# *The Cuban Lightning:*
## *The Zipper*

## Based on a True Spy Story

## Dr. Julio Antonio del Marmol
### *The Cuban Lightning*

ISBN: 978-1-68588-001-9 (sc)
ISBN: 978-1-68588-000-2 (hc)
ISBN: 978-1-68588-002-6 (e)

Because of the dynamic nature of the Internet, any web addresses or links contained in this book may have changed since publication and may no longer be valid.
Any people depicted in stock imagery provided by Thinkstock are models,
and such images are being used for illustrative purposes only.
Certain stock imagery © Thinkstock.

*Cuban Lightning Publications, Int rev. 06/19/2012*
www.cuban-lightning.com

All people and events described in this book are real. Only the names and select details regarding places and times have been changed to protect them.

# Acknowledgements

I am a very lucky man because I have a great group of people by my side that I not only consider my friends but also who are the most capable, sacrificing professionals equal to the ones I've risked my life with over the past 50 years in their dedication and values. This group has made possible the publication of this book. To them, with all my heart today, I give the best of my love, gratitude, and sincerest thanks to every one of these fantastic warriors. In order of seniority, I would especially like to thank O'Brien: a great friend, a great individual with extraordinary values, thank you for your contributions you have made in many different ways to this project, as well being loyally by my side and watching my back for almost all of my career. I know for a fact you have never done that before for anyone. To my right arm and great friend, Tad Atkinson: for your dedication to every detail in research and many hours of hard work with me, never hesitating to sacrifice even your personal and private family time in order to make this happen. To Steve Weese: thank you for the many pieces of computer and graphic work as well professional enhancement of photos to improve the quality of the book. To Carlos Mota: my thanks for your dedication and multiple contributions and sacrifices you have made in order to make this happen. To Gervasin Neto: for your constant loyalty and many hours standing on your feet or hiding between cars in order to maintain our security with your group of people you've coordinated to watch our backs, continually keeping us informed of any suspicious activity that occurs in our surroundings. To Chopin: for your great companionship, loyalty, and support for the last 50 years with me in our fight for freedom and that beautiful, generous letter you wrote in behalf of the project. To our editor, Jen Poiry-Prough: who managed to make this book as easy to read, using her magic touch to polishing this piece of coal and bring to you, the readers, what I consider to be a very rare diamond. It makes all of us very proud to be involved in this project. Your professionalism, vast knowledge, and dedication, has made this book a great piece for future generations. To all of you, my friends who remain in the shadows, who contributed in one way or another in making this book and help me to bring the truth to the public, you have given the best of yourselves, putting forth your best effort to educate future generations. God bless you all. I embrace you as the Christian warriors that you all are.

Dr. Julio Antonio del Marmol

# "The Tyrant"

*At dawn the rooster crowed*
*In the guise of a Messiah he came*
*Promising peace, freedom, and roses*
*The sun rose on his works*
*And in its light we saw:*
*Strife, bondage, and thorns*
*Covering the land and its people in blood.*

Dr. Julio Antonio del Marmol

# Chapter 1–The Lightning and the Conception of Conspiracy

*"Principles for Them and Us"*

"The abuse of other people's freedom is the beginning of the extermination of our own freedom and the abuse of freedom itself."

Dr. Julio Antonio del Marmol

**September 6, 1971**
**Havana, Cuba**

I was walking towards Coppelia Ice Cream Parlor to meet my contact. He had already been waiting in line a couple of hours for a table, so popular was this establishment. It wasn't just its popularity, which even before the revolution was undeniable; all the other ice cream parlors had been shut down, leaving this one as the only one in existence in the entire city of Havana.

I saw him from a distance standing outside, dressed casually. We both checked the area carefully, cautiously, to be certain we weren't being watched. He finally sat down on the outdoor patio at a corner table. I joined him momentarily. A pretty young girl dressed in a red and green uniform with white stripes came to the table and asked us what we would like to have. I ordered an Indian Canoe, a combination of three different flavors of ice cream with tropical fruit, and my contact ordered a single ice cream cone. I was holding the communist newspaper *Granma* folded in my hands—just as *Pravda* was the sole newspaper of the Soviet Union, this was the only one allowed in Havana, controlled by the Castro regime.

I placed the newspaper on the table. The other man smiled, picked it up, and said, "Is there any good news in the paper today?"

I replied, "Yes, there is great news for us but very sad news for others. You will find inside all the microfilms detailing the invasion by Castro of the African coast in support of the rebels. It will start tomorrow. Millions of dollars are being used in this operation, sending not only troops but also weapons, ammunition, and food supplies, while people in our own country are deprived of the most fundamental things to live. They are dying for lack of medicine and food while we spend all this money to support Castro's ambition of world dominance."

"Let's hope it's not too much longer that Castro is in control, or else we'll have nothing left for future generations."

"Let's hope so. Now I want to make it very clear to the people who receive this information that it is very important they use it to stop or deter these actions, but under *no* circumstance to make it public. The only place this information could come from is my office. I do not want to jeopardize my life or those of any of the others who are working with me. I want to make this very clear: *no* public announcements—*please*. Do you understand?"

He nodded. "Yes, I understand very clearly what is at stake."

At that moment the young girl arrived with our orders. My contact took his cone, stood up and said goodbye, and walked away with the newspaper under his arm. I remained at the table, ate my Indian Canoe, and watched him leave. I thought all the while that I hoped the people who received this information would treat it with the respect I had asked for.

## September 7, 1971
## United Nations Building, Washington, D.C.

The delegate of the United States was finishing his statement: "— and it is clear that Cuba is an international base, exporting terrorism and revolution to stable, democratic countries all over the world with the intention of disrupting the good function of their systems, creating chaos in order to establish their own communist regimes."

The Syrian delegate rose to ask a question. "Do you have any proof of these allegations?"

"Even as we speak, Cuban troops are disembarking in Africa. We have proof of this."

The other delegates began to talk amongst themselves in surprise and trepidation. Immediately, the scandal hit the press. Headlines read along the lines of "United States accuses Cuba of exporting terrorism and intervening in the internal affairs of other countries around the world." The President of the United States called a press conference to reaffirm the accusations made by the United States delegate to the U.N.

## September 8, 1971
## Prime Minister's Office, Vedado, Havana, Cuba

Fidel Castro's office was lavish but cluttered. An assortment of twelve officers stood around, listening to him. He was holding one of the United States newspapers in one hand while he pounded the desk with his other. In full tantrum, he kicked the wall and strode back and forth before the three most senior officers: Commanders Escalona, Piñeiro, and Valdez, as well as his brother Raul, waving his lit cigar in the air as he screamed and yelled. Ramiro Valdez sat in a chair with his feet up, watching Fidel rant and rave. He knew this wasn't a joke, but he didn't look as worried as the other men. He, too, was smoking a cigar. He exchanged a quick glance with Piñeiro.

Fidel stopped in front of him and asked, "This must be the work of very sophisticated intelligence. Who is behind this? Do you have any information for me? Only a small group of people in our circle has access to this information. How in the hell did this get out and into the hands of our enemies?

Ramiro reclined in his chair and took a long drag on his cigar. He had been waiting for this question for months—he had not dared until now to tell Castro the answer, fearing the reaction it would elicit. He rested his cigar on the glass ash tray next to him and looked straight into Fidel's eyes. "My commander and chief, I am sorry to tell you that the Lightning, our worst nightmare for the past ten years, is the one who not only passed this delicate information to the North Americans but has been sending these secrets to the rest of the world. As you know, he has been impossible to detect, and I have finally come up with an answer why. It is because he is right here—in your office!"

3

Castro's eyes popped out of his head like a cow with diarrhea. He yelled at Ramiro, "Are you crazy!? Or did you drink too much Bacardi this morning? You know better than anyone else that everybody in my office is bulletproof because you've tested them a thousand times!"

Piñeiro had been listening intently to the conversation and interjected, "My commander, I agree one hundred percent with Ramiro. It cannot come from any other source. The traitor has to be here."

Castro clapped his head with his hands in frustration and disbelief. "I don't care how you do it but get that son of a bitch! He has been making fools of us for ten fucking years!! I want results *immediately*! We can send a man to kill another man in any part of the world, but we can't get a spy in our own circle! My patience with you guys is running out! Bring me this man, dead or alive, but get him—once and for all!!"

The others murmured their wholehearted agreement, and Piñeiro added, "We are on his trail already and we will get him in the next few days."

Castro threw down the newspaper and stormed out of the office, foaming at the mouth like a rabid animal and followed by his bodyguards.

## September 9, 1971
## Prime Minister's Office, Vedado, Havana, Cuba

It must have been 90 degrees. It was hotter than any other day that week. My handkerchief was soaked. I needed a glass of lemonade, and the ancient air conditioner was broken for the fourth time that month.

My military uniform stuck to my body, making every movement uncomfortable. On top of my regular job at the Department of Economics in the Prime Minister's Office, I had to play guard there one day a week. I did my rounds in the building, making sure there was no one around.

I walked into the Prime Minister's private office at the end of the corridor. When I got to the office, I noticed it was at least ten degrees cooler. I propped my rifle against Castro's desk. Opening my lunch box, I took out three components and assembled a very small camera with an attached tape recorder.

4

Julio Antonio's government ID card

I knew just where to look. I carefully laid out the printouts of the economic status of Cuba. To my surprise I found something I did not expect: documents detailing the relationship between the Cuban government and the drug cartels. The documents detailed billions of dollars involved in creating out of each cartel leader a president for each country in Central and South America, who would still be able to function freely with the drug business and also having the political power to change the destinies of these nations with no interference from the "imperialistic" United States. This alliance in Spanish was dubbed the ASU; in English it rendered into the USA: the United Socialist Americas. I could not believe what I was seeing. I began to look around more cautiously and over my shoulder as I immediately realized that this document was too confidential to be simply lying around on Castro's desk. Was it a trap of some sort? I began taking pictures quickly so I could get out of there as soon as possible. My stomach churned every time I heard the click of my camera. I thought that anyone who might be near by could hear it. I had been doing this for so long, and luck had been with me—but my luck could run out at any time, and I would then be shot in the head, like so many others before me.

As I moved some of the files, one folder with pictures of airplanes in it fell to the ground. I opened it and looked through the folder. These planes were hidden amongst the other commercial planes in the Jose Marti International Airport in Havana. They bore the logo *Cubana de Aviacion*. My instincts told me there was more to this story, so I began to read the files closely. I discovered that these airplanes were being used to supply guerillas in South and Central America with clothing, food, medicine, guns, and ammunition. At first glance, the pictures showed soldiers carrying what I thought were bodies of people; but when I looked at the pictures under a magnifying glass, I could perceive that the bodies were actually dummies and were being loaded onto the planes in alternating window seats in order to make it appear to be a passenger plane. This method was extremely clever; if the International Intelligence Alliance took pictures of those planes in international airspace, they would appear to be normal passenger flights. Without these files they would never be detected. However, each plane that was being used in this operation was marked in the blueprints with a red dot on top and the number of each plane was shown. It was no wonder that the International Intelligence Alliance had no idea how these communist terrorist guerillas survived when they were isolated in remote regions by the governments of the countries in which they were operating. Even the Mexican government had not been able to comprehend how the guerillas in Chiapas had survived when the government had exhausted all methods to isolate the terrorists.

I started to get very anxious as I knew I had to take pictures of these files as well while still needing to get out of there—but then I ran out of film. I had to have all these blueprints, especially the ones with the red dots. I thought I might go into another office and make photocopies, but just then a buzz at the front entry door made me jump. I decided to simply take the last page and return it later. I knew if they found me in this office, I was a dead man, so I hurriedly left.

The buzzer sounded insistently. I hadn't noticed how much time had passed until I looked at my watch and saw that it was almost 4 am. I gathered my things together and reached for my rifle. As part of my normal guard duties, I went to see who was ringing the door buzzer. I relaxed when I saw that it was Chong. He was a small Chinese man who worked with me and had been my friend for many years, though of course he had no knowledge of my double life. He had come to relieve me.

"What kind of guard are you?" he asked in a joking manner as I opened the door for him. "I've been banging on that door for almost half and hour, and now you've finally come to answer?"

I smiled and said, "I was in the bathroom, for God's sake. Can't anyone even take a crap in peace in this country anymore?"

He joked back, "Don't give me that excuse again. Be a little more original. If you said you were sleeping, I'd believe you more!"

Without admitting anything, I shook my head and mumbled, "God, this guy's always thinking of the worse of everything."

"Think the worst and you're probably right!" he blurted as I was leaving.

I walked to the parking structure and got into my car. It wasn't really a car; it was a jeep used by the military. I called it the Russian Green Pig. I started the engine and drove home for the night.

A few days later I received a phone call in my office. I picked up and heard my contact's voice tersely ask if I was free. "Yes," I replied, "I can meet you." I hung up and headed over to the Coppelia Ice Cream Parlor, where I saw him sitting in the back corner reading a newspaper and drinking a Cuban coffee. I got an ice cream and sat down next to him, casually sliding an envelope across the table to him as I did.

He as casually slid it off the table and put it in his bag. "Julio Antonio, you have to leave Cuba right away." I stared at him in surprise. He had shocked me speechless. "I'm sorry. The information about Castro's troop movements in Africa was released to the U.N."

Anger returned my capacity for speech. "I made it clear that information was not to be released!"

"I know," he said with equal outrage, "damned politicians, nothing we could do. People from your office are already being taken in for questioning, even as we speak."

"I can't leave now!"

"They will find you, Julio Antonio. And then they will kill you. We've made arrangements."

"No!" I said as I buried my face in my hands.

"It will be tonight."

"No!"

"I'm sorry."

"You don't understand—Sandra is pregnant!"

He thought for a moment. "Perhaps we could arrange for her to go as well."

I cut him off with a gesture. "I will have to consult with her. She cannot leave. Her family, her mother, her father, her brother, are all here…she won't leave them. She doesn't know about my double life."

"If you want to live, you and your associates will have to leave tonight."

I said nothing but nodded in resignation.

Map of the Guantanamo Bay area

Late that night, I led my friends Kinqui, Pablo, Cisneros, and Joachim on a week-long ordeal to the naval base at Guantanamo. We navigated deadly minefields, losing only Cisneros in the process, we ran through the jungle, dodging soldiers shooting at us. Finally, we swam several miles around the coast to reach our destination. Sandra, my love, was arrested at the train station. I can still hear her sorrowful cries as we had no choice but to leave her behind.

We were dressed in Navy fatigues, weary and drinking hot chocolate as a US Navy officer spoke to us. "You've all been vaccinated, so as soon as we verify your identities, you'll be clear to fly to Miami."

"I already gave you the name of my contact already," I objected.

"Yes, I know. Be patient; it will all be over soon."

Julio Antonio's vaccination card

We were flown to Miami with a slight detour to Jacksonville. Castro, knowing the only place I could have gone to would be the US Navy base, had released information to the press describing me as a mass murderer being illegally sheltered by the Americans, since at that time political asylum could not be granted at the Guantanamo Base. My new friends in intelligence, O'Brien and Addison, wisely had the plane rerouted to a private airstrip first before continuing on to the scheduled stop. No sooner had we stepped onto the rolling tarmac ladder than it was wheeled back from the aircraft, which had not even shut down its engines so that it could immediately take off again.

O'Brien, a tall, blonde-haired man of clearly Irish descent, jokingly asked, "Did you fly that thing all the way here?"

I caught his sense of humor as the four of us clung to the ladder and so joked back, "No—we had a plane when we left. Now all we have is this ladder!"

He laughed and extended his hand to shake our hands as we descended the ladder. "Welcome to the United States. We have one stop in Miami where you'll have to be debriefed, and then you can start your new lives here."

The debriefing was conducted by a man named Steffan. The way he questioned us went beyond debriefing—it was more like an interrogation by one of Castro's men. I shared my concerns with

O'Brien, who assured me that the man was only doing his job. In spite of that, I could tell from his expression during the one time he was present that he was outraged by Steffan's approach.

We were in a plain office with grey and white walls. I recall the clock on the wall read 3:30 pm. "Once again," Steffan said in his surly manner, "tell me who you conspired with against Fidel Castro!"

"I'm just a researcher in animal genetics," I replied wearily. I don't like Castro, and his men found out about it. I knew I had to escape."

"Do you want me to send you back to Cuba? I know you are lying!"

"What do you want from me?" I demanded angrily. "I barely made it out alive!"

Steffan got up and paced around behind me. "One more time: who did you work with against Castro? Who were your partners?"

Shortly after that, there was a break in Steffan's interrogation, and O'Brien brought me some sandwiches. "Pretty rough in there?" he asked gently.

"That Steffan is a royal zero," I said as I ate hungrily.

"He's just doing his job, making sure you're not a spy from Cuba."

Eventually, O'Brien was able to relocate the four of us to a safehouse near a local restaurant. After he left, we decided to celebrate our new freedom with a lunch there. I was called away to the telephone in the back—a call which saved my life. A man entered and took a table next to my friends just before the owner took me over to the phone. He left mere moments later, but the briefcase with the bomb in it remained under the table. I had just hung up the receiver when an explosion tore through the restaurant, killing my three friends who had just barely escaped from Cuba.

O'Brien came to get me and revealed what I had suspected all along. "Steffan never showed up in Washington. We now have proof that he's a double agent. I'm sorry, sorrier than you can imagine." I smiled mysteriously. O'Brien gave me a curious look. "He's probably reporting what you told him back to Havana."

"I lied to him," I said with a smile of satisfaction.

"What?" O'Brien asked in surprise.

"I gave him false intelligence. I had a bad feeling about him."

"How do you feel about me?"

"I don't know yet."

"Well, maybe this will make you feel better. It's clear that it's not safe for you to stay in Miami, so we're going to relocate you."

"Where?" I asked in astonishment.

"I hear California is nice this time of year." He smiled. Then he glanced at me in deadly seriousness. "Castro has you marked for death. It will be safer if we never process any official record of your entry into the U.S. No paper trail for Castro's agents to follow you and track you down. As far as our government's concerned, you don't exist. From now on, you, my friend, are a ghost."

# Chapter 2—The Ghost

For the next 17 years, my life was completely changed. Everything I knew was gone, and as a freedom fighter, a spy, and a "ghost" I was involved in global events of historic proportions.

After I completed my training in 1971, I began my work. In Cuba, Castro hosted a reunion of the Tri-Continental Conference (the first taking place officially in 1966, though it was formed by Che Guevara in 1959). The purpose of this reunion, in their words, was "to create many Vietnams around the world." This would, in turn, spread the U.S. so thinly in terms of resources and political capital that no effective resistance could be offered against the propagation of Castro's brand of communism. This conference was disrupted by me and my team, causing the hotel to be evacuated. Protesters arrived on leaked information about the true nature of the conference.

In 1972, the Lightning team provided information to the South Vietnamese forces about Chinese infiltration along with counter propaganda. This slowed the advance of the Chinese in converting peasants into Viet Cong. That same year, my team provided President Nixon information concerning a secret deal made between Cuba and various members of the U.S. government, causing the President to authorize a small intelligence team to enter the Watergate building and investigate.

The following year, the entire town of Wajay in Cuba was organized to protest the shortage of food. The protesters were only women, children, and the elderly. In an unforeseen countermove, Cuban troops fired on and killed these protesters indiscriminately in the streets. Even pregnant women were slaughtered in the violence.

In 1974, Portugal's "Carnation Revolution" took place. Democracy was restored after over 30 years of dictatorship with the help of the Lightning team. In 1975, O'Brien introduced me to his personal friend, Governor Ronald Reagan of California (and future President of the United States), who outlined to me his plans for his Presidency, specifically the importance of freedom and democracy in the world. Our meeting took place in the historic Culver Hotel.

Intelligence from my team contributes to the 1976 strikes in Poland, undermining the strength of the Soviet communist bloc. The following year we exposed a plan by the Cuban government to back the Sandinistas. The cover of the Cuban advisers in Nicaraguan territory is blown and exposed to the press. President Anastasio Somoza Debayle is forced to lift the siege of Nicaragua by the Carter Administration. This, however, weakens the government and allows communism to gain a foothold.

The presence of Cuban troops and support in the conflict in Ethiopia is made public through information provided by my team in 1978. These troops were being used against Somalia in Ogaden in order to set up a communist regime—controlled by Castro, of course. The Ethiopian government is forced to admit this scandal. This same year, information is leaked in the USSR state of Georgia about Soviet attempts to change the constitutional status of their language. The ensuing protests were also assisted by my team.

In 1979, through the hard work of local resistance, intelligence forces, and the Lightning team, the dictator Idi Amin (a personal friend of Castro's) is ousted and flees Uganda as its capital of Kampala falls. That year, Pope John Paul II visits his native Poland in what would become known as the Nine Days That Changed the World. A revolution of conscience sweeps Poland, and they begin their struggle to free themselves from communism. Information from my team and my direct relationship with that Pope influenced this event.

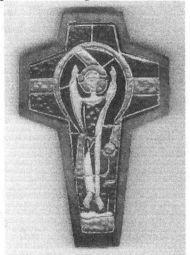

Gift cross to Julio Antonio from Pope John Paul II

In 1980, something extraordinary happens in Cuba. A mother fights with Cuban police who drag off her homosexual son for being "inappropriately dressed." The woman is killed, and the rest of the witnesses, standing in a food linen for hours for bread, angrily attack the police and force them to retreat. Upwards of 10,000 people riot, breaking into the Venezuelan and Peruvian embassies, often using vehicles as battering rams. This becomes an international embarrassment for Cuba, now forced to show how conditions in the country have caused thousands to want to leave. My team was present at the time and aided a bus filled with people to smash through the gates of the Peruvian embassy in Miramar. Under pressure, Castro is forced to open the Mariel port, allowing many people to leave Cuba.

In 1981, President Reagan signs the top-secret National Security Decision Directive 17 (NSDD-17), authorizing the intelligence community to recruit and support Contra rebels in Nicaragua. The decision was made based on intelligence provided by my team.

During the Falklands War in 1982, my team sends intelligence directly from Argentinian government sources to the United Kingdom and United States. The original concept of this conflict was developed by Che Guevara before his death and carried out by his remaining associates in Argentina. Designed to cast the U.K. and U.S. as imperialist aggressors and unite all of Latin America against them, it ended instead with the resignation of military dictator Leopoldo Galtieri.

In 1983, a violent coup in Grenada resulted in the deaths of 40 people, including Prime Minister Maurice Bishop. Extreme leftists in the government, in league with Cuban advisors sent by Castro, are behind the takeover. When my team sends proof of Cuban involvement, the U.S. deploys troops to invade the island.

In 1984, the Sandanista Front wins the general elections due to massive fraud financed through Cuban intelligence agents. My team helps the Contras denounce this fraud, which establishes strong opposition.

In an attempt to create hostility between the U.S. and Mexico, Castro orders the 1985 kidnapping and murder of a DEA agent through his Mexican cartel connections. Once again, the plan fails as my team provides the evidence connecting Cuba as the responsible party in the event.

In 1986, Yoweri Museveni's National Resistance Army succeeds in taking over Uganda after a five-year guerilla war with Idi Amin's successor, Obote. Museveni is sworn in as President. Over the years, my team provided economic and intelligence support to the freedom fighters in this conflict.

The next year, my team discovered plans by Cuban and Nicaraguan agents to expose the Iran-Contra affair, using bribes and social engineering to obtain details of the operation. Later, Ronald Reagan addresses the American people on the subject after details are leaked and admits his overtures had deteriorated into an arms-for-hostages deal.

In 1988, the U.S. House of Representatives rejects Reagan's request for $36.25 million to support the Contras. As a result, soon after, the operation called "the Zipper" is born.

During these years there were several attempts on my life. I had been kidnapped, attacked, and even shot. Seventeen years since that fateful explosion in the restaurant, I was still alive and fighting for freedom. My team consisted of only childhood friends: Hernesto, Elizabeth, Yaneba, Arturo, and a few others—all freedom fighters like me, all despising the corrupt communist system. We had just had some time off in Las Vegas at the conclusion of our latest mission, where I had discovered my long-lost cousin, Narciso Caletano Barriety, was very wealthy and tied in with mafia kingpins. We were now on our way home. When we arrived in Orange County, it was nearly three o'clock in the morning, and my girlfriend Loren was sound asleep. I received a call from O'Brien the next day.

"Are you back already?" he said in surprise when I answered. "I thought you'd take a little more time to come back before we debrief you."

"I want to get re-established before I take vacation time. What do you have in mind for me out here?" It was about ten o'clock in the morning.

"I'll pick you up in an hour. I will have an interview lined up for you—if you like it, we'll go with it. If not, we'll find something else."

I was still in bed with Loren while we had this conversation. I hadn't slept well the night before: a cousin in Las Vegas had once warned me not to trust people who work in intelligence. "Your best friend today," he had cautioned, "could be your worst enemy tomorrow."

My recent debility combined with the most recent attempt and O'Brien's abrupt decision to deprive me of a sound sleep. "All right,

I'll see you in an hour," I said, determining to push those doubts from my mind.

An hour later I was in O'Brien's car, driving to the Herald Examiner building. As we walked along the hallway, he explained what he was thinking to me. "This will be your new cover job—working with the newspaper."

"I have to come here to work every day?" I asked in concern.

"No, not at all. This is your new cover. You will be the owner of many vending machines. You put in a few appearances, but most of the work will be done by others."

I grinned. "I should have taken this job years ago!"

O'Brien chuckled as he ushered me into the office of the newspaper representative. I only caught his first name: Frank. He gave me a briefing of what would be expected of me. "You will be responsible for the distributorship for these five cities in Orange County," he finished after several minutes.

"It sounds ideal, Frank," I agreed.

"Then just sign here," he said as he pushed several documents toward me. I signed it and we shook hands. I caught the tail end of a huge grin on O'Brien's face. I had some misgivings at that point but had no time to dwell on them as he ushered me out of the office, telling me to take a few days to get into the new job, and that he would be in touch later.

**HERALD ☰ EXAMINER**

P.O. BOX 2416, TERMINAL ANNEX
LOS ANGELES, CALIFORNIA 90051

To Whom It MAY CONCERN:

This is TO CERTIFY THAT Julio A. MARMOL IS AN INDEPENDENT DEALER FOR THE Los Angeles HERALD EXAMINER. MR. MARMOL'S AREA INCLUDES IRVINE, COSTA MESA, Newport BEACH, CORUNA del MAR AND SANTA ANA. WE ESTIMATE THAT MR. MARMOL DRIVES Between 75,000 to 80,000 Miles per YEAR IN COVERING THIS VAST AREA.

SINCERELY,

▓▓▓▓▓▓▓▓▓▓▓▓▓

ZONE SALES MANAGER
Los Angeles HERALD EXAMINER

Letter from the Herald Examiner

In the meantime, my team had reassembled, and I had no difficulties with this new cover in helping them get established, as there was much that they could do to help me to get this business up and running in the cities contained in my new distributorship.

**LIMITED TERM INDEPENDENT CONTRACTOR AGREEMENT**

THIS AGREEMENT, made this ___3rd___ day of ___November___, 1975, at Los Angeles, California, between Los Angeles Herald Examiner Division, The Hearst Corporation, herein called the "Company" and ___Julio A. Marmol___, of _____
State of ___California___ herein called the "Dealer."                           # A-31

WHEREAS, Company is engaged in the publication of newspapers, and whereas, Company desires to have these newspapers delivered and sold to the reading public, and whereas, Dealer represents himself as being engaged or prepared to engage in his own business of distributing and selling newspapers by purchase from Company and resale to Dealer's customers.

NOW, THEREFORE, IT IS AGREED:

1. In accordance with the mutual intentions of Company and Dealer this contract establishes between them an independent contractor relationship, and all of the terms and conditions of this agreement shall be interpreted in the light of that relationship.

2. The Dealer agrees to purchase from the Company and the Company agrees to sell to the Dealer, for resale by the Dealer, such quantities of the Company's newspaper as the Dealer may require in the independent business conducted by him.

3. The Dealer will pay the Company at Los Angeles, California, for all newspapers furnished at the Wholesale Prices, as from time to time established by the Company. Such payment shall be made by the Dealer within ___7___ days upon receipt from the Company of a Statement of Account.    **Daily Rate Per Copy .0600**
**Sunday Rate Per Copy .1840**

Independent Contractor Agreement

Julio Antonio in the newspaper office

It was a good way to unwind after our previous mission, and I was not surprised when O'Brien contacted me a few days later, just as he had promised.

Arturo and Hernesto had slept in my house that night, joining Loren and me for breakfast. Arturo loved to cook and so eagerly took over the duty to fix things up for us that morning. He asked who wanted French toast and who wanted waffles, adding, "I'm going to make both."

I smiled and said, "Maybe one or two slices of French toast will be good enough for me. You'd better slow down on your eating or you're going to have a heart attack one of these days."

He laughed and replied, "Brother, we only live once."

"Well, you only live once, that is true," I said, "but at least live healthy."

He patted his stomach and said, "I'm healthy!"

Loren laughed and said, "Waffles for me."

Hernesto said, "French toast for me."

Loren asked us, "How do you guys like your eggs?"

"Over easy for me," I said.

"Same here," Hernesto chimed in.

"Me, too," Arturo agreed. "That way we make it easy for you, girl."

O'Brien's call came after breakfast, so I said after we were through, "Do you guys mind taking Loren back to her home? I have to go and meet with O'Brien."

"No problem," Arturo replied.

"OK," I said. "I'll see you guys later." I stood up and bent over to kiss Loren, who was still finishing her breakfast. I walked to the garage, pushed the button that opened the door, and got into my Jaguar sportscar. I opened the electrical gates and drove off to the ferry on Balboa Island which connected the island with Balboa Peninsula.

**Jaguar XJSC**

When I arrived at the French café by the ferry, O'Brien was already waiting for me on the patio at a table beneath an umbrella, drinking coffee. "Hello," he said happily, "are you OK?"

"Yeah, I'm fine." I wondered why he had asked me if I was OK—he had never done that before. It made me curious if my recent ordeal had shaken his confidence in my overall health. I asked, "And you, how has everything gone these past few days? Anything new?"

He nodded. "Yes, a lot of good news. Do you want something to eat, or did you have breakfast already?"

I looked at my watch. "Breakfast? It's nearly lunchtime now."

He paid the bill, took my arm, and said, "Let's walk back to the ferry to cross back and forth a couple of times. We'll be able to talk privately that way."

We walked to the ferry not even fifty feet from the little restaurant and sat down on the long benches that were there for the pedestrians that crossed on the ferry. There was no one around us, only a few cars with people inside, minding their own business and listening to music on their radios. The ferry began to cross the bay. He looked around at the big, beautiful yachts and the scenery around the ferry. He said, "God, you sure didn't pick a poor place to live, did you?" He smiled ironically.

He looked at me thoughtfully, put his hand on my shoulder, and spoke in a very quiet voice. "The old man has already given us the green light for our operation. The official name for the operation will be the Zipper. Officially, it does not exist. Nobody will have any idea of what we are doing. Nobody! Not even the other people in our agency. We are going to close the Zipper on the Soviet Union, Cuba, and the rest of the totalitarian regimes around the world. We expect the Zipper to completely bankrupt the communist regimes."

"The Zipper?" I repeated with an ambivalent expression on my face. "Well, it's original."

He looked at me closely. "Are you OK? Is anything wrong?"

I looked him straight in the eyes and smiled. "No, nothing is wrong with me. Everything is fine. Maybe I'm just a little tired from that last trip and still worried about a few things. Nothing important. I'll tell you later. Why do you ask if something is wrong with me?"

He stretched and said, "I don't know. I feel as if you're losing your passion. Your passion is very contagious and that is what inspires people to follow you and do what you want them to do. I always say to Addison and the old man that your passion is capable of converting the Pope to Judaism."

I tried to divert his attention from my demeanor, which he had obviously noted. "Listen, it is nothing important, but it is something that has been worrying me a little bit. I will tell you later. Let's talk about this operation, the Zipper, which is more important. Who will be in charge of this operation, and what is it about?"

O'Brien smiled. "The old man, Addison, and I all agree that you are the person most qualified to lead this operation. Not only are you qualified but you are the ideal person because of the characteristics you possess. They make you unique for this."

"Me?" I asked in total surprise.

O'Brien smiled again. "Yes—you don't appear on any of our papers or official documents, not even on the payroll of the agency. You aren't even a citizen of the U.S. You're only a resident. You're the ghost. That makes you an ideal person just in case something goes wrong, and our plans get discovered; no one will be suspicious of us, the intelligence service, and certainly not the old man!"

I leaned back and asked curiously, "Is there something illegal in what you guys plan to do?"

His look turned serious—deadly serious. "Yes, very much illegal. We are going to clone the billions of dollars we need to tear down the Berlin Wall and bankrupt the Soviet Union. We are going to sweep, once and for all, the influence of the Castro communists from South and Central America."

I looked at him in awe. "What? You want me to make counterfeit money? Are you going crazy, or am I just dreaming?" I took off my sunglasses and laid them on the bench. I slid closer to him, put my finger in my ear, and jokingly tried to clean it out. "I must have a bad connection, or my ear misheard what you just said. Do you mind repeating it to me?"

He clearly didn't think this was funny. "This is not a joke," he said with deadly earnest. "This is very serious. You said many times in the past that you wanted to take down Castro's regime. His horrendous crimes against humanity and the U.N. violations he commits every day against political prisoners in his prisons were the main reasons you felt you had to leave the country. Not to mention the fact that they almost killed you and would have for certain if you hadn't slipped through his fingers like butter."

"Calm down, man," I said. "I was just joking with you. I know anything we do will have no comparisons with the crimes Castro commits each day."

"Do you know what the Europeans call Cuba these days?" he asked. "They call it the island of sex and pleasure. Not only in Europe, but all over the world."

"Why? Why is that?"

He smiled grimly. "Because that is the cheapest place on Earth where you can get sex, even a virgin or an under-aged girl for just a few dollars."

I controlled a sudden flash of temper. "Why do you tell me these things? Do you want to piss me off even more than I am already with these people? Or are you just trying to pump up my adrenaline even more than it already is against these people? You guys don't have to justify what you plan to do. Don't screw with my intelligence."

He calmed me down and put his hand on my shoulder. "We really need you for this operation. I promise you that if something goes wrong, we will not let you down." He squeezed my arm emotionally.

I turned to him. "I'll feel a lot better if you tell me that *you* are not going to let me down—not *we*."

He said, "If it will make you feel better, I give you my word of honor. *I* am not going to let you down."

I saw the sincerity in both his face and eyes. I still shook my head. "I don't like this at all. I didn't come here to break the law in this country. I don't mind breaking laws in any other country, but not here. This country is to me my second mother. She opened her arms to me when I had to leave my first mother of Cuba. The idea of doing any harm to the economic stability of this country or breaking any of her laws makes me feel very uncomfortable. I love this country, the USA, equally as much as the country I was born in."

O'Brien tried to calm me down. "We're not going to do any harm to this country. We're going to protect her from her enemies. Remember, this is my country, and I will never do anything against her." I stood up, shook my head, and pace around with my hand on my head. "Sit down, please—you're calling attention to yourself. The people in those cars are looking at you. Stop moving your hands so much. It looks as if we're fighting."

One of the men sitting in a car close to us opened his door and got out. He began walking around, pretending to look at the scenery and the yachts passing by. It looked, however, like he was curious and wanted to eavesdrop on our conversation. Fortunately, the ferry was docking at the Balboa Peninsula, and so the guy had to run back to his car because the other cars were starting to leave. The attendant came over to us to collect the fare, and we paid him for another trip so we could get back to Balboa Island. New cars came onto the ferry until it was filled up, and a few pedestrians also came on board. A person dressed as a panda bear also came on board, selling flowers and postcards to the tourists. The panda bear had a name plate pinned to its chest which read, "Doby, the Panda Bear." The costume had a red lining in its ear and its paw held a small camera, so well hidden you could hardly see the lens.

**Actual panda suit used for surveillance**

We crossed back to Balboa Island on the ferry. O'Brien took my arm and led me away from rest of the pedestrians. He did not even notice the panda bear. He whispered to me, "We are going to provide you with everything you need: legitimate currency paper and magnetic ink. The only thing the printer has to do is copy the plates we are going to give to you. This is because if there is any screwup we don't want the original plates in the wrong hands. If you follow my instructions step by step, everything will be fine. We need you to supervise the whole operation."

I shook my head again. "This is going to be a very interesting experience."

He looked at me with a small smile. "Does that mean I can count on you in this?"

I looked at him. "How can I say no to the man who opened his arms to me when I first came to this country, and has always protected me right up until now? You can count on me, but I still say I don't like this at all. What do I have to do?"

O'Brien extended his hand to me. "I promise that if anything goes wrong, I will protect you and will take care of the problem myself." We shook hands and he pulled an envelope out of the pocket of his sportscoat. "There is a list of equipment you will have to buy. Rent a warehouse in an industrial area with an office in the front. Make sure you put up a business sign outside. I don't need to tell you anymore details because you've already been doing this all over the world. Create a ghost company."

I nodded. "OK, I got it. Who is going to be the printer?"

He pulled another envelope out of his coat pocket. It was full of cash and had two plane tickets to Buenos Aires, Argentina. "All the information is inside the envelope. Our people have already talked to him, and he's agreed to do the job. All you have to do is negotiate with him as to how much he wants to do it."

"OK. If I need anything, shall I call you at the same number?"

"No." He took out a business card for a Chinese restaurant in Costa Mesa. He turned the card over and wrote a number on the back and then handed it to me. "Use this number from now on if you need me. Only use the old number in case of an emergency. Never call me from the location where you will be working. Another thing I want to ask you—because Addison asked me to—from now on, since you are involved in this operation, please don't send any more contributions to the Republican Party."

"For God's sake—I didn't give money to the Republican Party. The contribution I sent was because I believe in an individual: the old man. If he were a Democrat, I would have sent the same donation to them. I am not a Republican. I am not a Democrat. I am not even a citizen. I have no political affiliation. I simply believe in the old man and sent my support."

O'Brien shook his head and smiled gently. "I know, I know. But just a couple of days ago you sent five thousand dollars to the Republican Presidential Task Force. That is the same thing as the Republican Party. This would not look good at all if something goes wrong. It would not be prudent."

"Oh my God! Now you guys are checking me out to see who I send money to?"

"Calm down. It's only routine. The same people we sent to watch your back and protect you are the same ones who report back to us what you are doing." O'Brien smiled and put his hand on his chest. "We are like Papa God. We see everything, we hear everything, and we know everything."

"God!" I exclaimed. "This is exactly what I heard from the mafia a while ago."

O'Brien smiled a little more broadly. "How do you think Mr. Caletano found out that he's a member of your family? Where do you think he got that information from?" I kept silent and stared into his eyes. He continued, "Do you remember when you came into this country some 17 years ago, when we met for the first time, and you asked me if I could walk on water? I said to you 'almost.' It's actually very good for you that I have all this power, since I'm your friend and my people love you. They will protect you all the time because you are a man with integrity."

"Do you guys work with the mafia?"

He looked at me very sincerely. "We work with all kinds of people. That does not make us bad. We only try to protect our country, and that is good."

I remained silent for a few seconds, thinking about what he had said. Finally, I said, "Thank you very much for your trust in me, and for being on my side all these years. Please don't disappoint me this time, because what I am about to do may require you to walk on water to get me out when I am drowning."

"Let's try to think positively and hope there will be no need for any of that. Maybe you and I can take a trip to Cuba together at last and drink a real Cuba Libre when the island is really free again."

We had by now gotten off the ferry and returned to sit at the same table in the little French restaurant. We stood up and he gave me a big hug. I could see over his shoulder, not too far away, the panda bear taking pictures of us. Doby was acting very casual to avoid attracting any attention to what he was doing. There were several children around him.

O'Brien and I said goodbye and I got into the Jaguar. When I put the two envelopes he had given me on the front seat, I saw the plane tickets to Buenos Aires. I thought about what a strange coincidence it was that my cousin had been talking about Argentina and his adventures in Colombia with Fidel Castro. I thought about that irony. The printer who was going to do the job for us was an Argentinian. I drove along the Pacific Coast Highway towards home. When I arrived, I telephoned Arturo and told him we were going to pick up Hernesto to go out to dinner that night at 7:30 pm. There I would talk to them about a new project before I hung up the phone.

# Chapter 3—The Argentinian Contract

The phone rang and I heard Loren's voice teasingly say, "Hey, stranger, what happened? You didn't call me all day. Did you decide to give me a day off?"

"Oh, no—I've just been extremely busy all day. Have you had dinner yet?"

"No, I've not even had lunch because I thought we were going to do some work today. Remember, you're my boss. I spent the whole day doing nothing because you didn't give me any homework to do."

I smiled. "Don't worry. You'll be working overtime all week!" She laughed her sweet, contagious laugh. "We are going to pick you up in about half an hour in our new limo to take you to dinner. Arturo and Hernesto should be here any minute. I am just waiting for them." At that moment the intercom buzzer rang. I said to Loren, "Just a second, don't go away." I pushed the button of the intercom and saw Arturo and Hernesto at the gate. I pressed the gate opener and told Arturo, "Hey, brother—put one of those remote controls in the limo. That way you won't have to ring the bell next time; you can open the gate yourself."

"OK," Arturo replied.

I picked up the phone and said to Loren, "We'll be there in fifteen or twenty minutes. Arturo is here already."

"OK, love. Bye."

We left my house and drove to pick up Loren. She was wearing a beautiful, low-cut red dress. When she got in the limo I said jokingly, "Wow! The lady in red!" Chris de Burgh's song by that title was very popular at that time. "You are beautiful!"

She turned as red as a tomato, like a ten-year-old girl. "You are very flattering, and you are a gentleman. I'm not used to that because American men normally aren't like this. Every time you say something like this to me you make me blush."

"Do you like it?"

"Blushing, no. What you say, yes."

"Well, all you have to do is get accustomed to my nice compliments and then you won't blush anymore because I never tire of telling you how beautiful you are."

She blushed again and hit me on the shoulder. "I think you like to see me blushing."

Arturo drove down the Pacific Coast Highway towards my restaurant, Julio's Caribbean Grill. It served typical Caribbean food: lobster, filet mignon, shrimp, pork chops, all cooked on the grill. Everything was served with white rice, black beans, and fried plantain bananas with a fresh fruit salad. It was very elegant and had a dance floor. There were live bands that played not only Caribbean music but whatever customers requested. When we arrived at the restaurant, I told Arturo to let the valet park our limo.

He shook his head. "For your security and mine I won't let anyone else drive this limo or have the keys in their hands until you assign a permanent driver. It must be someone we know and have complete trust in."

"OK, brother. If you feel better that way, you park the limo. You are in charge of our security, anyway. We will meet you inside the restaurant."

When we went inside, Manolo, the manager, gave me a big hug. He was not only the manager but a good personal friend. He said to Loren, *"Mucho gusto, señorita. Bienvenida a* Julio's Caribbean Grill." He took Loren's hand and kissed it.

Loren blushed again and said, "I have to get used to being around Cuban people. They are such gentlemen."

Manolo replied, "Thank you very much, *señorita*. We try. Follow me, please, to your table."

We sat down at the table I always used when I came here. It was on a balcony that was separated from the rest of the restaurant by glass, hanging over the marina where the yachts docked. We could see the boats crossing by as they came in and out of the bay. Looking inside the restaurant the glass provided a view of people dancing while music softly played in the background. The glass barrier, however, provided enough soundproofing so that the customers inside would not hear our conversation, so I used the opportunity to explain the new project to my friends. I gave them the primary outline of the project and said that I would tell them all the details later.

They were playing a beautiful ballad inside, and I asked Loren to dance. We went inside and danced with the other customers; after the ballad ended, I went to the bandleader, shook his hand and said hello. I then whispered, "Would you play 'The Lady in Red', please?"

"For you, anything," he answered.

Loren was waiting for me on the dance floor, wondering what I was doing. I walked over to her, but before I could take her in my arms the band began to play. She recognized the song at once and began to giggle and blush. I kissed her tenderly on her neck and around her ear as we danced for a little while. Then, using this opportunity, I began to talk quietly into her ear. "I cannot tell you everything I do because I do not want to put your life at risk. This, however, I must tell you, because if you decide to involve yourself with me in this project, you have to know what the possible consequences are so that you know what you are getting into."

She moved her head to face me and looked into my eyes. "I know what you do. I know you own vending machines in town. You have properties. This is what I know." She smiled mischievously and continued, "But I know there's something else you haven't told me yet."

"I will tell you now, but you must promise not to repeat it to anyone. It could cost me my life—yours, too."

She gave me a tender kiss. "Don't worry about it. I'm a Cancer. Cancers are very loyal. Whatever you say to me I will never betray you. Whatever you tell me I will put in the safety of my heart, and it will remain there until I die. Besides, I think I've falling in love with you. I'm also really grateful for everything you've done for me. I swear to you on the memory of my mother, who passed away many years ago and is now in Heaven, I will never betray your trust."

I saw sincerity in her eyes, and although it is difficult for me to put my trust in anyone until I had known that person for a long time, I was also evidently falling in love. I opened my heart to her, even though we had known each other only a short time. "I work with several intelligence organizations around the world and the Cuban freedom fighters. We are trying to prevent our enemies from swallowing the world and our freedoms."

She stopped dancing and put her right hand over her mouth. She smiled, and her eyes were shining, reflecting a wild joy in what she had just heard. She pointed at me. "I know—I know. You're working for the CIA!"

30

I put my index finger over my mouth. "Shh. Lower your voice. No, I don't work for them, I work with them. There is a big difference. Please don't repeat that word ever again. The people I work with are far above the CIA, at another level. Just call it the intelligence community."

"OK, I understand. I'm sorry."

"No, that's alright." We walked back out onto the balcony to rejoin our friends. On the way I let her know I would give her more details later at home about what we were going to do.

With a joyful smile she said, "You must be kidding! I love what you do and have always wanted to be a part of it. This is like a dream come true for me. I don't want to wake up."

I shook my head. "Don't think this is as glamorous as it appears in the movies. Just remember the bad time you went through in Vegas not too long ago. Our enemies and the people we deal with are not precisely gentlemen. They are assassins, murderers, and drug smugglers."

We arrived at the table as we spoke. Hernesto heard part of the conversation and asked, "What movie are you guys talking about? I love movies."

I replied, "We are not talking about movies. We are talking about real life, my brother. Do you guys want dessert?" They shook their heads, protesting they had already eaten too much. I raised my arm and Manolo himself brought me the check.

"Is everything OK?" he asked.

"Excellent like always, Manolo," I replied. "Keep it that way and we will bankrupt all the other restaurants in Newport Beach." I grabbed the check, signed it, and kept a copy for myself.

Arturo stood up. "I'm going to get the limo. I will meet you guys out front."

We left the restaurant, got into the limo, and drove down the Pacific Coast Highway. I said, "I'm going to give you the details of the project. That way, you guys will know what you have to do while I'm out of town."

All three of them looked at me. Hernesto said, "You are going to leave town?"

"Yes, very early tomorrow morning. I'm going to Buenos Aires, and Arturo is coming with me. Hernesto and Loren will stay here to buy some things and run several errands. When we come back from

Argentina, everything will be ready to start work. When we get home, I'll make cherries jubilee for you guys."

Loren smiled. "Really? You know how to make that fancy dessert?"

Arturo laughed. "Lady, you don't even know what this man can do in the kitchen! He is a Cordon Bleu chef." He tapped Hernesto on the shoulder. "Tell her, brother. Tell her what he can do in the kitchen."

She smiled again. "Really? You can do that?"

I smiled and winked at her. "You'll see." I took a list out of my pocket and said to Hernesto, "You guys buy exactly what is on this list, even the same brand name. I don't want the printer to have any excuse if he does a bad job, like blaming the equipment." They looked at me in wonderment. "Yes, the man I am going to get from Argentina is the man who is going to clone twenty-, fifty-, and one-hundred-dollar bills for a special mission."

Hernesto jerked his head around so fast that he nearly broke his neck. "You must be kidding, brother!"

"No, I am not kidding at all. If any of you has a problem with this, I understand perfectly. You can jump out now or shut up and do the job until we finish."

Arturo said, "This is very damned serious, brother."

"Yes, very serious. Billions serious."

Loren looked at me mischievously and said, "You make all my dreams a reality. The only thing in life I hate is routine. With you, nothing is the same from one day to the next. As a matter of fact, not even from one hour to the next!"

I smiled and nodded. "Like I told you before, in theory this all looks glamorous and exciting, like in the movies, but in reality, it is not like that at all. You can get hurt. You can end up in jail and under the worst circumstances you can lose your life. That is the reason I say again, before you get involved think carefully before you commit yourself to this project. I don't want to be blamed or held responsible if anything goes wrong and you end up in jail or getting hurt in any way. It is your decision."

Loren smiled again, leaned over to me, and put her hand against my cheek. "That is one of the qualities I like best about you, though you have many other qualities that I'm discovering each day. For me, it really is a pleasure to join you in this project and this time I will follow your instructions to a T. I promise. But I'm going to ask you a little favor." She leaned forward and kissed me on the cheek. "Will you please not worry so much about me and the others? Be more concerned about your own personal wellbeing and safety. Nobody is invincible. I've observed that you have the impression that you somehow will be able to get out of the worst situations with no problem at all. You are so self-assured that you let your guard down sometimes, and that could cost you your life. Promise me that you will try to control this. Worry about yourself a little more and less about us."

I nodded. "OK. I will try, but it is my nature to worry about the people I love and care for."

We arrived at my house. Hernesto said, "You can count on me for whatever you're going to do."

Arturo said, "Count on me, too. I feel the same. You know I won't put any conditions on whatever you need me to do."

I replied, "Thank you brothers. We are probably going to need more of our people to join us on this project."

Hernesto said, "I'm going to call my sister, Elizabeth, in Miami. She can help us tremendously. If you don't mind, I can call Yaneba, too." He glanced at Loren as he spoke.

Loren picked up on that and looked at me with questioning eyes. I simply nodded my head and replied, "Of course. Yaneba is perfect. She can help us, too."

Almost immediately, Loren burst out, "Who is Yaneba?"

Arturo said, "Yaneba is one of our freedom fighters. She has many talents. She can disguise you in fifteen minutes so that even your own mother won't recognize you."

Loren didn't ask any more questions about Yaneba, but I knew that she would ask me more later.

Hernesto asked, "If you want, I can get in touch with Jacobo, your Mexican friend in Costa Mesa. He's helped us out before."

I considered that briefly. "OK, but this is on a need-to-know basis. Tell him he might be needed but don't give him any details. Just ask him to be on standby. If we need him due to an emergency, then we will contact him. The man has a wife and two kids, and this job is extremely delicate and dangerous. I don't want him getting hurt and seeing those kids and his wife ending up alone with Jacobo in jail or dead."

"OK, I understand," he replied.

Arturo parked the limo in the driveway, and we all went inside. I went to the kitchen to make the cherries jubilee. When I served it to them, I poured the brandy over the top and lit it on fire. Loren exclaimed, "My God, this is fancy! Real high cuisine!"

We all ate our dessert. As always, Arturo said, "If you don't mind, I'm going to have another helping."

I said, "There's plenty there, brother. Knock yourself out."

Hernesto said, "Well, it looks as if we're going to have to sleep in your house again tonight."

"Yes, that's a good idea," I agreed. "After you drop us at the airport tomorrow, you can come back here, get Loren, and then begin to purchase the equipment while you look for a good location for our office and warehouse. Then, when we return in two or three days, you will have everything in place, and we can begin to work without delay." Out of the blue, Arturo burst out laughing. All of us looked at him and I asked, "Why are you laughing?"

He got himself under control and replied, "Well, I was just thinking to tell Hernesto that we spend so much time in your house, sleeping here nearly every night, that one of these mornings we'll wake up to find a bill under the door for room and board!"

We smiled and I shook my head. "Is that how you entertain yourself? You make your own jokes and then laugh at them. Are you your own audience?"

Hernesto said, "He does that all the time. Joking with me, driving me crazy and eating like a pig! You know what he did to me the other day?"

Loren asked, "What did you do to him, Arturo?"

Arturo smiled but did not answer. Hernesto asked him, "Why don't you tell them what you did to me the other day?" Arturo still didn't answer, instead eating the last of what was left in his bowl. "He's like a big kid. He filled up a balloon with water. Not a little balloon—a big one. He put it on the seat of my car. When I came out it was dark, so I didn't see the balloon. I sat down on it and got my ass and balls soaked. I had to drive all the way home with wet pants and underwear!"

We looked at Arturo and Loren clucked her tongue. "Tsk, tsk, that was not nice."

I said to Hernesto, "He plays jokes on you because he loves you. My mom used to tell me that if people did not like you they would not even talk to you let alone play with you or joke with you."

Hernesto said, "Sometimes I wish he wouldn't love me so much. Just a little less!"

I said to both of them, "My house is your house, brothers. You can stay here. You can sleep here as much as you want. Consider it your house. I bought this house because it has many bedrooms. If my plans materialize the way I expect them to and my diplomatic connections don't fail me, very soon I will have my mom and dad out of Cuba and in this house with me. Let's hope this works, because otherwise I will have wasted all the money that I put into it."

"Congratulations, brother," Arturo said. "I hope all your wishes come true. I waited for nearly ten years to bring the rest of my family out of Cuba. Finally, the Cuban government let them go to Spain last year, and from there I was able to bring them to the United States."

Loren said, "It is very beautiful and noble of you to try and bring your mom and dad from Cuba. That says a lot about your character. My mother used to tell me that if a man is not a good son, he won't be a good husband, father, or a good person at all, and not to get involved with a man who wasn't."

I smiled and nodded. "That is what my mother told me ever since I was a little boy, except she warned me to be careful of a girl who wasn't a good daughter. What a strange coincidence. You are of a different origin and culture, but you hold the same values we Cuban people hold, and you even have the same sayings!"

She replied, "I'm half Hungarian from my mother and half Irish from my father. According to what I've read about race and cultures, the Hungarians are very similar to the Spanish and Italian cultures. Maybe that is the reason we connected so well. Maybe it comes from my mother's side because I'm very much like her. I'm not like my father at all."

"Maybe, honey," I said. "Maybe that is also the reason you like fried plantain bananas so much. Every time we go to a Cuban restaurant, we have to order an extra side for you!"

She slapped me on the arm. "I'm not going to eat any more bananas. Arturo is the one who eats them all!"

Hernesto laughed. "Arturo eats everything!"

We all laughed and had a good time until I looked at the clock and said, "Well, guys, let's go to sleep. We have to get up early." I turned on the stereo which was connected to the intercom and pressed the automatic button so that it would turn itself off when the tape was done. I put in "The Velocity of Love" by Suzanne Ciani, a beautiful instrumental piece. I took Loren by the waist, and we went into the master bedroom. Under the influence of the passionate and exquisitely refined music we made love deliciously until we were both physically exhausted and had used our last drop of energy.

The next day at four o'clock in the morning I dragged myself out of bed. I hated getting up early, but I had no choice. I jumped in the shower and then dressed. Once I was ready to go, I tucked the covers around Loren and kissed her on the cheek. "I will call you," I whispered in her ear.

I thought she was half asleep, but she opened her eyes, grabbed my arm, and pulled me to her. She gave me a little kiss on my lips. "Don't worry about anything. I'm going to take care of everything, and I'll make sure things are done the way you want."

"Thank you. You take care of yourself, too. I will call you in a few days."

She got comfortable again. She put her head back on the pillow and snuggled into the comforter. I left the room and went to meet Arturo and Hernesto, who were already waiting for me out in the limo. Hernesto drove and Arturo sat with me in the back. We drove all the way to the airport in Tijuana, Mexico.

# Chapter 4—The International Bank Arrangements

Hernesto dropped Arturo and me off at the airport and a little while later we took off on a plane headed for Buenos Aires, Argentina. I had been there before and liked it very much. The people were very cordial and generous, always ready to invite you to their homes to eat an Argentinian meal, typically different kinds of barbequed beef. While on the plane I thought about the irony of my cousin telling me about Argentina and his story about Peron and Evita, and now here I was, flying to Peron's land.

Arturo brought me out of my meditation when he asked, "Hey, brother, this man we're going to see in Argentina—is he trustworthy?"

"Just remember this," I answered, "trustworthy to me means only you, Hernesto, and a few people in our group. The rest are question marks."

He nodded. "I'm glad I brought my pistol. It's better to be safe than sorry."

The plane began its final approach into Buenos Aires and the flight attendant's voice came on the intercom with the usual announcements about fastening seat belts and all the other safety precautions for landing. A short while later the plane had landed and we walked into the airport, claimed the rental car which was already reserved in my name, and drove all the way to Rosario, where the printer, Romero, was supposed to live.

We drove around the city looking for his address. Finally, we arrived in the right neighborhood. It was very middle class, neither rich nor poor. We found his house and saw that it was the nicest house in the area, clearly standing out from the others. We parked the car and knocked on his door. A man about fifty years of age, a pot belly in spite of his otherwise thin frame, mustache, glasses, black hair, and about five foot seven inches in height answered the door. "Yes? Who are you looking for?" he asked nervously.

"Romero?" I inquired politely.

He hesitated before replying. "Who are you? Why are you looking for Romero?"

I extended my hand. "I am Dr. del Marmol, and this is my friend Arturo. I believe you were expecting us."

He smiled in relief as he took my hand and shook it. "Oh, I'm sorry. I wasn't expecting you guys until tomorrow. Come in, please." He was clearly nervous and embarrassed. He called out loudly, "Isabel, come here!" The pleasure he expressed was so great that one might think I was there to give him a new Cadillac.

A lady came into the living room where Romero had ushered us into and had been seated. She was very beautiful, exotic, with an excellent body. She was dressed in a very slutty manner, and it was clear that Arturo could not take his eyes off her.

Romero said, "This is my wife."

She extended her hand to Arturo. "Pleased to meet you."

"Nice to meet you," Arturo responded as he took her hand.

She turned to me and said, "Pleased to meet you, Dr. del Marmol."

"The pleasure is mine, *señora*."

Arturo looked at me and I could tell he was wondering what this beautiful young woman was doing with this disgusting old man.

She asked, "What would you like to drink? I have coffee, lemonade, Pepsi-Cola, or iced tea."

I replied, "If it wouldn't be too much trouble, I will have a lemonade. If you have some rum, put a little bit of it in for me, please. That will help me to relax."

"Of course," she said. "That is what my husband drinks all the time."

I looked at Romero and said, "Maybe you have some Cuban taste buds."

Romero said to her, "Bring me one like that, too."

Arturo asked, "Me, too, but instead of lemonade could you put Pepsi in mine?"

She gave us a beautiful smile, turned around, and walked into the interior of the house. Arturo followed her with his eyes.

I coughed loudly and said, "I have something in my throat. Maybe it is the change in the climate."

Arturo understood my signal and took his eyes off Isabel.

38

Romero said, "The lemonade and rum will make your throat feel better." He didn't appear to notice I was signaling to Arturo, or at least gave no indication that he had.

I said to Romero, "I understand you are the man who has been selected to do the work for us. My people told me to negotiate the price with you and if we can agree I will arrange for you to cross the border safely into the United States where we going to do the job."

He reclined in his chair and said, "I want one *palo verde* because I calculate it will take at least two months of work due to the huge amount of money your friends want me to make. That is not counting they want me to copy the original plate." He removed his glasses and continued, "This is a lot of work because they don't want me to use the original, which would be a lot easier."

"I beg your pardon," I said, "and excuse my ignorance, but I don't know what one *palo verde* means. I assume this is some kind of name or slang, or maybe I'm just getting old because I don't recall my Spanish vocabulary—aside from the literal meaning of one green trunk."

He burst out laughing and said, "I'm sorry, my friend—one *palo verde* means one million dollars."

I shook my head. "That is way over my limit. They only authorized me to offer $250,000. I cannot play games here. I don't have the time. That is why I'm telling you up front how much I can offer. That way we can wrap this up quickly—or I can leave quickly."

He stood up and paced around in great distress. "No way—going all the way to the USA for only $250,000! These guys must be kidding! Leave my wife and family here for that little money? No way!"

I knew what was going through his mind thanks to the information O'Brien had given me about him. His beautiful, sexy wife had been a prostitute prior to marrying him. He had met her in and taken her from a whorehouse. One of the things mentioned in his file was to be very careful of what one said about his wife. He was very much in love with her and adored her, but he did not trust her, was very jealous of her. Although she had been entirely faithful to him the four years they had been married and given him two children, he could not forget her past and was afraid that if he left her for any length of time, she might get an itch to go back to her old ways.

So, using a little psychology, I proposed another way. "Why don't you bring your wife with you? Find someone, maybe a member of your family, to care for your kids and you two can have a second honeymoon. I live close to Disneyland, the San Diego Zoo, Sea World, and many other attractions. You guys could have a ball." He sat down and thought about it at least, so using the momentum I added, "Of course I will pay for your wife's airfare out of my own pocket. All you have to do is accept the $250,000 offer, a quarter of a million dollars, which is not bad for only two months of work."

He put his hand on his chin, still thinking about it. He looked up at me but was clearly still not convinced. He shook his head. "I don't know."

"What about the money you are going to make? You are an expert at this. We are going to give you all the necessities. The real currency paper. The magnetic ink. With this, you will be able to make a masterpiece. What if I give you the *palo verde* you asked for out of the money you are going to make? You cannot tell anyone. Not even the people who previously contacted you because I am not authorized to do this. Then you have the *palo verde* you asked for as well as the $250,000."

He stood up, came over to me, and put his arm around my shoulders. "You know, Doctor, I think we're going to be friends. You are a good man. You understand other people's needs. Those bastards, your 'friends', told me that under no circumstances could I take my wife over there. She cannot be mixed up in my work."

"No, she will not work with you. You will never bring her to the place where you will be working, but I will arrange to rent an apartment for you or in order to avoid calling attention to you, maybe you will be able to stay in my girlfriend's condo. She doesn't use it much, anyway. She sleeps at my house most of the time."

"Well, thank you very much. I will be much happier having her there. I'll be able to do much better work without any worries in my mind."

"I'm glad we were able to reach an agreement. I'm sure it will work out fine."

"Did you know that my wife cannot get into the United States legally? Like me, she was deported many years ago."

"Don't even worry about that. My friend, O'Brien, is probably arranging your crossing right now with one of the border patrol agents. We will cross your wife in the same car with you. No one will bother you or her."

He smiled in satisfaction and held out his hand to me. "Then the business is closed. We are in complete agreement."

I took his hand and shook it. "OK, we will meet you in Tijuana in a couple of days. We will pick you up from the airport."

He nodded. "A couple of days will be good enough. I have to arrange the passport for my wife to get her from here to Mexico."

"OK. How much money do you need in advance to take care of these little things? You will get the rest of the money when you finish the job."

He smiled. "If you give me twenty thousand, I will be able to pay off all my obligations and arrange for someone to take care of my house plus have enough left over for my personal expenses during the trip."

"No problem. Save all your receipts from the time you leave Argentina, and we will reimburse you for all your expenses." I opened my briefcase and gave him two wrapped bundles from the bank, each containing a printed bank seal stating the bundle contained $10,000. I gave them to him. "Count it. If it is less, let me know right now before I leave. If it is more, I don't even want to know."

He unwrapped both bundles and counted the money to verify it was correct. He nodded in approval.

I took a notepad out of my briefcase and wrote a phone number on it, which I handed to him. "Call me as soon as you leave Argentina. That way we will know what time your plane will arrive in Tijuana so we can pick you up at the airport."

He shook my hand again. "It really is a pleasure doing business with you."

"The pleasure is mine."

Isabel came back with a tray which held our drinks. I wondered why she had taken so long. Then I realized that they probably had agreed previously that she should not interrupt us until we had completed our negotiations. We sipped our drinks and talked for a little while.

Romero was very hospitable, and after we had spent a little time together asked, "Why don't you guys stay here tonight? My wife is a great cook and I make the best *asado* in Rosario. I have a special sauce that I use to marinate the beef."

Isabel smiled and insisted. "I assure you that you won't regret it."

"Thank you very much," I said. "I really appreciate it, but we have to go back to Buenos Aires tonight." I had noticed that Isabel had been checking out Arturo. They had been talking together and giggling. They seemed to really like each other, and I felt there could be a problem brewing.

"Dr. del Marmol," Arturo chimed in, "actually we could leave early in the morning and do the things you have to do before our plane leaves tomorrow afternoon."

"There can always be unpredictable problems," I disagreed, "and I want to be sure we sleep in Buenos Aires tonight, even if it's for a few hours. That way, tomorrow morning, we will be there for sure to do what I have to do before we leave."

Isabel said, "It's such a pity that you just arrived in Rosario, and you have to go all the way to Buenos Aires in such a rush."

"That is the way of life is sometimes," I answered. "But I assure you that the next time we will accept your hospitality and will stay for a few days."

Romero said, "We would be delighted. You can stay for as long as you want."

I said to him, "OK, by the way—repeat with me: American citizen."

He said, "American citizen" with a slight accent.

I took a small tape recorder out of my briefcase. "Play this many times until you can pronounce it without an accent." I pushed the play button, and a voice repeated those words over and over. I turned it off and handed it to him. "Repeat this for the next two days as many times as you can until you get it in your brain. Remember, even though everything is arranged at the crossing with the border patrol officer, and he is waiting to pass us through without any problems, we should be prepared.

"If he says anything to you, even if you don't understand what he is saying, you answer 'American citizen.' That is all you have to say. Normally, that is what they ask: 'what is your citizenship?' That is the routine question they ask everybody. They have put cameras on the border lately because of all the problems they have with drug smuggling and some of the border patrol guards have been wounded or killed. They are a lot stricter now."

Romero asked, "Do you think there will be a problem with my wife? You say they know about me, but they don't about her."

"Don't worry about it," I replied. "They don't look at people, just the license plates of the car. Arturo will be our driver. I will bring my girlfriend with me and that way everything will look normal. We will look like tourists crossing the border at Tijuana, but we have to be prepared just in case some unexpected problem happens."

His eyes opened wide, and he looked a little scared. "Do you expect any kind of problem at all?" he asked anxiously.

"No. They already have the license plate of my car. My friend, O'Brien, will be there waiting for us just to make sure there are no problems."

"Yes, yes. I understand. It is good to be prepared anyway." He turned to his wife and said with a nervous smile, "You have to learn to say 'American citizen' without an accent."

Isabel repeated, "American citizen." There was no accent at all— she was even better than Romero.

We all laughed, and I said, "Isabel, you are good. You have no accent at all. If you dyed your hair blond and with your light skin and greenish eyes you could easily pass for a North American woman."

She laughed, liking the compliment. Romero said, "Yes, she is very beautiful."

We all hugged and said goodbye. I noticed she hugged Arturo a little longer than she did me. The two had most certainly hit it off. Arturo and I returned to our beautiful hotel in Buenos Aires.

The next day we went to a nearby bank in the city: the International Bank of Tokyo. While we were in the bank, I asked one of the bank attendants for the branch manager, Mr. Hugo Zuzki. She went at once to find him. The bank building was beautiful, with marble floors and walls decorated with surrealistic designs in different colors, giving it a very contemporary look. I thought that this bank must be doing very well, since everything around us was luxurious.

When she returned, she invited us into an enclosed office with beautiful engraved glass partitions.

We sat down and she offered us something to drink. The chairs we sat in were extremely comfortable. It felt like sitting on a cloud. Arturo asked for a Coke and I asked for iced tea. A few minutes later she came in with a plate full of very delicious almond cookies and drinks. She put the plate down on a table and said, "Mr. Zuzki will be with you in a few minutes."

While we were eating the cookies and enjoying our drinks, I asked Arturo, "Do you want to open an account here? It could be very beneficial to you in the future. If anything goes wrong in the States, you will be prepared. This would be your cushion because the first thing the authorities do when you get in trouble is freeze your bank accounts. Then you cannot even defend yourself because you have no money to pay a good attorney. This bank is bullet proof and does not provide information to anybody. You can put your mom or dad or any member of your family as beneficiary. You can name up to five persons who can claim the money in case of your death. In whatever order you prefer. This is all absolutely confidential."

He smiled and leaned over in his chair to take a few more cookies and said, "Brother, you are extremely smart. You always think of every single detail."

"No, not always," I disagreed. "Sometimes I forget something, like anybody else. But I try to cover my back because if a problem arises, I think, 'Why didn't I do this that way, or why didn't I do this another way?' Anyway, thank you very much for your compliment."

He shook his head and said, "No, brother, this is not a compliment. This is reality. You are very modest but also very smart, and I appreciate having you for my friend."

I smiled and just then Mr. Zuzki opened the door and greeted us. "I apologize for making you wait," he said. "Well, Dr. del Marmol, you are much younger than I pictured you to be. Based on our conversation on the phone, you are either an old banker or you have a lot of experience in the banking business and the financial world. Are you a banker?"

I smiled and shook my head. "No. I have been in many businesses but never banking. I do have a lot of friends in high finance all over the world. I guess I have learned a little from them."

"Not a little—you have learned a lot. Some of the questions you asked me about the power of law enforcement to obtain information about clients through the court of law I did not have the answers to. I had to make some calls to our attorneys to verify the answers I gave you."

"Well, as you know, every country has different statutes of limitation and different laws and regulations for bank institutions."

Mr. Zuzki was Argentinean descended from a Japanese family, probably second or third generation. He appeared to be more European, except for his eyes. He looked very distinguished—tall, with a full head of dark hair. He had a very pleasant expression and appeared to be trustworthy. I liked the man, and that was why I asked him a few straightforward questions. "How can you guarantee the confidentiality of this account that I am about to open?"

He smiled as he pulled open a drawer in his desk, took out some documents, and extended them to me. "Dr. del Marmol, if you feel comfortable, you can call me Hugo. That is okay with me."

"Thank you," I replied.

He leaned over, opened the documents, and pointed with his finger to the day that document had been filed in the Argentinean courts. "You see here, it has been five years that the court has been trying to get the financial status of one of our clients. They have not been able to do so. Maybe it will be another five years that they will try, and maybe another five years after that, and maybe they will never get it." He smiled and winked. "By that time, if they are able to accomplish their goal, the statute of limitations will already be over and the client will be able to move their funds anyplace in the world, leaving only a small amount in the account. That is the record we will provide to the court."

He reclined in his chair, tapped his desk with his fingers and continued. "We are bonded with the same confidentiality between attorney and client as a priest and the confessor. That is our banking principle. We have the best legal corporations behind us, not only here in Argentina, but all the way around the globe. We are an international banking institution. We are going to defend this principle and the right of our clients always."

I smiled and said, "I love what I am hearing from you. More than that, I like very much your passion because the personal privacy of an individual is so important. It constitutes the basic principles of his rights and the most beautiful thing any man has. If we lose this, we lose a very precious gift. Our individual freedom is not a privilege. It is a right for every one of us."

He smiled and looked at me and said, "Very well said. I think we agree one hundred percent. When any government or any other institution, using any excuse, tries to violate the rights of an individual, they kill the basic rights of the average man and his individuality and break in pieces the most precious right that a person can have, which is his personal freedom."

We stood up and shook hands firmly. I said, "Absolutely. We agree, one hundred percent." We sat back down. "I intend to make large deposits in your bank. Maybe through wire transfers. Bank to bank. From the United States. But I don't want to transfer directly to Buenos Aires. I don't want to leave any trace. Is there any way to do this where there is no trace of it?"

"Of course," he answered. "We do this all the time. We open two different bank accounts. We open one here and one at our mother bank in Japan. Both are your accounts but they are not attached to one another. When you wire money, you wire it directly to your account in Japan. When that money arrives in Japan, we convert it to yen and there will already be verbal, not written, instructions given to the bank officers there to immediately wire transfer any money that comes into that account to our branch here in Buenos Aires." He stood up. "Do you have any more questions?"

"Nope. I am completely satisfied."

"Okay. Then let me go and get the necessary documents for you to open your accounts and we can register your personal information and your exclusive code signature, which will only be for your extraction of money from our bank. That particular code signature will protect you from any fraudulent impersonation or attempt by anybody to withdraw your money from here. Even if I die or am replaced by another person, that code signature will be on file in an extremely confidential safe. No one except the branch manager of our institution will have access to it."

As he was stepping out of the office to get the forms, I asked, "Would you mind bringing an extra set of those documents? My friend, Arturo, would like to open one of those confidential accounts also." I looked at Arturo and nodded at him, asking for his approval. He nodded back.

Hugo said, "Sure. I will be delighted to bring an extra set for your friend."

"Thank you very much."

He left the office and closed the glass door behind him, leaving us alone for a while. Arturo said, "Wow! This is what we call financial sophistication!" He smiled and tapped my shoulder. "Brother, every day I learn something new from you! Do you have enough money with you to open your accounts and mine? I am so used to you paying for everything that I don't think I brought enough cash with me on this trip."

"Don't worry. I don't think the requirement for opening an account is too much. But if it is, I think I have enough cash anyway."

A little while later, Hugo came back with his documents and after a few questions back and forth we managed to fill out all the paperwork. Hugo told me the required amount to open a confidential international account was a minimum of one thousand dollars. I looked at Arturo and we smiled at each other. I opened my briefcase and took out an envelope containing $25,000. I extended it to Hugo and said, "Put ten thousand in each of my accounts and five thousand into Arturo's account."

Arturo turned to me and said, "Brother, as soon as we get to the States I will give you that money back."

"That's okay," I replied. "There is no rush."

Arturo smiled. "Thank you very much."

Hugo smiled and said, "Evidently you are not too worried about the interest we are going to pay on your money. That is the only question you have not asked so far."

"I know it will be the normal rate you pay to everybody," I answered. "I have read it already in the documents you have given me: three-point-five percent, compounded every three months."

He verified the cash I had given to him. After making sure everything was okay, he gave me a receipt and a copy of the documents we had just signed. We said goodbye and shook hands again. "It was really a pleasure doing business with you, Dr. del Marmol."

"The pleasure is all mine," I replied.

He shook Arturo's hand and we left the bank and back to our hotel. When we arrived there, I made a phone call to Loren. She was very happy to hear from me. She told me they had already bought everything and rented a warehouse with an office. She had decorated the office herself. They had also gone to the city hall and obtained all the licenses and permits we needed to operate the business, including the DBA. I told her to drive my four-door Jaguar to Tijuana and meet us in the Hotel Lucerna in *zona del rio*, or the zone of the river. She did not even ask why, which made me feel very proud because she was learning so very fast.

"When?" she asked. "When do you want me there?"

"Tomorrow. Drive carefully. I love you, sweetie."

We said goodbye and hung up the phone. The next day we went back to Tijuana.

# Chapter 5—Money Plates

We took a taxi from the airport to Hotel Lucerna. Loren was waiting there and had already booked rooms for us and for Arturo.

"Wow!" I exclaimed. "This is efficiency. I will have to give you a bonus for this. This is overtime!"

She smiled, hugged me, and gave me a passionate kiss as if we had not seen each other for months. "Are you horny, honey?" I asked jokingly in her ear.

She turned red, like always, and hit me on the shoulder. "You love to do that to me!"

I laughed and said to Arturo, "Make a reservation for Romero and Isabel. I'll see you in a little while."

Arturo could see that I was anxious to be alone with Loren. "Go ahead. I will take care of everything. I want to take a shower. I will see you later."

"I am going to take a shower, too," I said. "I will call you when we are ready." We took the elevator and went upstairs to our room.

After we made love and took a shower, I called Arturo, and he asked, "What are we going to do today? Romero will not be here until tomorrow."

"Let's relax," I suggested. "Let's go to the horse races."

He laughed. "Okay, man, I love that. I love the horse races."

When we got to the stadium, Loren exclaimed, "My God, this is the first time I've ever been to a horse race!"

"We love this," I replied. "We come here all the time."

When we walked into the stadium, Loren saw a horse getting out of a trailer. She asked the person leading the horse, "What's this horse's name?"

"Relampago," he answered. "It means 'The Lightning,' *señorita*."

Arturo and I looked at each other and smiled. "Can you believe this, brother?" I asked him.

"My God, I like that horse. Is he going to run today?"

"Yeah."

We went to the betting area and I picked out the horse I liked for the first race. I placed my bet. Arturo did the same. Loren placed a bet for one hundred dollars on Relampago. We looked at the history of the horses and found that Relampago had never won a race. He always ended up last or next to last. We laughed and joked with her about it. I explained to her that she needed to pick a horse that had won once or twice before. She said she didn't care. She liked that horse.

We got some hot dogs and were having fun when the first race started.

The horses began to run. We were all excited. Loren's horse was number seven. He began to move ahead and as they came down to the final stretch he was in second place. Everyone was screaming for number 12, who was the favorite and in the lead. As they came near the finish line, Loren's horse was neck and neck with number 12. The people were screaming loudly for number 12. The finish was so close that we could not tell who had won. We had to wait for an announcement.

Arturo said, "My God. You are going to make a lot of money because even if your horse came in second, the odds were so great, you are going to make like 40 to 1! A killing!"

I looked at her ticket and shook my head. "I am sorry to burst your bubble but Loren placed her bet on winning only, not on place."

Arturo threw his arms in the air and said, "Why did you do that?"

She smiled calmly, still sitting on the bench and waiting for the decision.

She said to me, "I liked that horse because he has spirit. He has class." She smiled maliciously and added, "He reminds me of you."

"Oh, thank you, sweetie," I answered. "You are something."

Just then, the announcer's voice came over the loudspeaker. "The winner is: number 7!"

Loren screamed and jumped up and waved her arms in the air, shouting, "Yes! Yes!"

Arturo was upset. "Look at this girl! First time she ever came to a horse race and she has won four thousand dollars or more! This is amazing. I lost all my money!"

"Congratulations, sweetie," I said.

We went down to cash in the ticket. After we cashed it in, Loren extended one thousand dollars to Arturo and said, "You don't have to return this to me. It is a gift for you. Let's go to the best restaurant in Tijuana and I will pay the bill. It's on me."

Arturo was embarrassed because he should not have complained about losing his money, but Loren insisted he take it, and so he put it in the pocket of his shirt. Then he took the money out of his pocket and tried to give it to me, asking me to give it back to her later.

"No, don't give the money to me," I said. "I do not want to be involved in this. That is between you guys. Leave me out of it. This is a good lesson for you for the future. Don't gamble your last dollar. Only gamble with money you don't need."

Loren said, "You Cubans have too much pride. You deprive me of the satisfaction of sharing with you. I know you just lost your cash here and we're in a foreign country, but if it makes you feel so bad, you can return it to me when we get back home. Meanwhile, don't spoil the party. Let's go out and eat and drink some good champagne and celebrate my winnings."

Arturo gave up and said, "Okay, when we get back home I will give it back to you."

Loren smiled. "Okay, whatever makes you feel good."

We left and went to a Spanish restaurant and ordered *paella valenciana*, plantation bananas. As soon as Arturo saw the waitress bringing the *paella* to the table, his eyes shone and his mood changed. He said to me, "Brother, this is the good life."

We ate the bananas, green and ripe. They prepared a great avocado salad with spinach, boiled eggs and anchovies. We ate and drank for a while, and as always, Arturo ate more than he was supposed to.

The waitress brought the bill to me and Loren snatched it out of my hands. "Why do they bring the bill to the man all the time? Don't they think women can have money?"

"Honey," I said, "this is a man's world. The man should always pay the bill for the lady. That is the custom, especially here in Mexico."

Arturo smiled and said, "We should ask them that question. Why did they bring the bill to you? I am here, too. Why didn't she bring it to me?"

"I assume it is because I am the one who placed the order," I surmised.

"But I am the one who ate the most!"

Loren smiled and said, "You are not kidding!"

We left the restaurant and Arturo began to complain that his stomach was beginning to ache. We stopped at a pharmacy and bought some Alka Seltzer. The pharmacist offered him a glass of water and

Arturo drank it with the seltzer before we left. On the way back to the hotel I asked him if he felt any better.

He bubbled like a baby. "Oh yes, brother. I feel a lot better already."

"You know, you eat too much, my friend. You are still young, but you need to cut down a little bit the size of the portions you eat. You can eat many times a day, but only small portions. That way, your digestive system will work even better."

He nodded. "Thank you, doctor. I am going to follow your advice from now on because for a little while back there, I was feeling miserable."

We arrived back at the hotel and after we went to our rooms and changed, we went down to where the swimming pool and the Jacuzzi were. We sat down in the Jacuzzi and talked. We ordered a bottle of champagne and Loren told us all the details of what she had been doing while we were out of the country in order to prepare for our project.

We went to bed very late. The next day, early in the morning, Arturo did not wake me up but instead went to the airport to pick up Romero and Isabel. When I awoke, it was nearly ten o'clock in the morning. I looked at my watch and jumped out of bed, filled with concern. I knew Romero and Isabel had been due to arrive around nine o'clock. It crossed my mind that perhaps the front desk had forgotten to give me my wakeup call. When I looked at the telephone I saw a small red light flashing, indicating that I had a message. I picked up the phone.

A young lady answered the phone, "Front desk."

"What happened? You guys were supposed to call me at eight a.m."

She laughed. "Yes, Dr. del Marmol. Your friend, Arturo, called and told us not to bother you. He said we should let you sleep. He canceled your wakeup call and is already back from the airport. He wants you to call his room when you're up."

"Oh. Okay. Thank you."

"Oh, he brought two more guests."

"Oh, that explains it. Thank you very much."

The conversation woke Loren. She sat up in bed and hugged me and kissed my neck. "Sweetie, I'm going to take a shower. If you want, we can take a shower together."

I hung up the phone. "Sure, I'll be there in a minute." I picked the receiver back up and dialed Arturo's room.

After a few rings, he picked up. "Hello."

"What happened? Why didn't you wake me up this morning?"

"I didn't think it was necessary. I decided to let you guys rest and enjoy each other. I went myself to pick them up from the airport."

"Thank you, brother. Did you put them in a room close to you?"

"Yes, they are right next to me."

"Okay, I am going to take a shower. Bring them down to the lobby around noon, and we will all have lunch together down there."

He giggled a little bit. "Man, I think this guy is extremely jealous of his wife. He won't leave me alone for even a second with her."

"Stop staring at his wife," I chided him. "I know she is a beautiful woman but you have to control yourself. By now he probably realizes you like her, and if I noticed it, I am sure he noticed it, too. We don't want any problems. We need this guy."

"No, brother. I am not going to fool around with his wife and create a problem for us—"

"Don't give me that rubbish," I interrupted him. "You and I both know that if she opened her legs to you, you would jump in there like a bee in a honeycomb. At least be discreet about it. Please."

He understood my message. "Okay, I'm sorry. I understand."

I knew Arturo wasn't the only one who was intrigued. I saw the way Isabel looked at him, too. She looked at him in the way a woman looks at a man she wants to jump into bed with. I hung up the phone and went into the shower to join Loren. She was waiting for me. I opened the glass door and began to rub her back with soap. Then I soaped her breasts and the rest of her body. We began to kiss, and after a few minutes we started to make love under the water. Evidently, the rails which held the glass walls were loose because as we were moving the frame started to move. With our motion the whole thing started to fall apart.

Fortunately, the door opened and supported the rest of the structure, and we fell out onto the floor. We were both laughing as she lay on top of me and the water ran all over the floor of the bathroom.

We stood up and decided to go into the bedroom to dry ourselves off and to continue making love in a more secure place. After we finished, we got dressed and I called hotel maintenance to come and take care of the shower. Fortunately, nothing was broken. It was just loose.

We went down to the restaurant and enjoyed lunch with the rest of our group. I introduced Loren to Romero and Isabel. Loren commented on how beautiful Isabel's hair looked. She had dyed it a copper red, making her look even more beautiful. She looked more French or European now, rather than South American.

I smiled and said to Romero, "That is a very good idea. You look more like you belong to the country you are going to. Whose idea was it to dye Isabel's hair? By the way, you look very nice," I added to her.

Romero replied, "It was her idea. Actually, did you notice my hair? I have no more white hairs. She touched mine up, as well."

I looked at him and, sure enough, he did look younger, and dressed in a suit, he looked cleaner and better. After we had a good lunch we ordered dessert. The hostess approached our table to tell me I had a phone call. They brought the phone to the table and I answered it. It was O'Brien.

"You need to be at the border a few minutes after three o'clock. That's when they change the guards. I'll be waiting for you at the last border crossing on your right. Everything is already taken care of, but I'll be there to make sure everything's okay."

"Okay," I replied.

We said goodbye, and I looked at my watch. It was about one-thirty in the afternoon. I said, "This is the call I have been waiting for. We need to go upstairs, pack, and check out of the hotel. I don't know how long the wait is at the border and I don't want O'Brien to have to wait for us for too long."

We finished our dessert and went upstairs to our rooms, packed, and checked out. At around 3:15, we approached the gate at the border, where an immigration officer with an Asian appearance was waiting. He smiled at me and said, "What is your citizenship?"

I extended my immigration card and replied, "I am a Cuban citizen who has resided in the United States for many years."

He glanced at my card, bent down, and looked in the window. "What about your friends?"

I maintained silence and Loren, who was sitting next to me in the passenger seat replied, "I'm an American citizen."

Romero said in perfect English, "I'm an American citizen."

Isabel and Arturo also repeated the same reply with perfect English. The immigration officer smiled, extended my green card to me, and said, "Have a good trip."

As I slowly drove through the gate, I saw O'Brien walking towards his car in the parking structure. Our eyes met and we both smiled. He continued walking towards his car and we drove slowly out of the structure.

We stopped at a gas station, filled up the tank, and bought some cold sandwiches for the road. We continued our journey towards Orange County. A few hours later we arrived at Loren's place in Costa Mesa. After we cooled off and drank some lemonade and beer, Loren showed Romero and Isabel the room she had prepared for them. They liked it very much and were very happy.

We left Isabel in Loren's house and the rest of us went to the warehouse office Loren and Hernesto had prepared in the city of Santa Ana. It was situated on Grand Avenue in an industrial area among several other businesses. It blended in very well and did not stand out at all from the other buildings.

Loren took the remote control from the glove compartment in the Jaguar as we approached the building. We drove into the alley and the huge doors opened automatically into the storage area, which was in the back of the building. When we were inside, Loren pushed the remote control again and the doors closed behind us.

Hernesto was waiting for us and came out smiling to say hello. We all got out of the car and Romero practically ran to check out the enormous cameras and printing equipment. He was in love, he said, with what we had bought for him to use. He said with a beatific smile, "I asked for the best, but I never expected you would buy the best. This is unbelievable. This is great equipment!"

"You got what you asked for," I said. "No more and no less."

"I can do great things with this equipment."

"Well, if you are not too tired, you can start right now!"

He rubbed his hands together and said, "Of course I am going to start right now! Why wait?"

I pointed to a corner and showed him some boxes and said, "We bought some ordinary photocopy paper for you. That way you can do your tests and we won't ruin the original paper which will be here tomorrow together with the magnetic ink and the rest of the chemicals you will need for your work."

"Very well," he answered. "I am not tired at all. The sooner we start, the sooner we finish. Where are the original plates?"

"I have them in my safe in my home. If you want, I can have them here in twenty minutes."

"Perfect," he said. "I am going to work tonight with the plates because I want to make the duplicates. That way you can return the originals to your friends."

**Old currency printed in the warehouse**

"Okay, I will go and get them. Arturo will stay here with you right now and Hernesto and Loren will go with me. If you need any help, Arturo can help you.

"In the future, I will most likely not be around all the time, but you can ask them for whatever you need. I don't want you to leave this place by yourself. Even if you just need cigarettes, send one of them to get them for you. Remember, you are not legal in this country and immigration is making a lot of raids around here because there are many illegal Mexicans working in these factories." I showed him a little folding bed in the corner. "If you ever get too tired you can rest there for a while."

"Thank you very much. You have thought of everything. Even the smallest of details."

"You are welcome, but even the smallest details are sometimes very important to the security of this operation and to keep us out of trouble." I pointed to the telephone on top of the desk. "Only use that phone for emergencies. You have a paper on top of the desk which is scotch taped to one of the corners with all of our numbers. Under no circumstance call long distance. Not to Argentina or to any of your family or friends in all of the USA. If you want to make a personal call, tell one of us and we take you to a public phone. Do you understand?"

He had a long face, but he replied, "Yes, I understand."

"These are the rules. They are for your security and for our security. There is no excuse for breaking these rules because if anything goes wrong the first thing the authorities do is check the telephone bill and every single one of the persons you have called from that phone is recorded on that bill and you will involve them in what we are doing; those people will contradict you if you try to defend yourself." I looked him directly in the eyes. "Do you understand?"

"Yes, I do. Everything will be done exactly you say, Dr. del Marmol. I don't want to end up in jail here in the United States."

"I am glad we understand each other. That makes me feel more secure." We said goodbye and left the warehouse. As we were driving away, I told Hernesto and Loren, "Keep your eyes on that guy. I know he looks very humble and friendly, but remember he has been an outlaw all of his life. Those who live that way sometimes think they are smarter than the rest of us, and he might try to shit all over us."

Loren said, "Don't worry about it. We're going to keep him on a very short leash and under a magnifying glass."

"I don't know why," Hernesto told me, "but I don't like this guy. From the minute he came into the warehouse with you guys I had a bad feeling about him. His smile is not sincere. It is like he borrowed it from someone else."

We both smiled.

When we got to my house, I went to my safe and pulled out the plates O'Brien had given to me a few days before. They were in a small box wrapped in a protective fabric to prevent them from being scratched. I stood next to Hernesto and told him, "Guard this with your life and tell Romero to treat it very gently because I have to return this to O'Brien as soon as we finish copying it."

Hernesto said, "Don't worry about it."

Loren went to the bathroom and Hernesto pulled a little note out of his pocket. "Read it when we leave."

I took the note from him. "When you get back to the warehouse, please tell Arturo to come over here to rest. He can relieve you tomorrow."

Loren came back from the bathroom. She gave me a little kiss and we said goodbye. When they left for the warehouse, I opened the note Hernesto had given to me. It had a phone number and an address and two initials: E and Y. I realized immediately that E was for Elizabeth and Y for Yaneba. I went to the phone and dialed the number.

Yaneba answered the phone. "Hello."

"How are you guys doing?"

"Oh, my God!" she exclaimed. "The mystery man! We have been here for almost a week and we have not had the pleasure of spending some time with you or even saying hello to you in person."

"That is the story of our lives: close but not together."

She giggled a little bit.

"How is Elizabeth?" I asked.

"Just fine. She is right here with me. She says hello to you."

"Say hello to her. I will be there in fifteen or twenty minutes."

I hung up, and took my car back to Costa Mesa to the hotel where Yaneba and Elizabeth were staying. When I arrived at the hotel room, Yaneba opened the door and gave me a small kiss on my lips.

With a mischievous smile, she said, "Somebody told me you have finally found the love you lost when you left Cuba."

I smiled. "Well, I don't know if it is love, but I feel very good whenever I am with her."

She rubbed my shoulder. "I wish you the best. I hope it lasts."

In one of the corners on one of the chairs lay the panda bear outfit with the head on top, complete with the name tag marking it as Doby the Panda Bear. Elizabeth, who had been in the restroom, came out and hugged me. She took a big manila envelope full of pictures and spread them out on the table. They were pictures of O'Brien and me when we were on the Balboa ferry talking about the Zipper operation. She took a micro-cassette and a small tape recorder and put the earphones to my ears so I could hear the conversation she had recorded.

After I had listed for a while and had double checked that the quality was good, I turned it off, took the micro-cassette out, and said to Elizabeth, "I want you to make several copies. Every time I meet with O'Brien or anybody important, do the same thing. Put the pictures and cassettes in different packages in safe security boxes in different banks every time you record. Use banks not only here in the United States but in other countries as well. This will be our insurance to protect you guys and to protect myself just in case something goes wrong."

Yaneba asked me, "Do you think if something goes wrong O'Brien will abandon us? Do you think he would do something like that to us?"

I smiled and touched my chin. "No, no. I don't want to think like that. But it's better to have a weapon in your reach to defend yourself if somebody attacks you, even if you never have to use it, than to need that weapon and not have it. Let's pray to God that we never have to use this."

They both nodded their heads, and Yaneba said, "You are right. It is better to be safe than sorry."

Elizabeth came close to me and rubbed my shoulder. "You know what? I love you. You are always thinking of our safety before you think of yourself."

I smiled and she gave me a hug.

"Thank you," she said close to my ear.

"You guys had better pack," I said, "because we are out of here. I have a better place for you guys to stay. I have a beautiful house right on a cliff on top of the ocean in Corona del Mar where I know you will wake up every morning with a smile on your faces. You will not miss Miami at all!"

They both smiled, and Elizabeth said, "We are already packed. We only have to put our panda teddy bear in a garment bag and we are ready to go."

"Okay, let's do it," I said.

I picked up the phone and called for the bell boy. A few minutes later, he arrived and we all went down to the lobby and checked out. We got into my car and traveled to Corona del Mar. When we arrived in Newport Beach, I stopped in front of my house on Lido Island.

Yaneba said, "Remember, we've been in town for almost a week, and you told us where you lived. We crossed by here many times, hoping to see your face."

"Well, I just wanted you guys to see how the house looked, but you obviously know already! I forgot how good you are at what you do. I guess when I was in Argentina you had plenty of time to drive around and explore the town."

We continued on to Corona del Mar, and I said to Elizabeth, "The perfect place for you is to be close to me. You are going to be my limo driver. In other words, you will probably sleep more often in my house than where I am taking you now with Yaneba. I have already prepared a room for you that you will be comfortable in. When I am not in town or not around, you can stay in Corona del Mar."

When we arrived at the house, we took the luggage in. Yaneba said, "What a beautiful house! What a view! If this is what it looks like at night, I don't want to see it in the daytime."

We could see the full moon, and it was gorgeous from the house which was on the top of a cliff. Elizabeth asked me, "How much did you pay for this house? It must be millions. And nobody lives here?"

"No," I answered, "this is a safe house. When I bring somebody from out of the country I want them to be safe. No matter what I paid for it, technically it is not my house because it is not in my name, but the person whose name is on the deed is very happy because I let him use it as a tax deduction."

Elizabeth said, "My God. I feel like someone special. I feel like royalty." I replied, "You and Yaneba are special and you deserve royal treatment, because I trust you with my life. That is the reason I want you guys to be very comfortable for the time this project lasts."

Elizabeth hugged me again and said, "You are the one who is very special. Whatever my brother Hernesto and Yaneba tell me about you is not enough compared to the way you really are."

Yaneba came close to me and said, "I don't want your girlfriend to be jealous, but I agree one hundred percent with what Elizabeth just said. You deserve a big hug and a big kiss from me."

She did not wait for my approval. She hugged me and kissed me right then and there. "I'm not going to feel like I'm working while I'm here. I feel like I'm on vacation."

I smiled and told them both, "Follow me."

I went to the kitchen and opened the door to the garage and turned on the lights. They could see a brand new metallic green Range Rover and a black four-door Mercedes sedan. "The keys for those cars are in the kitchen, hanging in the cabinets. You guys use them for the time this job lasts. I suggest you alternate the cars when you follow somebody or are doing undercover work. That way you don't call attention to yourself. I know you guys are professionals and I don't have to tell you this, but that is why I put two cars in there. You don't have to worry about anything. The cars are registered to a different address in the name of a telecommunications company as are these two pagers where I will call you in case of an emergency or you can call me if you need me at any time."

I handed them the pagers and a card with my pager number on it. "In case of an emergency we will always meet here. When we talk over the phone and say location number one; that means here at this house. Place number two, just in case this place is not appropriate or you do not want to expose this location, will be the French café on Balboa Island."

I handed them a card with the address of the café. "Place number three in extreme circumstances will be the Baskin-Robbins on Harbor Boulevard at 19th Street in Costa Mesa."

Elizabeth nodded. "Very well. Understood. But this applies more to Yaneba than to me because I will be close to you most of the time, since I am going to be your limo driver."

"Yes, that is true, but you will not be around me all of the time. I will be out of the country a lot because I need to establish banking connections all over the world. We need to be prepared for any eventuality."

She nodded again. "Okay. I understand now."

I opened the refrigerator, a huge, beautiful subzero one that was full of goodies, and said, "I told Hernesto to fill this up with all kinds of stuff, including wine. That way you can relax when you come back from work."

Yaneba went to the fridge and took out one of the bottles. "My God. You remembered to buy the wine I like. Do you have a few extra minutes so you can have a glass of wine with us?" she asked with a smile on her face.

"Yes, I have a few minutes. I cannot stay too long as I have men working at the warehouse and I want to check on them to see what is going on. But I can stay for a few minutes with you and have a glass of wine."

While Yaneba was opening the wine, Elizabeth pulled out some Brie cheese, some olives, and a little container of salmon caviar from the fridge. She put it all on a big plate and put some crackers around it. We sat down and drank a glass of wine and snacked for a little while.

Later, after we talked for a bit and had a good time, I had to leave. I said goodbye to them and drove back to the warehouse in Santa Ana.

Newer 1996 currency

# Chapter 6–Doctor Franklin and My Frustrations

When I arrived at the warehouse, I opened the doors with the remote control and drove in. The first thing Romero told me when I approached the bench where he was working was that the job was a lot more complicated than he had expected. He was having problems reproducing the original plate of the one hundred dollar bill.

"What, exactly, is the problem?" I asked.

He took a deep breath. "Well, the back of the bill is no problem. I already have that done. The major problem is the front of the bill. There is a very thin line, almost microscopic, between the long hair Franklin has and the fur coat his is wearing. This has to be separated. They cannot meet. There is a little tiny color separation in between the fur coat and his hair. If I cannot get this thin line in place when we print the bill, both inks will mix, and that will form a continuation between his hair and the fur coat. That is not good because when we print it you will be able to see the flaw."

"Do you think you will be able to resolve this problem? If you can't, maybe I can bring someone to help you."

He was a little irritated at my suggestion but said, "Yes, I think I can get it. That is what I have been trying to do for the last few hours." He showed me the results of the different plates he had made and shook his head. "This is something new they have added because I never had this problem before."

"What about the fifty dollar bill?"

He smiled and took a plate from the desk and showed it to me. "This is perfect. It is already taken care of. The problem is with this damn hundred dollar bill and Franklin," he added in frustration.

Loren came close to us, bringing a plate she had been working with. She showed it to Romero. "What do you think?"

I smiled at her. "Do you know about these things?"

She smiled back. "Yes, I studied graphic arts and painting for many years. The principle is the same. It's the separation of colors, the mixing of pigments to obtain the optimal color."

I took the plate in my hand and looked at it. "I don't know, but to me, this looks a lot better. What do you think?"

Romero smiled. "Yeah, but let's put it to the ultimate test." We walked to the magnifying glass and put it under the glass. "You see— to the naked eye, it looks okay. But when you put it under the magnifying glass you can see that it is touching in the corners. As soon as we start this running in the printer, the inks will mix together and that line will disappear. Not good."

I scratched my head, confused and frustrated. I had been expecting this guy to be a master. So I asked again, "Are you sure you can fix this?"

I did not like his answer. "I am not sure about anything, but I will try my best."

Loren could see the frustration on my face as I squeezed my chin with my right hand. She came close to me and said, "Don't worry. I'll stay close to him and try to find a solution to this problem."

"Okay," I said, "Hernesto will be here with you guys and Arturo will come with me. That way he can rest tonight and he will come here tomorrow. We cannot leave the warehouse without someone here all the time. We have too many valuables here, and for security measures, we should not leave this place alone."

We left the warehouse, and when we arrived at my house my beeper began to vibrate. I checked it and saw that it was O'Brien. I dialed his number and talked to him. He told me he wanted to see me in location number one. For us, that meant the terminal train in Santa Ana. Arturo, who was standing beside me, asked me if I wanted him to come with me to the meeting.

"No. You just try to rest. Tomorrow will be a hectic day."

We said goodbye and I took my red DeLorean and drove to our meeting place, which was actually not too far from the warehouse where I had just been. When I arrived at the train terminal, I parked the car and walked to the lobby. O'Brien was already there and waiting for me, smoking a cigarette. I smiled when I got close to him and shook his hand.

"Those are going to kill you before the bullets of our enemies."

He smiled and, feeling a little guilty, put out the cigarette in one of the ashtrays on the arm of the chair. "How is everything?"

I held out the little box that contained the plates. "The twenty and fifty dollar bill plates are here."

He looked at me in surprise. "What about the hundred?"

I did not want to worry him, so I said, "Well, our man is having a little bit of a problem with Franklin and he is hassling with the details. He has already done the back so it should not be too long before he does the front."

"Don't rush him too much, but tell him the importance of getting that plate back as soon as possible."

"He already knows, but I will make sure to put a little more emphasis on it."

He moved a little closer to me and put his right hand on my shoulder. "I want you to be extremely careful. The Cuban agent, the Dolphin, is on the loose again, and he just prevented us from completing an important operation in Nicaragua. We think he's responsible for the death of two of the best agents we had in place in Columbia. They showed up dead, with their heads cut off, in a hotel in Bogota where they were supposed to have an interview with a Cuban female double agent."

I shook my head. "Well, well. Have you ever considered the possibility that our famous Dolphin could be a woman?"

"Yes, there is that possibility. Remember, in the line of business we're in, nothing looks the way it is. It could also be a decoy to throw us off in a different direction. Anyway, I want you to be very careful. We just got some information from reliable sources that the Dolphin is going to be in California very soon on a special mission. He may be here already. Our sources cannot verify what the mission is, but we all know very well what kind of mission the Dolphin takes. It's either to kill somebody or to destroy one of our major operations."

I nodded my head and said, "Don't worry. I will put my people on alert and will be waiting and watching for him. If he comes close to us we will cut him to pieces, put his ass in a sardine can, and send him back to Castro."

O'Brien smiled. "Don't be too self-confident. Be prepared for the worst. Remember that Castro will never forgive you because for ten years you took classified information out of his office right under his nose."

I nodded. "Yes, I know. We are going to take all the pertinent precautions and we will be waiting for him. We are ahead of the game now that you've told us he is coming. Besides this, I have something on my mind that worries me a little bit."

"What's that? What's happening?"

"You checked out this guy, Romero, right?"

"Yeah. He's been working with us for many years."

"Are you sure he has no connections to our enemies?"

"Well, we're never sure about that, but we have no indication that he's working for the other side. You know better than anybody that these people work for whoever pays the most. Keep it under the loop, anyway."

"Well, it just doesn't make sense to me. I have no knowledge of this printing business. Maybe he is just a little lazy and he doesn't want to hassle too much, making a copy of the plate of the hundred dollar bill. He might just be delaying this in order for us to let him use the original plate."

O'Brien raised his arm. "Oh, no. Under no circumstance will we let him use the original. That's the deal. That's the reason we're paying him two hundred fifty million dollars."

I smiled. "Try a million two-hundred fifty thousand."

His eyes bugged out. "*What?*"

"Yes, I had to offer him an extra million over and above the money he was going to make because he didn't want to leave Argentina for two hundred fifty."

"Son of a bitch! We never paid him more than a hundred fifty before for any job, and now two-fifty isn't enough!"

"Calm down. I figured that would be an incentive to him to make better quality money because he is going to use it himself."

O'Brien stood up, clearly unhappy with this. "Well, if he cannot make completely excellent work, send him back to Argentina and don't pay him shit! But under no circumstance let him use the original plate for the hundred dollar bill."

I also stood up. "Don't worry about it. Take it easy. I have somebody on standby. If Romero cannot do this to perfection, this person might just do it as a favor to me with no charge. But we should let Romero work with this for a couple of days to see what he is capable of doing. After all, the man just got here. He is probably tired from the trip, and I think we should not be too impatient."

"Okay, I'll leave it in your hands. Handle it however you think is best." We began to walk towards the entry door. "Remember, the quicker we do this operation, the less risk we have that something will go wrong."

"I know."

We shook hands, said goodbye, and left the terminal in different directions. I drove out of the terminal and, since I was so close to the warehouse, I decided to stop there and check out how much progress Romero had made. I drove into the garage and, after I said hello to Hernesto, I went into the area where Loren and Romero were working.

The first thing I noticed was a big trash can that was full of rejected plates and photo negatives. I waved to Loren and walked over to Romero. Even though the air conditioner was running full force, Romero's forehead was full of sweat. Under the potent light and using a spotlight as well, he was looking through the magnifying glass at the new plate he had just made. I came close to him and looked at me. "This is a little more complicated than it appeared to be."

He was just about to photograph the new plate, and I put my hand on his shoulder. "I think you should rest a little bit because you are probably tired from the trip, the tensions of crossing the border, and the long day you have gone through since we arrived. Maybe you just need to relax and sleep for a while. Tomorrow it will be much easier for you."

He looked at me and smiled just a little bit and then looked at his watch. I looked at mine, as well: it was one-thirty in the morning. He nodded. "I am going to give it a couple more hours. If I cannot accomplish what I want, I will tell Loren to take me back to her house where my wife will cheer me up maybe. I will take a shower and try to sleep away my frustrations. I will try again in the morning."

In an attempt to cheer him up and reassure him, I said, "I absolutely know for sure that you will do better in the morning because you are tired now. From my own experience, I know that when I am tired I cannot function well."

He ran his fingers through his hair in frustration. "Dammit! The fifty dollar bill I did in one hour. The twenty dollar bill I did in less than half an hour. But this goddamn Franklin, I cannot find the solution. This stupid little detail in his neck and his hair is driving me crazy!" He raised the plate again. He was ready to photograph it under the big powerful camera. He took a hand held magnifying glass from the desk and looked at the plate again under the big spotlight, just to make sure it was okay. He put it back on the table and began to prepare the equipment to photograph the plate.

I said goodbye to him and walked towards my car. Loren followed me and asked in a very soft voice, "Can I ask a favor of you, sweetie?"

"Sure. What is it?"

"I've not been home for so many hours, and I'm worried about my cat, BooBoos. Would you stop by my house and feed her for me?"

"Of course. It is on my way home, anyway."

"Thank you." She came close to me, hugged me, and kissed me on my ear, and then whispered, "If you want, I will wake you up in a couple of hours."

"Of course. I always like it when you wake me up in the middle of the night." I played with her and gave her a little bite on her neck. She giggled. While we were doing this, Romero came close to us, catching me by surprise.

"Where is Arturo?" he asked.

"My house. He is supposed to be resting because he is going to relieve Hernesto tomorrow. Why, do you need anything?"

"No, I just ran out of cigarettes, and I thought if he was coming back here he could bring me some."

Hernesto overheard us talking and said, "You don't need Arturo for that. I can go and get them for you. Give me one of your empty boxes. That way I will get the right kind. I don't know anything about cigarettes because I have never smoked in my life." Romero went to the trash and pulled out an empty cigarette package and handed it to him. Hernesto smiled. "Lucky us. We have a 7/11 just a few steps from us. I can walk over there."

I looked at Romero's shirt and noticed he had a full pack of cigarettes in his shirt pocket. He tried to hide it with his arm when he saw me looking at it. Loren caught it, too, and we looked at one another. I realized that it was not cigarettes Romero was worried about—it was the idea that Arturo was alone with his wife. I tried to reassure him. "I am going to stop at Loren's house to feed her cat. Do you want to give her a message from you or tell her something?"

He looked at his watch, smiled, and seemed a bit more relaxed. "No, no. *Mi gorda*[1] is sleeping already." With that, he went back to his work.

Loren looked at me and whispered, "What's going on between Arturo and Isabel?"

---

[1] An Argentinian term of endearment

"I think those two have a flame in their asses. I will tell you details later. I don't want to talk about it here."

I went to my DeLorean and drove out of the warehouse, closing the door behind me, and I drove towards Costa Mesa to Loren's condominium. When I parked in the driveway I noticed the light outside on the porch was off. This caught my attention because she always left it on. I assumed Isabel had turned it off in order to save electricity for Loren, trying to be considerate. I did not attach too much importance to this.

I took the key to the front door from under the cactus plant where Loren always left it for me. When I opened the door, BooBoos greeted me with a symphony of meows. Evidently, she was hungry and thirsty. Loren left little demo lights in nearly every outlet in the house, so it was unnecessary for me to turn on the big lights. I went directly to the kitchen and opened a can of tuna, put it in BooBoos' dish, and filled up her other container with water. She drank a lot of water, so she was thirstier than she was hungry.

I turned on the light in the kitchen, opened the refrigerator, and poured myself a glass of fresh orange juice. When I closed the fridge, I noticed a bunch of pictures of our trip to Vegas. I took one of them in which we were kissing each other. I smiled and then put it back on the door.

As I did so, I heard a scream. I turned off the kitchen light.

It sounded like Isabel was in trouble, as she screamed, "No. No! Why are you doing this to me? Ow!"

I pulled out my pistol, cocked it, and chambered a bullet. I followed her voice. It was coming from upstairs, from the guest room that Loren had given to them. I tried to make no noise and slowly walked up the stairs until I was in front of the door. I could still hear Isabel complaining.

I turned the knob slowly and opened the door quietly. When the door was completely open, I saw Isabel, stark naked. She was sitting on top of Arturo in complete ecstasy, making love and screaming like a woman possessed by the devil. At the same time, she was moving up and down, backwards and forwards, as if she were dancing an African ritual.

I looked at them in complete shock. My eyes locked with those of Arturo and he froze, looking at me in shame. I thought for a minute of what my father had told me many times when I was a kid. If a dog eats the eggs from the chicken on the farm we have to hang him

68

because even if you burn his nose he will always come back and eat the eggs again.

I thought to myself that it was a great shame because Isabel was such a beautiful and sexy woman—it would be a pity and a waste to hang her. Isabel did not even know I was behind her, as I'd made no noise when I opened the door, and she was still screaming. She would not have heard a bomb exploding right next to her at that moment.

Arturo stopped moving as he looked directly at me in the doorway. Isabel realized that something behind her had caught Arturo's attention, and she turned slightly towards the door and followed his eyes. To my surprise, she looked at me and smiled. She did not look ashamed at all, making no move to cover her breasts or herself in any way.

Instead, she beckoned to me with her index finger to come closer and join them. Evidently, Isabel liked orgies and was delighted to see me in the doorway looking at them and wanted me to be a part of this one. She never stopped moving. I was completely confused. I froze for a few minutes with the pistol still in my hand, watching that gorgeous woman with no shame at all continuing to make love to Arturo, even though he was still frozen.

She turned around again towards Arturo and pointed at me. It was as if she were asking him for his approval for me to join them. Arturo looked at me like a kid who had been caught with his hand in the cookie jar. He looked very guilty because of my warning to him about this situation. She turned again to me and made the same signal to me with her finger.

I shook my head and smiled but said nothing. I turned around and left the room, closing the door behind me. I went down the stairs as quickly as I could. When I got into my car, I called Loren immediately at the warehouse.

She asked, "Is everything okay?"

"Everything is okay, but do not bring Romero to your house under any circumstance whatever until I call you again. Do not ask me any more questions right now because I know Romero is close to you."

"I understand. I'll wait for your call."

We said goodbye and I drove back to my house. I took a shower and put on my bathrobe. I expected Arturo to show up at any minute. When I heard an engine in my driveway, I looked down from the window in my master bedroom and saw that Arturo had just driven up in my limo. I went downstairs and waited for him to come in. I sat down in the dining room, which looked out on the front door.

When Arturo opened the door, he raised his right hand high and said, "Brother, please let me explain to you what happened. Before anything else, let me say I am really, really sorry. The last thing I had on my mind was going to bed with that woman tonight. Especially in Loren's house."

"Very well. Go ahead and explain yourself because I have entrusted my life to you many times, and if you think with your dick, I am fucked! I will be very vulnerable and an easy target because anyone can get to you with some pussy. What's happened to you?"

"I'm sorry. I know how you feel. I am not going to try to justify my actions with lies. I am going to tell you the truth and let you be the judge."

"Arturo, Arturo. If Romero had found you guys the way I did, not only could he have killed you both, but you could have ruined our operation completely."

"I know. I know!" he said as he put both hands over his face.

"Arturo, do you know that crimes of passion in some countries in the world are forgivable. If a man kills his wife and her lover in a moment of jealous insanity, they get all the sympathy of the courts and the world. Nobody likes to see themselves in that position. They set them free. You had my limo. You could have even fucked her in it. Or you could have taken her to a motel or anyplace. Even though I am going to listen to what you have to say, there is no excuse in the world that can alleviate your irresponsibility and the damage you opened yourself to. I am going to try to calm down. I already took a shower, but I am still steaming. I am going to listen to what you have to say. Please. Go ahead. Explain yourself."

"You won't believe what I am going to tell you. Isabel called me. I was already in bed and half asleep. She asked me if I had some kind of sleeping pills. She said she could not sleep because of all the commotion."

"How did Isabel get your phone number?" I interrupted him.

"I gave it to them when I went to pick them up from the airport in Mexico. I told them both if they needed anything while they are in California to just call me at any time. I tried to reassure them they had nothing to worry about and tried to make them feel comfortable because they were a little afraid of coming to the USA, since Romero had some problems before when he was here."

I nodded and smiled. "I see. I see. What happened after that with Isabel?"

"Well, I recommended to her the remedy you gave to me a long time ago: a glass of hot milk with two or three fingers of Grand Marnier in it." I looked at him and smiled again. He was uncomfortable because he realized what my smile implied. "The problem was that Loren did not have any milk in the refrigerator and she did not have any Grand Marnier, either."

I interrupted and said, still smiling, "Of course, logically, since you are a gentleman, and you were so worried about Isabel being unable to sleep, you got out of bed and half asleep you went to the market in the middle of the night to buy a bottle of Grand Marnier and a gallon of milk. Well, in any case, you did not have to buy the milk because all she had to do was milk you and she would have her milk and Grand Marnier!"

He began to laugh while he shook his head. "Let me finish, okay?"

"Okay. I am very tired and I would like to go to sleep. Don't make a soap opera with ten chapters out of this."

"When I arrived at Loren's house, she opened the door and you won't believe it—she was completely naked." He kissed his finger and waved his hand. "I swear to God! I don't have to tell you how she looked because you saw her upstairs a little while ago. She jumped on top of me and I almost dropped the bottle of Grand Marnier and the milk on the floor. She grabbed the zipper of my fly and nearly ripped it off." He raised his shirt in order to show me half of his zipper which was hanging out of his pants. At the same time, he showed me his shirt which was missing three buttons and had only the holes left.

I could not hold myself any longer. I burst out laughing. "Damn! This woman did not want to fuck you! She wanted to rape you! She wanted to break you in pieces! If you had come in there unprepared she could have stuck the bottle of Grand Marnier up your ass! And bottom end first!"

He protested and in his defense said, "No, brother, I would not let her do that to me. You are exaggerating a little bit!"

"Well, it sounds like she did not just want to milk you or fuck you but she wanted to assault you. She must be a sadist." I laughed again. "When I saw her beckoning to me like that, I would have said 'Hell, no', turned around, and left! That is what you should have done! Heaven knows what kind of disease this woman has. I hope you protected yourself because before, any venereal disease you could get could be cured with antibiotics. But today, with the AIDS epidemic, you can die."

He looked at me with a long face. "No. I did not go over there with the intention of sleeping with her. Everything happened in a moment of passion."

"*Coño, chico!*   What were you thinking? If you keep acting so irresponsible,

I am going to lose my trust in you."

He tried to justify himself once more, but I interrupted him. "Don't tell me any more. I don't want to know the details. I know that Isabel is probably crazy and she raped you and all that, but you enjoyed it—when I opened the bedroom door, you were in heaven. The only reason you are repentant right now is that you got caught. Keep in mind, the next time you find another Isabel, it could be a Cuban agent sent by the Dolphin or from any other country and they could put a bullet in your head! Next time you put yourself in this kind of situation, remember what I am saying to you now because you would not be the first agent who died because of his dick. Never, never again repeat this stupidity. Especially in Loren's house or my house or any of your friends' houses because that will be the last thing you will do by my side."

He breathed deeply. "I give you my word of honor. This will never happen again. Especially with someone we're working with."

"Okay. That's good enough. I am very happy to hear you say that."

"I'm sorry, brother. I am really sorry."

"I know you are. But I am going to be even sorrier when one day I discover your body with a bullet in your head. This is exactly like eating. You are too impulsive. You have to exercise more control."

With that, I turned around and went to my bedroom. I was feeling bad because I knew he was just a big kid with a big heart. When I got to my room, I went to the bathroom, changed my clothes, and began to brush my teeth. As I did so, the story Arturo had told me crossed my mind, and I pictured how the whole thing with Isabel had happened. I pictured Isabel running behind Arturo with a bottle of Grand Marnier, trying to stick it up his ass, and I nearly spit the toothpaste out into the mirror. I could not stop laughing. I called Loren and told her the coast was clear. She could bring Romero home whenever she wanted.

---

[2] A Cuban expression roughly translated as "Damn, man!"

I crawled into my bed with a smile on my face and fell asleep. A few hours later, I felt a warm kiss on my lips. I opened my eyes to see Loren's smiling face. She took off all her clothes and climbed into bed with me, completely naked. Even though I was half asleep, she aroused me, and we made love. When we finished, we hugged each other and fell asleep holding one another because we were both exhausted.

# Chapter 7—Cloning Money with Father Salomen

The next day, we woke up at around ten-thirty in the morning. The sun was already hot. After we showered and had breakfast, Loren left the house to pick up Romero from her home and take him to the warehouse. I told Arturo to call Elizabeth and pick her up at location number two. I wanted him to bring her to the warehouse because I wanted her to meet Loren and get to know Romero.

After Arturo left, I called Jacobo. He said he had been expecting my call. I instructed him to meet me at the usual place at twelve-thirty.

I dialed another number, long distance. A female voice answered the phone.

"Is Father Salomon in?" I asked.

"Who is calling?"

"Dr. del Marmol."

"Wait a minute, please." With that, she placed me on hold.

A few seconds later, I heard Father Salomon's friendly voice, full of energy. "Dr. del Marmol, my son. Good to hear from you! We are so grateful for the package you sent. Thank you very much."

"You are welcome. It was a pleasure for me."

"I was just telling Father Lara and Sister Ella this morning that you are a blessing to us."

I smiled at that. "Thank you. It's okay."

"If there is anything we can help you with, please call us immediately. It will be a pleasure for us."

"In fact, Father Salomon, I called you because I want to ask a little favor of you."

"Yes, my son. What is it? What do you need?"

"Well, I think I could use your technical expertise. I am working here, and we are stuck with a problem. I know you are very knowledgeable. I wonder, if it is not too much trouble, could you come and spend a few days with me here in California? I would really, really appreciate this because we are in a jam and I know you can resolve our problem."

"When do you need me, my son?"

I smiled again. "Actually, I needed you yesterday, but I will know exactly this afternoon when I have exhausted all my remedies."

"Very well. When you know, call me, and we will arrange it."

"I will send one of my assistants to be your companion on the trip, and that way you will be comfortable both coming and going back."

"No problem," he said. "Call me and we will arrange it. Send your assistant and I will be there whenever you need me."

"Thank you very much, Father Salomon."

"You are welcome. I will expect your call this afternoon."

"Please give my warm regards to Father Lara and Sister Ella."

When I hung up the phone, I breathed deeply. In case Romero failed to resolve the problem we were having with the hundred dollar bill, I had no doubt that Father Salomon could.

I finished getting dressed and drove the red DeLorean to the warehouse. When I arrived, everyone was already there. I greeted them all when I got out of the car, and I told Hernesto to go back to my house and rest. After I introduced Elizabeth to everyone, I told Hernesto to also take her with him to my house. That way, he could give her a tour of the house and show her how everything worked, as she would be staying there most of the time as my limo driver.

Before she left, I told her that the next day she would be taking someone to the airport. I told her I would give her more details later. Hernesto and Elizabeth left, and Loren showed me a delivery that had come in a few minutes before I arrived. It was the special paper we were to use to print the money, the same paper used by the Treasury Department. There were also boxes of magnetic ink and other chemicals that would be used in the process of making the plates and printing the money. They were in huge boxes and were stacked against the walls so that cars could still get into the garage.

I stepped closer to Loren and whispered to her, "Has Romero been able to solve the problem of the hundred dollar bill?"

She looked at me with a long face and shook her head. "No. In my point of view, I don't think he's going to be able to do it. Evidently this color separation is a new technology. I don't think he has any experience with it. It isn't because he doesn't want to do it with all his heart; I just don't think he has the knowledge."

"I'm glad you just told me that. You have knowledge of these things. I know nothing about it. I trust you. This is exactly what I have been thinking, but I wanted to give Romero every chance."

She smiled. "Well, you don't know much about this, but you are a quick learner. You have come to the same conclusion that I already had come to last night." She pointed to the trash can. "Look at how many negatives he's ruined already, trying to correct the problem."

"Yeah," I said. "I see."

Arturo was standing close to us, and I told him, "Before you leave today, empty all that into plastic bags and take it someplace and burn it." I walked to Romero, who was still working with the negatives at his desk. "Stop trying to fix the problem. I don't want to get behind in our work. Prepare the equipment and let's begin printing the twenty and fifty dollar bills."

He looked at me in surprise. "Why? Don't you want me to complete the hundred dollar bill plate?"

"No, not now. I'll take the original plate. I want you to concentrate on printing what we already have done. Later, we'll deal with the hundred dollar bill. I might get somebody to help you. We'll leave it for the end. Let's do what we have now and not waste any more time."

He looked as though he felt a weight lifted from his shoulders. "Great! If that is what you want, there is no problem." He pulled the plate out of his desk drawer and wrapped it carefully in fabric, put it in a big envelope, and handed it to me.

"When do you think you can have the first bills printed?" I asked him. "That way I can see them and take them to my people for their approval."

He looked at his watch. "Maybe in a couple of hours at the most."

"Very well. I'll come back in a couple of hours. Loren and Arturo will stay with you and help you however they can."

We said goodbye and I left the warehouse for my meeting with Jacobo. I always met him at the Acapulco, a Mexican restaurant in Santa Ana. When I arrived at the restaurant, Jacobo welcomed me with a big smile on his face. "Hello," he said. "How are you doing?"

"Fine, thank you. How are you?"

Jacobo was a Mexican man, very tall, with light olive skin and long hair which he wore in a ponytail. He looked more Cherokee than Mexican. His wife was very small and had the same complexion as he. She had dyed her hair blond, which was a real contrast to her skin. They had two children, an eight-year-old boy and a six-year-old girl.

We had known each other for many years—ever since he had come to California illegally. Through my business and personal relationships, I had managed to make them all legal residents of the United States. Over the years, they expressed their gratitude to me many times. He had worked for me in several different businesses that I'd had. I gave him extra work whenever I had an opportunity. I sympathized with him because he was a family man: he loved his wife and cared very much for his kids. These qualities had earned my affection.

I sat down with him at the table. He had already ordered some food and asked me if I wanted something. I just ordered lemonade. After the waitress brought it to me and left, I told him I had a little job for him to do. I pulled out an envelope from the inside pocket of my sport coat. "There is ten thousand dollars in this envelope along with instructions for you. Also, there is a pager number for my driver, Elizabeth. Coordinate with her your departure and arrival times from the airport. Buy tickets to Nassau. I don't think all this will cost more than five thousand dollars. The rest is payment for the work you are going to do."

"What is my mission? What do I have to do?"

"You are going to bring—in one piece—a priest from Nassau, and you are going to make sure that when he leaves he will arrive back there in the same way. And you are to make sure he is comfortable during the trip."

"Is that all I have to do?"

"That is all you have to do. Do it well."

"Thank you very much. Five thousand dollars is a lot of money for that. Thank you for your generosity."

"It is your responsibility if anything happens to this priest. He is coming to do a job for me, and he is a personal friend. Do you understand?"

He looked at me very seriously. "Yes, I understand. I will be very careful with him. Don't worry."

I stood up. "Thank you. We will be in touch." I pulled fifty dollars out of my pocket and put it on the table. "This will pay for the food or whatever."

He also stood up. "Thank you very much. Thank you again."

We said goodbye, and I left the restaurant. As I was leaving, my pager began to vibrate. It was O'Brien. I called him and we agreed to see each other in one hour.

I went to my house, washed my face, and ate a little sandwich. I changed cars, taking the blue and black Lancia convertible. I drove to the Balboa Bay Club on the Pacific Coast Highway. When I arrived, I left my car with the parking lot attendant and went to meet O'Brien on the docks where we always met. One of my friends had a large yacht there, and O'Brien and I both had keys to the entrance.

We walked on the docks in complete privacy. He asked me, "How is everything going?"

"Even better than I expected," I answered. "In a couple of hours you will have the first twenties and fifties in your hand. You and your friends can check them out and give me the green light to begin printing in massive quantities."

"What about the hundred dollar bill?"

"We still have a little problem with the Franklin side of the bill, but I decided to start anyway with what we have already completed—the twenties and fifties. That way, we don't waste time, and I can bring some help for Romero. I came to the conclusion that he doesn't have the technical expertise to resolve the problem. We can always print the hundred dollar bills at the end of the job, so if anything goes wrong, God forbid, at least we have most of the job done and out of there."

O'Brien smiled ear to ear. "Very good thinking, my friend," he said. He reached into his pocket and pulled out a card, which he handed me. "I want you to get in contact with this woman. She has extremely good contacts in the Caribbean and Cayman Islands. She knows a lot of bankers who can help us process our operations in South and Central America. Through their banks, they may be able to arm the people fighting on our side with the weapons they need to defend themselves from Castro's aggressions."

I looked at the card and said with a laugh, "Amelia Coborrubia. Shit. Can you repeat that last name two times quickly?"

He smiled and said, "I like your sense of humor."

"Does she work for you guys?"

He looked at me and smiled. "She works for whoever pays her the most. That's why I want you to be with her when she goes to the Caribbean Islands, so you can get to know her banking contacts. At the same time, you can protect us so we don't get ripped off in our transactions."

"Okay." I paused. "Maybe I can find an opportunity to sneak a trip into Cuba and take care of some unfinished business."

O'Brien looked at me very seriously. "Watch out. We can't afford to lose you now."

"Don't worry. They are never going to get me. I'm too sneaky."

He smiled and said, "Well, actually you can get in touch with her tonight. She'll be at a Cuban party in the Social Hall at the Red Lion Inn in Costa Mesa. You can find her through our contact there. His name is Sanchez. He'll find you at the party. He's expecting you tonight."

"Alright. I will be there tonight. Don't go too far, because I will call you in a little while to show you the bills."

We said goodbye and I drove to the warehouse. I was anxious to see the bills that Romero had probably already printed. When I arrived at the warehouse I opened the door with my remote control and drove in. Sitting in chairs right in front of me were Romero and the others eating donuts and drinking coffee.

I got out of the Lancia and said, "This looks like a police station. You guys reversed the coin. You bring the donuts to your place of work."

Romero smiled with satisfaction. He had a bunch of bills already cut and stacked in his lap. He raised his coffee and said, "Look at this! I am rich!"

I smiled and walked towards them. "You are not kidding. You will be rich."

"I will never be rich like you, Dr. del Marmol. How many cars do you have? Every time you come here you come in a different car."

I smiled but did not answer. Arturo said, "Believe it or not, Dr. del Marmol has fifteen cars."

Romero raised his hands. "Oh, my God! This is crazy! Do you really have that many cars?"

I did not answer. I kept looking at one of the fifty dollar bills I had taken from his lap. I held it up to the light.

Arturo asked Romero, "Are you a Peronista?"

Romero rushed to say, "No, no, no, *che*. I am not a communist."

Arturo smiled as he was having fun with Romero and said, "If you are not a communist, what difference does it make whether he has two cars or twenty cars? It is up to him to spend his money however he pleases."

Romero became defensive at that point. "No, no. I don't mean it in a bad way. I think Dr. del Marmol has very good taste, because all of his cars are beautiful and expensive." He came close to me, bringing one of the twenty dollar bills. "Look at this. You can touch it and it is still warm. It just came out of the oven."

I shook my head. "I have to tell you this is a job well done. It is perfect. Of course, I have to show it to my friends and get their okay before you run this off in major quantities."

He looked at me. "How long will it be before you give me the okay? We are like horses in the cage on the race track waiting to be released."

I smiled. "Not too long. Maybe half an hour. I am going to take off right now and bring a few examples of these bills to my friends. I will call you as soon as I get the green light so we don't waste any time."

I called O'Brien from my car before I left the warehouse. I told him I would see him in ten or fifteen minutes at location number one.

"Okay," he replied, "I will see you there in a few minutes."

Lancia with "Marmol" license plate

A little while later, we met in the bathroom of the Santa Ana train station. I handed him the envelope and he closed himself in one of the latrines. After a few minutes he came out with a big smile on his face.

"Go ahead," he said. "Start any time you want. This is more than good enough for me. It's excellent."

"I will call you later when we are ready for the first pickup," I said.

We left the terminal using different exits. When I got to the parking lot, I called Loren immediately. "The mangos are green," I told her, using the code that signaled to her that they had the green light to start printing.

"Great," she replied. "We can eat them with salt and chili like they do in Mexico."

I returned to my house and sat down in the patio by the swimming pool with Hernesto and Elizabeth. I told them, "I will send Jacobo to Nassau to bring Father Salomon and you guys will be in charge of him during the time he is in California. I don't want anybody to know that he even exists because if something goes wrong, by no circumstances do I want him to be hurt. In other words, I want you to maintain this in complete confidence. Do you understand what I mean?"

They both nodded and Elizabeth asked me, "Where do you want us to house him?"

"Take him to the house in Corona del Mar with you and Yaneba."

"Okay," she replied. "That's good because we can keep our eyes on him. When is Father Salomon supposed to arrive here?"

"Actually, I don't know," I said. "Jacobo will handle that. It depends on the air flight schedules and so forth. This is his telephone number. He already has yours. He will call you when he has made all the arrangements. But if you want to double check with him, you are free to call and ask. I assume it will be in a couple of days because they have to fly from Nassau to Miami and from there to California.

"When you pick up Father Salomon, don't talk to Jacobo about any other subject. He only needs to know the basics. He does not need to know anything about the project or why Father Salomon is coming. Just tell him that when Father Salomon is ready to go back, you will call him."

"I understand perfectly," she said.

Hernesto asked, "What do you want me to do in this? With Father Salomon?"

"Actually, you will be doing very little," I told him. "You will continue to do your routine, watching Romero and helping wherever you can with Arturo. I want you to stand by just in case Elizabeth or Yaneba need you for anything at all. They will call you. Not Arturo or anybody else.

"Keep your eyes open because O'Brien just told me that the Cuban agent, the Dolphin, is being sent here to Los Angeles. He is either on the way or already here. O'Brien and his people don't know what his mission here is specifically, but we have to be extremely careful. He could be an informant in O'Brien's group or in our group. That could be the reason he was sent: to destroy what we have planned to do.

"Of course, this is just an assumption, but we have to be prepared, just in case. We all know they don't send the Dolphin for little things. He only is sent for major things, either to assassinate someone important or to disrupt an important mission that could do damage to them. That is the reason I tell you guys we have to sleep with one eye open."

Hernesto asked, "Are you going to be leaving soon?"

"Yes. I have to get out of the country for a few days."

He smiled and said, "I know when you make all these kinds of arrangements, it is because you do not intend to be around. Don't worry. While you are out of the country I will keep my eyes on everything."

I nodded and put my hand on his shoulder. "Thank you, but remember your priority is the warehouse. Don't take your eyes off Romero. Tell Arturo the same. Even though I have told him many times already, I think he is in love and his head is not in order. I put all my trust in you. I give all the responsibility to you."

He nodded. "Yeah. I think Arturo is in lust with Romero's wife, which is very dangerous. I have already told him to back off."

We all three shook our heads. I checked my watch and noticed it was three o'clock in the afternoon. "My God. The day is already slipped between our fingers. I have to go to the warehouse. You guys stay here and rest for a little while. If I need you, I will call you. Elizabeth, you have to drive me to a Cuban social function tonight where I am supposed to meet somebody important. Call Yaneba and tell her to be there to record and film everything that happens there, because the contact I am supposed to meet tonight is the international bank contact from the intelligence community. One of O'Brien's agents will introduce me to her. By the way, you guys are from Miami. Do you know a lady whose name is Amelia Coborrubia?"

They both shook their heads and Elizabeth said, "When I see her tonight, I'll tell you. Maybe that's not even her real name."

I patted her on the shoulder. "Very good thinking. Be here tonight at eight-thirty."

I gave her a note with the address of where the party was going to take place that night. We said goodbye, and I left the house and drove to the warehouse.

A little while later, I arrived at the warehouse. I went inside and was surprised to see how much money they had printed and cut in such a short time. It only needed to be counted, wrapped, sealed, and put in boxes.

After I said hello to everybody, I went to Romero and said, "My God. I am impressed. You really have experience in what you are doing. I can't believe you have done all this in less than one day."

He smiled. He was still working with some of the hundred-dollar bill negatives, which were spread all over the top of his desk. "I have not given up. Even though you took the originals away, I think I will be able to perfect this eventually. I made copies of series A, B, C, F, G, and H." He smiled mischievously and added, "I think I will be able to surprise you in a few days."

I smiled and shook my head. "Romero, you do not have to prove anything to me or to anybody. You are good in your work and you take pride in what you do. Forget about the hundred dollar bill. Concentrate on the printing of the ones we already have in process. I have someone coming in the next few days who will be able to help you, and we will print the hundred dollar bill at the end of the operation." I pointed to all the boxes stacked against the wall and added, "You should be proud of your accomplishments."

"Well," Romero said, "this is not all my work. This woman, Loren, is a working lion. Your friend Arturo is another lion. In other words, I have great helpers here. If it were not for them, I would not have been able to do all this."

I turned around and applauded them. "Congratulations, guys, for a job well done. Isn't it nice to work with a person like Romero? Someone who recognizes the quality of the work you are doing?"

Arturo and Loren smiled and nodded their heads. They were full of satisfaction, thanks to the compliments Romero had given them. I went to my car, opened the door, grabbed my car phone, and called

O'Brien while I was still standing up outside the car. "It's me," he answered. "Is everything okay?"

"Yes, more than okay. I think we will be able to send the first boxes of lemons tonight."

"So soon!"

"Yes. We have a team of lions working here. Their trainer has excellent qualifications from the African jungles." They all overheard me and were laughing. Romero was full of pride. If you had touched him just then, he would have blown up like a balloon.

"Very well," O'Brien said. "Call me when they are ready for delivery and I will send somebody to pick them up."

I said goodbye and hung up. "My friend is very impressed with your work. He told me to congratulate you guys."

They all smiled. It was not really true, but I had said it to stimulate them. I believed in my heart that although O'Brien had not said anything, he probably felt it in his heart based on the conversation we just had.

I dialed another number on my phone and a female voice answered. "Hello. Mr. Laden's office. May I help you?"

"Yes, please. Is Mr. Laden available?"

"Who is calling, please?"

"Dr. del Marmol." I don't know whether she recognized my name or my accent, but she giggled.

"Wait a few seconds. I will get Mr. Laden for you right away."

A few seconds passed, and Mr. Laden came to the phone. "Hi, how are you doing, my good friend? Where have you been? I haven't seen you for a few days. What can I help you with?"

"Remember when we talked about I might need your fax machine and you said no problem because you have an extra one?"

He paused a moment. "Oh, yeah, yeah. If you need it, just send someone for it. I will put it in a box for you."

"Okay. I will send my friend and associate, Hernesto, in a little while to pick it up."

"Okay. I will be waiting for him. Tell him to ask for me when he gets to the bank."

I hung up and dialed Hernesto's number. As I was dialing, Loren was looking at me very seriously. Evidently she had overheard my conversation with Mr. Laden and was shaking her head as she had no fond memories of him.

"Hello," Hernesto answered.

"Yes, if you are not too tired, I am going to need your and Elizabeth's help here in the office."

"No problem. I have already taken a shower and I was just watching TV. I am completely rested."

"Okay, I need you to go to Mr. Laden's bank and pick up a few boxes for me. Ask for him when you get there. He will be waiting for you."

"Very well," he said. "We will leave for the bank right now. We will be at the office in a little while."

A short time later, Elizabeth and Hernesto arrived at the warehouse. They unloaded four boxes from the car. In one of them was a machine for counting money that Mr. Laden had sent, and in the others were paper wrappers for bundles of $20, $50, and $100 bills. That way, it was much easier to count the money and to determine how much each box contained.

I said, "You guys count and bundle as much money as you can. O'Brien will be sending someone to make the first pickup tonight."

They said okay, and I reminded Elizabeth that she was to be at my house at eight-thirty that evening in order to take me to the Cuban gathering. They arranged themselves in the front office and began to work.

At the same time, the press was continuing to make more money in the back. Romero was attending to the press. Arturo began to help Hernesto bring the boxes of money, which was already cut, into the front office, where Elizabeth was running the counting machine and sealing the money in wrappers. Arturo and Loren were putting the bundles of money in boxes and putting the boxes against the walls in the storage area, and they marked on each box the amount of money it contained, ready for delivery.

I looked at all this processing and said goodbye to them. I muttered aloud to myself, "My God. We have a money manufacturing plant here!"

I left the warehouse and went back to my house. From there I called Jacobo and told him to make sure to get the plane tickets as soon as possible and to call me back with all the details of the flight. I said goodbye to him and hung up.

A little while later, he called back and told me he would be leaving the next day from LAX to Miami and gave me all the details of the flight from Miami to Nassau. I told him to make sure he called

Elizabeth and gave her the same information. That way, she would be able to take him to the airport and pick him up when he came back.

After I said goodbye and hung up, I called Nassau and spoke with Father Salomon to give him all the details of the flight. I told him I would see him soon and hung up the phone.

I put on my swimming suit and went out to the pool to do a few laps in order to keep myself in shape. After I had worked out for a while, I took a shower and began to get ready for my meeting. Half dressed, I went to the kitchen for a glass of orange juice. To my surprise, Elizabeth arrived.

"All the money has been counted and wrapped and is ready for pickup," she said.

"Oh, my God. Good job. You guys finished early. Thank you, sweetie."

"You're welcome. I'm going to take a shower now and get ready. I have plenty of time since we finished so early. You know how we women are. We need lots of time!"

"Take your time, Elizabeth. I don't like to get to a party too early. Besides, these parties always finish very late. If we get there too early, people will get bored too quickly with our faces."

While she went to take a shower, I called O'Brien. "Okay, you can send your guys to pick up the first batch of lemons."

He laughed, and I could tell he was very happy. "Congratulations. You've broken another record."

"I didn't know we had any competition here!"

"Well, it's not competition, but it's a great satisfaction, and you should know you've done this in record time."

I said, "Well, it's not complete yet. It's not over 'til the fat lady sings!"

He laughed, we said goodbye, and I hung up the phone.

# Chapter 8—Insurance with Panda

A little while later, we left the house in my limo and headed for my important meeting at the Social Hall in the Red Lion Inn in Costa Mesa. When I arrived, I saw roughly one hundred well-dressed people laughing, drinking, and enjoying themselves. Some were dancing to instrumental music played by a live orchestra.

After she parked the car, Elizabeth joined me. She said, "Let's dance. That way, we'll blend in better."

We started to dance, and as we did we heard people clapping and shouting at one end of the dance floor. A circle had formed around a couple. The woman was wearing a short, sexy dress which revealed her legs and her cleavage. Her outrageous moves, dips, and dives showed off almost all of her body for all to see. She seemed to be dancing more for the crowd than for her partner.

Elizabeth squeezed my hand. "I think I've found your contact!" With this, she turned me around so I could see the couple everyone was watching. The lady who was dancing looked at me and our eyes met. She smiled and nodded to me. I nodded back at her. She continued laughing and dancing.

"Would you like something to drink?" I asked Elizabeth. "I am a little thirsty."

"Yeah," she answered.

We stopped dancing and went to the bar. I asked Elizabeth what she wanted.

"Whatever you are drinking."

"Are you sure?"

"Of course I am sure. Whatever you order for yourself is fine for me. Order two."

"Okay." I turned to the bartender. "Do you have mango and kiwi juice?"

"Of course, sir. We have everything," he answered.

"Put three or four fingers of each juice and squeeze a couple of limes in there. Fill the rest of the glass with white Bacardi rum."

"This is something different," he said. "Do you mind if I taste it?"

"No, of course not. Make three of them. One for my lady and me and one for you. I will pay for all. Let's hope you like it."

A gentleman came close to me. "Dr. del Marmol, how about making four? Another one for me, and I will pay for all four." I turned around and he said, "I am Sanchez." He extended his hand and we shook.

"You don't have to pay," I protested. "I will pay for all. This is Elizabeth."

"Nice to meet you, Elizabeth," he said as he kissed her hand.

He did not look like a Cuban at all. He looked more like he was from Pakistan or some country in the Middle East. He was tall, handsome, muscular, and balding. His remaining hair was mixed black and white, and he had long sideburns and a mustache. He was very well dressed.

"Are you Cuban?" Elizabeth asked him.

"Yes, I was born in Cuba. My ancestors were Hungarian. They ran from Hungary to Cuba because of the communist regime in their country, but it caught up with them, and they had to run again. They took me out of Cuba when I was twelve years old, but I remember it very well. I remember the long lines just to get a piece of bread, exactly the same as my parents told me they had to do in their native country many years before."

The drinks came and the bartender exclaimed, "My God, Dr. del Marmol! This is excellent! I love it. I think I will suggest to my boss that we put it on the drink menu. This is really something! What do you call it?"

Elizabeth smiled and answered, "Marmol's Wild Dreams!" Elizabeth and Sanchez raised their glasses, and she added, "To no more bread lines."

"To no more running from communism!" Sanchez added.

I raised my glass as well and quipped, "That is my Wild Dream!" We all sipped and laughed. They both made sounds of appreciation, so I said, "You guys really like it, huh?"

"Yes," Elizabeth said.

"You can't even taste the rum," Sanchez said.

"That is the only danger with this drink. There is a lot of rum in it. You could end up in real trouble before the night ends and wind up having to take a taxi home."

Sanchez pointed to the lady everyone had been watching dancing with such outrageous abandon and said, "That is Amelia Coborrubia from Miami. She opened some physical therapy clinics here in southern California. She is also one of us. She has done a lot to help the Cuban freedom fighters."

I looked at Elizabeth and said, "You are good, honey. Do you know her?"

She looked at me and frowned. "I think I've seen her someplace before, but I can't remember where. Introduce me to her after you've met her, and maybe it will come back to me."

Sanchez observed, "She likes to be the center of attention."

"What woman doesn't?" I laughed.

Elizabeth touched my arm in protest. "I don't!"

"You are a different breed, honey," I smiled.

Sanchez grinned. "You know what? Amelia is a very different breed of woman. She is actually like a business woman. She attracts men, uses them, and then tosses them away when she doesn't need them anymore."

"You sound as if you are speaking from your own personal experience," I observed with a smile.

"No, not me," he said quickly in self-defense. "But a friend of mine went through that with her. It's my duty to inform you. That way, you know what waters you are swimming in. That water has very powerful currents, my friend. Do you still want to meet her?"

"Yes. I am interested, but only from a business perspective and nothing else."

"That's what they all say, but they usually wind up in bed with her."

I looked again at the dance floor, and I realized that the man who was dancing with her was Jacobo. I hadn't recognized him before because he was dressed very elegantly. He was wearing a white suit with a black shirt with no tie, and a white hat with a black bandana. His ponytail was hidden by his hat.

"Well, well, well," I said. "Look at Jacobo dance. I didn't know he had that quality. Actually, he is really a good dancer."

"Yeah," agreed Sanchez, "he thinks he's her boyfriend. And he is— for the next hour." We all three laughed at Jacobo's expense. "Do you know him very well?"

"Yes," I replied, "I have known him for many years. As a matter of fact, he works for me."

Sanchez nodded, but said nothing. We all watched the two dancers, and once in a while, Amelia glanced at me. She felt threatened because she had not expected a woman to be with me. She was used to seducing every man who did business with her.

Elizabeth was dressed very beautifully, with a long black dress, open on the side up to her thigh. She looked elegant, and her behavior was classy. She touched me occasionally on my shoulder and put her arm around my back in an affectionate way. It looked as if we were together and more than friends.

We watched them until the dance was over. Jacobo looked like a proud lover. Amelia looked around the room for approval. Everyone clapped, whistled, and raised their drinks. Amelia turned, looked at us, and smiled. Sanchez beckoned to her to join us. She signaled okay with her hand. "In a minute," she mouthed. Sanchez nodded in the affirmative. She went to the other side of the salon and came back by herself a few minutes later.

Sanchez said, "This is Dr. del Marmol, and this is Elizabeth."

"I am Amelia Coborrubia," she said. She smiled at Elizabeth and looked her up and down. "Dr. del Marmol, you have a beautiful wife."

Before I could answer, Elizabeth said, "No, I'm not his wife. I'm his limo driver. Thank you for the compliment. I think you're a beautiful woman, too."

I put my arm around her shoulders. "She is not only my limo driver; she is a very special friend."

Amelia laughed loudly. "God, I don't want to see your wife if this is your limo driver!"

"Well, that will be hard to see because I have no wife. But eventually, I will have one and that one will be by my side for the rest of my life. I have already had the misfortune of losing the love of my life under very strange circumstances. I don't want to go through that experience again."

Amelia became very serious. "I really respect what you say. These days, it is very hard to find a man with integrity and who wants to be with only one woman. They are all jerks and have only one thing on their minds: sex, sex, sex!"

I smiled. "Why do you have sex when you don't have love? It's like a flower with no perfume. It's like an ocean with no salt. It's like a sky with no moon or stars."

She put down her drink and shouted as she patted her heart, "Wow. Wow! WOW!" Her expression was a blend of disbelief and happiness, and she asked Sanchez "Is this man for real?"

Sanchez smiled and did not answer. Elizabeth leaned over a little bit in her chair and said, "Honey, he's as real as real can get."

Amelia picked her drink back up. She did not really want Elizabeth to get into the conversation, but she replied, "Honey, you probably know him a lot better than I do, so I will take your word for it. Are you sure you are only his limo driver?"

"Yes—and, as he said, I am also a very special friend," Elizabeth replied with a smile on her face.

Amelia said nothing else. She smiled and pulled one of her business cards from her purse. She wrote something on the back and handed it to me. "I believe we have some business to discuss. Why don't we get out of here? Meet me in fifteen or twenty minutes, alone, at this place and we will take care of our business." She extended her hand to me. "It's really a pleasure meeting you, Dr. del Marmol. I am looking forward to continuing our conversation shortly."

I took her hand in mine and shook it gently. As I was about to let it go, she smiled and asked me mischievously, "You are not going to kiss my hand? I guarantee you it smells good. I know that is an old custom in Cuba, and you look to me like a gentleman."

I smiled. Still holding her hand, I raised it to my mouth and said, "Of course, with pleasure." I then kissed it.

She said goodbye to Elizabeth, not extending her hand. Still smiling mischievously, she said "Nice to have met you. Take good care of Dr. del Marmol." She then extended her hand to Sanchez. "It was a real pleasure seeing you again, my good friend Sanchez."

He kissed her hand. "The pleasure is all mine, Señorita Coborrubia."

She turned and walked seductively through the whole salon to the exit. All the men watched her beautiful body as she walked and as she swung her hips from side to side.

Elizabeth could hardly wait until she completely disappeared to burst out laughing. She said, "Before this woman reaches her thirties she'll need maintenance and new shock absorbers, the way she moves!" She turned to me. "I'm a woman and I tell you as your mother would tell you: this woman is big trouble. She could be the worst nightmare of any man."

I smiled. "You're not kidding. Did you see when she raised her hands? Both tits nearly came out of her dress."

We all laughed, and Sanchez said, "But man—she looked good! That *mulata* Cuban woman can also be the wild dream of any man in bed."

Elizabeth said, "Oh, my God. I thought you had a little class, Sanchez. With all my respect, I don't want to offend you, but you are a typical man. You only see her ass. That is how you get your brain burned! Dream, my eye! She's a nightmare! She is right out of the Twilight Zone. Wake up. And you're in the intelligence forces! Man, you are in trouble. I see the way you look at her. You're asking for trouble."

We said goodbye to Sanchez, he thanked me for the drink, and we drove to Santa Ana to the Acapulco restaurant to meet with Amelia. When we arrived at the restaurant, I told Elizabeth I did not think I would be too long. I got out of the limo and went inside.

I looked around and did not see Amelia. Apparently, she was not there yet. I looked for a secluded table where I could see the door. When I found one, I ordered a glass of wine, a seafood platter, and a guacamole dip. The waitress brought my order before Amelia arrived, and I began to sample it and drink my wine. A few minutes later, she arrived. When she saw me, she came immediately to my table.

"Oh, you like Mexican food!" She exclaimed with a smile.

"I like all kinds of food as long as it is well done, but my favorite is French food."

"French, huh? You have very refined taste."

"Sit down, please, and join me."

The waitress came to our table. "Give me a glass of the same wine he is drinking," she ordered. When the wine came, she drank a little of it and delicately sampled the guacamole. She kept looking at me directly. "Mr. Sanchez told me a little bit about you. You are a very interesting man. There are a lot of people waiting for your merchandise. Is it already done? Is it ready for shipping?"

"No, not yet. We just began the process a few days ago. I will let you know when it's ready."

"I will be more than glad to pick it up."

"No. For security reasons, I will deliver it to you when it is ready."

Amelia made a disapproving expression, shook her head, and said, "Okay." With that, she reclined in her chair, leaving a larger space between us.

"I understand you have many offshore connections."

"You are right," she smiled. "I can have your merchandise wired to any place on this earth, but there will be a small fee for the bankers, of course."

"How soon can you wire the funds to the people in South and Central America?"

"As soon as you come with me and open each bank account. We have to do this in person and we use different banks in each country. I believe that is the way your friend O'Brien wants it."

"Yeah, he told me that is the way he wants it. Well, then, I will call you as soon as I am ready to take off. I need a little time to put things in order. I will get the tickets for the cruise ship."

"Oh. We're going on a cruise ship?"

"Yes, this is the way we always do these things. That way we do not call attention to ourselves. It will not be longer than a week."

She lowered her chin, smiled, and said, "You could call me sooner, if you like."

I smiled and shook my head. She did not finish her wine but instead stood up and prepared to leave.

"I will call you as soon as I am ready," I said.

She gave me her hand to kiss and said goodbye. She walked towards the door of the restaurant, the eyes of every man following the swaying of her hips as she walked away.

The next day, I met with Sanchez on Balboa Island near the ferry. I gave him the envelope with the tickets to give to Amelia. I had booked two cabins next to each other: one for her, one for me. I figured we could be close but we did not need to be together.

Sanchez smiled. "Boy, why aren't you using this opportunity to share a cabin with her?"

"Because she is your girlfriend and Jacobo's girlfriend, and I respect my friends' girlfriends," I replied.

Sanchez shook his head. "Boy, you are something, man."

"Make sure to tell her to be on time. Even though the captain is a good friend of mine, they are not going to wait for her."

I went back to the warehouse after our meeting and met with my friends. They were all working diligently printing, counting, wrapping, and boxing the money. Loren told me with a big smile on her face that they had already completed six deliveries.

"Oh, my God!" I exclaimed. "You guys are going to bankrupt the Treasury Department." I went over to Romero, who was still working on the hundred dollar bill negative. He said hello to me and seemed to be happy.

"I almost have it!" he exclaimed to me. He showed me one of the negatives he had been working very hard on. He held it under the light, and I could see it was almost perfect, but there were still a few hairs touching the fur coat of Franklin.

"Don't worry about it," I told him. "I have someone coming in a few days that can help you with this."

"I am not giving up. I am going to surprise you pretty soon."

My pager started to vibrate. It was O'Brien. I whispered to Loren, "I will probably be leaving tomorrow early in the morning. Keep doing the same thing you are doing now and don't let Romero know I have left town."

I said goodbye to my friends, left the warehouse, and called O'Brien. He said he wanted to meet with me before I left, so we went to location 4: a steak house in Long Beach, located on the docks in the Marina.

After we greeted each other, we sat down at an outside table. He was a little worried about my going out of the country, especially in the middle of this job when everything had been going so well. I told him I had several very trustworthy Cuban freedom fighters working on the job.

Everything would continue the same way and nothing would change. My friends would keep an eye on Romero, who was the only one we had to watch out for. "Besides," I reminded him, "you told me to go with Amelia."

"Yes, I want you to go and keep an eye on her."

"Well, my friend, I have not cloned myself yet. I cannot be in two places at the same time."

He smiled and nodded. "Yeah, I'm sorry. I wish I had ten of you."

I grinned. "You must be kidding. Ten of me! That would drive you crazy!"

"I'm a little worried about your side trip to Cuba. What if something goes wrong there?"

"Nothing has gone wrong in the past thousand times I have gone in and out of Cuba. What makes you think something will go wrong this time? If the Dolphin is coming to California looking for me, I am really going to throw them off. The last place in the world he would imagine me to be is in Cuba!"

"Yeah, you're right about that." Around us, Doby the Panda Bear was selling flowers. He caught O'Brien's attention. "Isn't that the same panda we saw a few weeks ago at Balboa Island in Newport Beach?"

"Don't worry about it. He is one of my people. He is watching our back."

O'Brien smiled. "Shit. You have better security than I have."

"My security is your security." The panda bear hung around, utilizing every opportunity to take pictures of O'Brien and me. "Remember, every time I go to Cuba I always bring fresh information from there about the next move Castro is going to make against us."

He nodded. "I guess I'm getting old. I'm getting too worried. I even worry about our Secret Service."

"What do you mean?"

"If the Secret Service finds out about this...oh, my God! We handle spies. They handle money. They don't have a clue about what we're doing. If they find out what's going on, there'll be hell to pay. You'll be on your own because under no circumstances can we expose the Agency or the old man."

I was very uncomfortable with what I was hearing. "Let's not forget this was you guys' idea. Not mine. I didn't come to this country to break its laws. Doing whatever we do out of the country is one thing, and I don't mind that, as long as we can stop Castro and his *mafiosos*. But doing it on our own soil is an entirely different thing. I told you from the beginning, I don't want to end up in jail here."

Doby continued walking around and staying close to us. He was about thirty feet behind us, playing with some kids and acting goofy. One of the children pulled on his leg and asked if he sold gum.

"No," the bear answered, "I sell flowers and fruits because I'm a fruit cake."

O'Brien gave me a concerned look but said, "Don't worry. If something goes wrong here, we have the power to get you out so long as you keep your mouth shut and don't implicate anybody else. If you do that, it'll be more difficult to get you out." He patted my shoulder. "Take it easy. We're almost there. When are you leaving?"

"Between now and Friday."

"You're beginning to sound like one of us."

"I thought I was."

"You are, dammit," he said, nonplussed at my taking his joke literally. "You *are* one of us."

I smiled. "I am leaving in the morning." We shook hands and said goodbye, and I drove back to my house to prepare my luggage and toiletries for the next morning.

# Chapter 9—The Caribbean Contacts and the Drug Cartel

Early the next morning, Elizabeth took me to the dock. I was dressed like the captain of the ship. After I boarded, Captain Pascual greeted me and introduced me to some of the officers. He jokingly told them that if he had a heart attack, I could take over the ship.

They showed me my cabin, and after I walked around and hung up my clothes, I went out onto the veranda balcony of my cabin. I looked at the scenery around the ship and at the smaller boats cruising by. I heard a knock at the door and thought it was one of the crew members bringing something to me. I opened the door and saw Amelia standing there with all of her luggage.

"Hello," I said, concealing my surprise. "Can I help you with anything?"

"No. This is my cabin."

"No, there must be some mistake. This is my cabin, but you can come in if you want."

"It's our cabin, honey. I told the Capitan we did not need two. We only need one because it will look funny if we have separate cabins. Remember, we are supposed to be a married couple."

"You are right, of course," I conceded. "Come on in. We will work out something."

"Don't sound so wounded," she chided me. "Many, many men would fall over and die just to sleep in the same place with me."

"I'm sure they would," I murmured.

"What?"

"Never mind. Come on in."

Amelia hung her clothes in the same closet and then threw herself on the bed with her arms over her head. She raised one knee and put her foot on the bed.

From where I was standing, I could see right up her dress. She was not wearing any underwear.

"Oh, there is something so romantic about cruise ships," she said. She rolled around the bed, arching her back like a cat, and added, "Oh, this is going to be a lot of fun." She stood up then and turned around. "Would you mind unbuttoning me? Will you?" She already had the straps off of her shoulders and was waiting for me to unbutton her dress. "I guess I will be teaching you how real banking is done."

"I am always open to learning new things," I said as I unbuttoned her dress. "I do have a little experience with international banking, though."

I finished unbuttoning her dress and she let it fall to the floor. She was completely naked. She walked over to one of her bags, unzipped it, and pulled out a red G- string and put it on right in front of me, as if I weren't there.

Amelia enjoyed flaunting her body as she walked over to the veranda and went outside. She turned around to face me and leaned back against the railing, brazenly showing her breasts. The ship started to move slowly out of the harbor, blowing its horn. People were outside, waving goodbye to family and friends. Some looked at her in awe; others were offended. Others just went back inside their cabins. She ignored everybody and everything as if she owned the ship and was alone on it.

I told her, "You'd better get dressed. If you want, we will go to lunch together. I will be back in a couple of hours."

"You're going to leave me alone?" she asked incredulously.

"Yes, I have to take care of some business." I closed the door behind me and went to the cabin of the captain. When I reached his cabin, he greeted me with a big smile.

"God, you have a package in your cabin," he said.

"Actually, it's not my package. It's anybody's. Do you want it? We can move it to your cabin."

"No, I'm afraid, old friend, that you are stuck with it."

"Well, someone has to do it. I guess this time it's me. Don't forget me tomorrow night when we pass close to Cuba. I'll be ready and will be in the same place as usual."

"Doctor," he said in mild reproof. "Have I ever forgotten?"

I smiled. "No."

We shook hands and I left his cabin.

That night I took Amelia to dinner. We danced and she went wild on the floor. She became the center of attention. While we were dancing, she tried to kiss me a couple of times on the lips.

"Don't you think you should quiet down a little bit?" I asked her. "You are calling too much attention to yourself and to me."

She laughed loudly. "Well, we are supposed to be husband and wife. We are supposed to kiss each other and make love once in a while."

"Sweetie, we are pretending, remember? You don't have to take your role so seriously."

She laughed again. "I always take my roles very seriously."

I decided to leave the dancing area, and so we went to the casino for a little while. We gambled for a while, and then I told her I would see her later. I took off and left her gambling. I bought some cologne in the little shopping mall and walked around for quite a while. Nearly three hours later, I went back to our cabin.

As I entered the cabin, the room was dark except for the moonlight shining in through the veranda. It took a moment for my eyes to adjust to the darkness. When they finally did, I saw a woman silhouetted in the moonlight on the veranda balcony. It was Amelia. She was leaning back against the railing, completely naked except for her high heels.

"Please, don't turn on the lights," she said.

"All right."

She raised her arms over her head and stretched again like a cat. The she gripped her breasts and squeezed them before walking to the veranda door. She stood in the doorway, her hands gripping the edges and looking at me. "Don't you desire me?"

I didn't want to offend her. I hesitated for a moment before answering. "You are a beautiful woman, Amelia." I maintained my distance from her, however.

She noticed that I did not move towards her. "Beautiful—is that all?"

"Is that all? What's wrong with that?"

"You don't feel like jumping on me when you see me naked like this? You don't want to fuck me?"

"I think you had too much to drink tonight, Amelia."

She grabbed me and said, "Let me take your clothes off. I know I can turn you on." With that, she began to unbutton my shirt and tried to take my coat off.

Gently I tried to stop her. "I don't want to do this, Amelia."

"Why? Why?" She pulled my zipper down and stuck her hand in my crotch.

"I'm sorry. I am not attracted to you. I'm sorry." I took her hand out of my pants.

"You don't have to do anything. Don't fight me. I am going to do everything."

By now, I was past irritation and moving into anger. I said firmly and loudly, "No! You fuck everybody. That is the kind of woman you are. You are not going to fuck me! I don't like your type."

That really upset her, and she pushed me and shouted at me, "Go away! Get out of here!"

I grabbed a blanket and a pillow and walked to the door. As I was leaving, I turned around and said to her, "You see? This is exactly why I did not want you to be in the same cabin with me. I know I am a gentleman and because I know that, I expected I would be the one who would end up sleeping on the upper deck on one of those goddamn sun bathing chairs!" I tried to button up my shirt and make myself presentable because I did not want to call attention to myself as I walked to the upper deck.

As I was walking there, I felt my blood pressure rising and my face growing red. I could hear my blood roaring in my ears, so high had it gotten. I was enraged at myself for letting that woman put me in this position.

When I arrived at the upper deck, it began to sprinkle. *Oh, no,* I thought to myself. *This is all I need. It looks like it is going to rain.* I wrapped myself up in the blanket, crawled onto one of those lounge chairs and tried to fall asleep. I slept very little.

It was perhaps an hour or two later when I felt an arm touching me. It was Amelia, dressed in a jogging suit and a raincoat.

"I'm sorry," she said with a very long face. "Come on back down to the cabin. You are going to get sick up here. I promise I won't bother you anymore."

"Are you sure, Amelia? Are you going to let me rest? I need to rest. I have something important to do tomorrow."

She raised her right hand towards Heaven. "I swear. I will not bother you anymore. I'm sorry."

"Okay. I will go down with you." I left the blanket and pillow there as they were soaking wet, and I did not want to carry them to the cabin.

On my way down, I asked one of the crew members to bring me another blanket and pillow, as mine had gotten wet.

The next morning, there was a knock on the door. I covered myself with a bathrobe and got up to answer it. It was room service with a tray of coffee, milk, orange juice, rolls, and fruit. The bellman handed the tray to me and then looked behind me, and his eyes bugged out. Amelia was lying with the covers shoved to one side, face down on the bed—and completely nude.

I tipped the bellman and closed the door in his face. Smiling, I shook my head, looked at Amelia and laughed, saying to myself, "What a crazy woman!"

That day, Amelia went to the swimming pool, wore her famous G-string swimming suit, and called attention to herself. Some women were offended, but some men loved it, enjoying the view of her large posterior.

While she spent the day at the pool, I spent the day resting as I had not slept much the night before. Early in the evening, I went to the bridge and met with the captain. We looked at the navigational chart of the Caribbean side of Cuban national waters. He said, "We are getting close. Be ready."

I looked at my watch. "It's eight-thirty now. In approximately forty-five minutes we will be at the right point."

I left the bridge followed closely by two crew members. We walked to one of the life boats. I was wearing my scuba gear and carrying my fins in my hand. I felt the ship slowing down, and with the help of the crew members crawled into one of the life boats and waited. I felt them begin to slowly lower the boat. The ship was moving very slowly. When I was about fifteen feet from the water, I put my fins on, stood up, sat down on the side of the boat, and slowly let myself slide into the water. I swam to the shore. From the water I could see the boat being raised back up onto the ship and the lights growing further and further away.

A few hours later, I was walking on the streets of Havana. I walked through the parking lot of one of the buildings of the El Vedado. I grabbed the keys from the front tire of a Soviet jeep and drove away towards Sandra's house.

I was hoping I would be able to see my son from afar as I always did when I went to Cuba. I never went near Sandra and my boy as I did not want to get them into trouble. I had told her on several occasions that she should find another man since she could never leave

Cuba and I could never come back until Castro was no longer in power. She assured me many times that she would always be waiting for me. She said she didn't want anyone else in her life replacing me in the eyes of my son.

I parked the jeep a few blocks away from her house, walked across the street from it, and hid behind the bushes. The lights were still on in the house, even though it was around 11:30 in the evening. This meant someone was still awake. I stayed behind the bushes for a little while, just watching the house and hoping to see someone.

I saw a government car approach the house and park in the driveway. A young, good-looking G-2 officer got out of the car from the driver's side. He walked around to open the passenger door. When he opened the door, Sandra smiled and stepped out. He kissed her hand, they hugged, and then they kissed on the lips.

I was shocked. I walked away before my emotional distress could provoke me to reveal myself. I had believed her when she told me again and again that I was the only man for her. I took the jeep and drove to my uncle's house in Miramar. After I had greeted my niece, my aunt, and my uncle, they offered me a Cuban coffee. Although I do not drink coffee, I did not say no. I knew how difficult it was to get coffee in Cuba because it was rationed, and I knew how special it was that they offered it to me. It was because they loved me and I did not want to disappoint them.

Twenty minutes later, the General arrived at my uncle's house. My cousin and aunt excused themselves and went to their bedrooms to sleep, or pretend to sleep, so the three of us could have privacy to talk.

The General said, "How very nice to see you. You are working on something big now, according to my sources."

"Yes, and very, very soon I may be able to put lots of money into funding the purchase of the weapons that are needed to overthrow Castro once and for all."

"I will be waiting. I have something extremely important to tell you. If you guys play this right, we may not have to wait for that money to buy those weapons. It is possible that the United Nations may intervene and finally take action for all the crimes against humanity that Castro is committing every day all over the world."

"Will you please explain yourself a little better? This sounds too good to be true!"

He lit a Cuban cigar and inhaled deeply. "Well, as you know, Cuba has intelligence officers in every single embassy all over the world. But in Panama, Castro has a special group of high officers from the Ministry of the Interior. They're up to their necks in drug trafficking and the cloning of human organs produced in Cuba. The use of official planes and ships to move all this contraband around the world proves the involvement of the entire Castro government.

"They sell to the black market. For instance, a heart goes for five hundred thousand dollars. A liver for three hundred fifty thousand. Kidneys, two hundred fifty thousand! This is illegal and breaches the treaty between Cuba and the United Nations. And they have been doing this for years.

"Even more outrageous," he continued, "is the cocaine trafficking from Columbia. There have been secret negotiations between the lord of the drug cartels, Pablo Escobar, and Castro's most trustworthy man, General Ochoa Sanchez. They're acting under the direct orders of Fidel and Raul Castro, bringing millions of dollars every month to Cuba to build new hotels for the tourists and for the enjoyment of the new class of the elite in the Castro circle."

"Oh, my God!" I exclaimed. "This is for real? It sounds like fiction! What can we do?" I asked. "How can we expose this?"

The General took the cigar from his mouth and said, "Let me tell you. A great opportunity has landed in my hands. You have to take immediate action. You cannot wait until you return to the USA and discuss it with O'Brien. We have to prove this right now! Later, we may not have another opportunity."

"How can we prove this?" I insisted.

"Our ticket is Capitan Jorge Martinez Valdez. He is an ignorant peasant, but he loves money. I have already arranged with him. If you put one million dollars in his hands, he will introduce you as a business man and an investor to the rest of his group, who are all a bunch of delinquents from the G-2 that Castro has placed in the Cuban embassy in Panama. This man, Valdez, is the direct courier between Pablo Escobar and General Ochoa Sanchez.

"He goes every weekend to the Ochoa ranch for the gatherings and parties in order to report the financial income and profits they have made that week. He also enjoys the parties, the luxuries, and the food. Try to record and video everything that will incriminate this man with the drug cartel. If possible, with General Ochoa and Tony de La

Guardia, as they are the strongest connection to the Cuban government and can prove Castro's involvement in all this."

"Okay," I said. "This sounds very good. I am traveling with a young lady. Perhaps she can assist me in this."

He gave me a small note. "When you get to Panama, call Capitan Martinez Valdez." He stood up and went to the window in the living room and looked out to make sure nobody was around, listening to our conversation. He closed the curtain and said, "Make sure that when you call you ask for Capitan Jorge Martinez Valdez. Use his whole name. He is supposed to reply to you, 'The same one is dressing and has his shoes on, comrade.' That is the signal. If he does not answer that way to you, hang up the phone. You can call again the next day."

"Okay. What is my name supposed to be to identify me to him?"

"You are going to be Dr. Antonio Rada Montiel."

"Very well, I will do it."

My uncle said, "Remember, this is a very unique opportunity because you can prove to the United States government and the intelligence community with pictures and recorded conversations that the Cuban government is using their planes and ships and their diplomatic immunity to move contraband all over the world. There is a great chance they will form a coalition with the United Nations and the rest of the world will intervene in Cuba. This is our chance to end the immoral regime of the Castro brothers."

I smiled and said, "My God. O'Brien will really be happy if I can bring this back to him. It will be like hitting the jackpot for the Zipper. Let's hope everything goes well."

The General smiled. "For sure, this time it will go well. All these people who are working with him are really disappointed and discontented with the economic disaster that Cuba has been going through for so many years. They know better than anybody because they travel all over the world; how different life is in those countries in comparison with Cuba, where you cannot even buy a piece of chocolate for your kids. They want to enjoy the good things in life also with their families."

He raised his hand and said, "Did you know that a few weeks ago they brought orthopedic mattresses for Castro, his brother, and a few of their friends? Do you know how much each one of those mattresses cost? I saw the receipts with my own eyes. Each one cost six thousand dollars! At the same time that Castro and his brother are sleeping like on a cloud on these mattresses and building luxurious resorts all over Cuba with drug money, they are poisoning the world with their drugs and their political ideas. There is no other name for these people. They are parasites. They get inside a country under the guise of helping it and suck it dry until there is nothing left, and the country dies."

"Yes," my uncle agreed, "you are right. That is exactly what they did in Luanda, the capitol of Angola. A beautiful and wealthy city, full of prosperity—and they sucked all the resources and massacred a large part of the population of the whole country."

"Yes," I said, "but remember: everything has a beginning and an end. One of these days, Castro will run out of tricks, and his diabolical games will be ended. He is like Machiavelli. He always instigates conflict everywhere. When he gets caught doing so, he blames everybody else, including his close friends and allies. He washes his hands and pretends to be innocent like Pontius Pilate and then sits back and enjoys watching all his friends die."

The General made a face to show his agreement. "Yes, this man is extremely dangerous and we all know that by now." He reached inside his pocket and pulled out a little plastic bag that contained five rolls of microfilm. He handed it to me and said, "Be extremely careful with this. Tell O'Brien this is for his eyes only because in here is some of the conversation between Capitan Valdez and myself. In this conversation, he not only incriminates himself but also some of the people working with him in the Cuban embassy in Panama, including General Ochoa Sanchez, Antonio de La Guardia, and the Panamanian leader, General Noriega. Make sure you seal the container that you use to transport this film very well. This is extremely valuable."

"Don't worry," I said. "I will make sure this gets into O'Brien's hands in the same condition you are putting it into my hands right now."

We hugged each other and said goodbye. They wished me luck as I left the house. I drove towards Sandra's home again. I parked my jeep several blocks away and walked to her house. The government car I had seen earlier was still in her driveway, and all the lights in the house were off.

I got close to the car and pulled a small explosive out of my pocket. I unwrapped it, set the timer, and crawled under the car to stick it under the fuel tank. I crawled back out and walked away slowly. I turned around and looked the car from a short distance away, and then walked to my jeep. When I was driving away, I heard a tremendous explosion behind me and a big cloud of smoke went up into the sky.

I drove to the same location where I had picked up the jeep. I parked it in the same position and put the keys back where I had found them. I walked to the coast, and about forty-five minutes later was at the same place where I had earlier left my equipment. I uncovered my gear from where I had hidden it and put it back on. Then I got back into the ocean and swam to the place where the ship was supposed to pick me up.

I surfaced and saw the lights of the cruiser not too far away. After swimming for a while, I got to the ship. I signaled to the captain with my transmitter watch, and they lowered the life boat until it practically touched the water. I climbed into the boat, and they raised it back up. When we got to the upper deck, some members of the crew and the captain were waiting there for me. I had already taken off my scuba equipment. The crew and the captain helped me get out of the boat and back on board the cruise ship.

So ended my brief visit to my home country.

# Chapter 10—One More Attempt

Captain Pascual had a huge grin on his face as he asked, "Is everything okay?"

"Well," I answered, "not everything is perfect, but everything is okay."

"Well, not everything in life is perfect, my friend."

"Yes, you are absolutely right," I conceded.

"I hope you have a good excuse," the captain said slyly, "because the package you have in your cabin has come unwrapped. She has been everywhere, asking all the crew members and officers where you are. In order to calm her down, I told her that you were doing something important and very confidential and you will explain it to her later. I asked her please not to ask any more questions about Dr. del Marmol of the crew members."

I shook my head in disgust. "Thank you, *Capitán*. I will handle that when I get to my cabin."

The captain clapped his hands together and said to the crew, "Roll it up! We have to get out of here." The crew began to cover the life boat. I said goodbye to the captain and walked to my cabin.

When I arrived, I opened the door and was surprised to see Amelia standing a few feet from the door—pointing a pistol at me. I raised my hands. "It's me. Don't shoot! It's me."

She put the gun down and exclaimed, "Oh, my God! I thought something had happened to you. Where have you been?"

I tried to calm her down. Her agitation was so great I feared she might grow even more indiscreet. "I'm fine. I had to step out for a while to take care of something important."

She put the little pistol back in her handbag and shook her head. She calmed down, though her eyes were still a little wild. "You disappeared yesterday, and when I asked around for you, the *capitán* said you would explain it to me later. It was confidential, whatever you were doing." She raised her arm in frustration. "The *capitán* gave me no explanation or anything. I thought the worst had happened to you. I thought maybe someone had killed you!"

I smiled, drew close to her, and touched her face. "Thank you for worrying about me, but I'm fine. By the way, I may need your help for something extremely important that I have to do in Panama before we get back to Miami."

"I don't want to know," she said, turning away from me. "I have enough problems in my life. I'm in this for the money and nothing else."

"You are Cuban, aren't you?"

"Yes," she answered, "so what?"

"Wouldn't you like to see Fidel and Raul Castro out of business forever?"

"With all respect to you, my friend, Dr. del Marmol—"

"Why don't you just call me Anthony?" I interrupted.

She paused. "Okay. My friend Anthony, I live very well and I don't want to complicate my life. Cuba is my homeland where I was born, but now I am a citizen of the United States of America. I don't want to end up in jail in one of the banana republics where they change presidents like they change underwear because I did something illegal or crazy."

She placed one hand over her breast and said emotionally, "Right here, in my heart, I love Cuba and would love to see her free one day. I believe everything that has been going on in the past years is bullshit. If the international community wanted to take that son of a bitch out of Cuba because of the crimes he has committed against humanity, they could have done it a long time ago. However, they choose to close their eyes and turn their backs and ignore the suffering of the Cuban people."

She raised her arm as if to hold me back. "I don't want to get involved in anything that will put me in jail or cause me to lose my life. In the end, they could put another man in power who would be just as bad as or worse than Castro. I believe that Castro's brother will die of old age. Don't waste your time, honey."

I raised my hands as if in surrender. "Okay, okay. No problem. I will find someone else to help me with this. It will cost me more time because I will have to fly someone from California to Panama. That is the reason I asked for your help— because you are here already."

"Okay. Do as you want. I'm sorry; I cannot help you with that. That is way over my head."

"Oh, by the way," I said, changing the subject, "that red dress you are wearing is beautiful. That diamond necklace must have cost you a fortune."

"Yeah. It cost a few dollars, but isn't it gorgeous?"

"No, it's not gorgeous. It's radiant. You look like a star in the sky."

She grinned from ear to ear, and then raised her fist as if to hit me. Instead, she shook her finger in my face. "Oh, no. You are not going to bribe me with your compliments."

"No," I protested. "Honestly. That is a true compliment. You look wonderful. When people say no to me, I take it literally. I will not ask you again."

"No doubt about it, honey. You know how to compliment a woman. You really mean it, so I thank you very much."

She paused then and reverted to the previous subject. "Please, next time you are going to take off for a while, let me know. A couple of people around me have been killed or have disappeared. When a person is with me and I cannot find them for an hour or two, my stomach goes crazy. I cannot even digest my food. I think the worst things, and my head goes crazy thinking how many ways they can be torturing or killing you. Most of the time, I end up sick. That is not fair."

"I'm sorry. Next time, I will tell you in advance if I am not going to be around."

"Thank you," she said. "I appreciate that very much. Will you come with me to dinner?"

"Yes. Either you can wait for me for fifteen or twenty minutes while I take a shower and dress up to your standard, or else you can go ahead and I will join you in the dining room in a little while."

"Okay. I will go ahead and you can meet me in the dining room. I will wait for you and we can order at the same time. That way, we can eat together."

"I will be there as soon as possible," I said.

She closed the door and left.

Instead of using the main hallway to the dining room, Amelia went to the outside deck and walked along, looking at the ocean in order to leave more time before the dinner meeting.

The hallways were well lit, but the decks had dimmer lights so people could see the stars and moon. This made the decks much more romantic. Along the decks there were benches which rested against the walls and on the other side was the hallway where people were walking back and forth. Occasionally, there were windows with very thick glass so people could look outside without going out on the deck in case it was cold, windy, or raining.

Amelia sat down on one of the long benches and rested her back against one of the windows. She laid her head back and looked up at the stars and moon. She began to remember her childhood days in Cuba. She rested for a while, and then she heard some footsteps. She did not open her eyes, as she was comfortable and peaceful. Her stomach had been upset all day with worry. She heard footsteps and asked, "How did you know I was here?" With her eyes still closed, she added, "Oh, I know. You saw me through the glass."

She moved her head in the direction of the sound of the footsteps. Before she opened her eyes, she realized that the cologne she smelled was an unfamiliar one. She opened her eyes quickly and saw a tall, skinny man. He was in his late fifties. His hair was nearly white except for the area on the sides of his head, which was still dark. He looked like an Anglo, but he could have passed for European. He appeared distinguished and his clothing was very elegant. He wore black leather gloves and held something in his hand—it looked like a gun. Before she could react, he hit her very hard on the forehead with the object he was holding.

Amelia's tall and curvaceous body was limp, unconscious in the chair.

The man tried to lift her up but was unable. He decided to take another approach. He embraced her, putting one of her arms over his shoulder and his right arm around her waist. He dragged her to the railing with the intention of dropping her overboard into the ocean. Before he made it to the railing, one of the doors to the hallway opened. He heard the door and he embraced her again, pretending they were a couple.

He held her against his body with her head against his chest. Three couples came through the door, talking loudly and with drinks in their hands. They walked close by Amelia and the man. One of them said, "Good evening."

"Good evening," the man with Amelia replied calmly.

One of the ladies exclaimed, "Oh, look! A falling star!" Everybody turned around and looked in the direction she was pointing. The man with Amelia continued to hold her with difficulty. He used this moment to move Amelia from the railing back to the bench where she had been sitting before.

He tried to make Amelia look as if she were conscious by moving her head a little. However, the man who had said good evening noticed she was drooping, and asked, "Is your wife okay? Do you need help?"

"No, no. She is fine. She has just had a few more drinks than she can tolerate. She always gets like this, but she will be okay. That is why I brought her up here where she can get some fresh air." He gently pushed Amelia's head up against his chest and stroked her hair to cover her forehead that was bleeding from the blow he had given her.

The man in the group said, "Okay."

They remained on the deck for a little while before deciding to go back inside. The same man said, "Have a good evening. I hope your wife gets better."

"Thank you very much," Amelia's assailant said. "You folks have a good evening, too."

The three couples disappeared through the door they had come from and went back into the hallway. He waited for a few minutes after the group left to be sure they did not return. He then looked through the window and up and down the deck to be sure the coast was clear.

He lifted Amelia again and dragged her to the railing. He pushed her body against the rail and tried to raise her up and over. He realized she was too heavy for him to lift that high, so he twisted her body around so she was facing the rail, but she slipped from his hands at that point and her stomach hit against the railing quite hard. Amelia's face was looking down to the ocean, which was exactly the position he wanted.

He crouched down to grab her feet, raise them up, and so drop her into the ocean. The pressure from her falling against the rail so hard caused her to regain consciousness, feeling quite nauseated. She saw the water down below, and immediately stood up and turned around. The man was still crouched down, trying to grab her feet.

They both stared at each other in confusion—the man because he did not expect her to wake up so soon after he had hit her in the head so hard, and Amelia because she did not know what that man was doing there holding her feet. She was still bleeding from the blow he had given her. At that moment, Amelia put her right arm and hand over her stomach and her left hand over her mouth.

She gagged a couple of times and then threw up all over the man. All the food she had eaten that day came up out of her nervous stomach undigested. The smell was repulsive. The man looked up with vomit all over his face and his no-longer-elegant clothes. He tried to clean his face, eyes, and clothes from the goopy vomit and looked up at Amelia, enraged and frustrated. Amelia looked down at him, touching her stomach in relief from something that had been bothering her all day.

She felt something warm on her forehead and raised her right hand to determine what it was. She touched her forehead and felt something sticky and warm. She drew her hand away and looked at it and saw it was covered in blood. She suddenly recalled the man hitting her, and realization about her situation flooded in on her. She ran to the bench where she had been sitting before and where her handbag still was. She grabbed the bag, opened the zipper, and pulled out the little pistol. When she turned around, the man with the white hair was behind her and struck her again with all his strength.

She fell to the ground, badly stunned. The little pistol skittered down the deck and landed under the next bench, about six feet away from where they were. The man got down on his knees and grabbed Amelia by her clothes, trying to get her up.

"Do you know how to swim, bitch? That is where you are going. Nobody can stop me."

Amelia reacted immediately, and with all the strength she had left, she kicked the man in the groin, digging the point of her heel into the soft, vulnerable spot. He let go of her and could hardly breathe because of the intense, burning pain. He bent over and grabbed his testicles, grunting, "Ow! Ouch! You bitch!"

Amelia was crawling on the deck, looking for the pistol. She saw a small, dark object under the next bench. She tried to stand up quickly to get the gun, but the man hit her with both hands on the back of her neck. She fell down again, semi-conscious, and could not offer any more resistance. For the third time, the man dragged her close to the railing and put her in the position he wanted. He got on his knees, grabbed her legs, and threw her overboard.

As he flipped her overboard, she reacted and grabbed the railing in a desperate attempt to save her own life. She began to scream. "Murderer! Murderer! Why are you doing this to me? I don't even know you, you son of a bitch!"

The man tried to pry her hands from the railing, but she wouldn't let go. When he was able to pry one hand off, she held on with the other and scratched the back of his hand with her long nails. The man realized that this was not working, so he bent down and untied the laces of one of his shoes.

Julio Antonio in a tux

Meanwhile, I had been looking for Amelia everywhere. I was dressed nicely in a black tuxedo with a white silk scarf which had a black Pierre Cardin signature on it. It made the tuxedo look like a million dollars. I had waited for her in the dining room, but she did not show up. I looked up and down the hallway, but I did not see her. I decided to take the elevator to another level to check out the casino, thinking maybe she had gone there. The three couples who had been on the deck earlier with Amelia and her assailant happened to be waiting in the lobby for an elevator.

One of the ladies in the group commented, "You do not normally see a man dressed so nicely."

I smiled. "Thank you very much. By the way, have you by any chance seen my lady? I have been looking for her for a while. She was supposed to meet me in the dining room. I am a little worried because I have been looking everywhere and I cannot find her. She is wearing a beautiful long red dress, cut low in the front."

The same girl who had complimented me inquired, "Is she a brunette with long hair and wearing a beautiful diamond necklace? I saw a lady like that, but it was kind of dark. I don't know if that was your lady, but the necklace shone brightly and really caught my attention. However, I don't think that could be your lady...I don't know."

"Yes, that is her! Where did you see her?"

They all looked at one another warningly. Just then the elevator arrived, and they all prepared to get in it.

"Please," I asked the woman piteously, "before you leave, tell me where you saw her." Her husband grabbed her by the arm and practically dragged her into the elevator. They were all in a rush to get out of there, and they were looking at the floor as if they did not want to face me. The elevator door started to close, and I said once more, "Please, don't leave me like this. Please!" The door was almost closed and I was standing in the hallway in silence, not understanding why they did not want to tell me where Amelia was.

A hand stuck out just between the door and the wall, and the elevator door opened again. The woman pointed down the hallway in the direction of the dining room. "We saw her down there on the deck. She was wasted and was with another man. If you want to find her, you will find her there."

The elevator door started to close again. "Thank you very much!" I called.

"You're welcome," she called back.

I hesitated for a second because Amelia was not my girlfriend, let alone my wife. I had no right to confront her. But I began to think it was weird that she had told me she would be waiting for me in the dining room. She did not have to do that if she wanted to be with some man. She could have just told me she would see me later. But what gave me even more motive to look for her was the fact that she had invited me to join her for dinner and had said she would wait for me to arrive before she even ordered. Why would she do that if she was going to pick up another man?

Instead of going up in the elevator, I went down the hallway in the direction the woman had indicated where they had seen her, wasted in the arms of another man. When I got close to the door where she was supposed to be, I saw a man hitting the railing with one of his shoes.

Wondering what he could possibly be doing, I hit the window hard with my open hand to attract his attention. He turned around, looking like an idiot who had been caught doing something wrong. His face was familiar to me, but in the dim light outside I could not place him. He smiled at me and I rushed to the door to go out onto the deck to find out what was happening. As I came out of the door, he was standing with his shoe in his hand and his back against the railing. It looked as if he were trying to hide something.

"Can I help you with something?" he practically yelled at me.

I walked closer to him and said, "That is precisely what I was going to ask you." Something smelled horrible and I put my hand over my nose. I felt something gooey under my shoes and looked down. It looked like diarrhea or vomit. "Are you okay? Have you seen my lady around here?"

Before he could answer, I heard Amelia's voice shouting, "Anthony! Dr. del Marmol! I am here! This son of a bitch threw me overboard and is trying to kill me!"

The man realized his cover was blown. He dropped the shoe and reached inside his coat for his pistol. I moved close to him before he could draw it. When he pulled it out I kicked it with my right leg. The pistol flew in the air and over the side where Amelia was hanging.

I heard her say, "Ouch! You son of a bitch! Now you are dropping things on my head?"

The man with the white hair and I looked at each other in the eyes. Then it came to me. "Steffan?" He made a face and tried to deny it, but I was sure, and said, "Steffan! You bastard!"

He knew I recognized him for sure and said, "I should have killed you years ago in Miami when you lied to me and gave me all those false names of people who were supposed to be involved in the overthrow of Castro. You are a fucking liar."

I smiled. "Did they reprimand you in Cuba for not giving them the proper information? It looks like you still serve the same master. Prepare yourself to die. I'm already pissed off about something I just saw in Cuba and now after what you just tried to do to my friend, Amelia… Well, that is the straw that broke the camel's back."

He did not answer me but instead jumped at me and tried to grab my neck. I was expecting that and moved to the left, putting my right leg between his legs. He tripped and fell to the floor, landing on the vomit and sliding on it. "God dammit!" he screamed angrily.

Amelia screamed to me, "Help me! I cannot hold on any longer! I am going to fall into the water!"

I looked at Steffan to make sure he was not going to be able to get up. I saw him try, but he slipped again on the vomit and fell once more. It was only a temporary disability, so I put my right hand down and grabbed Amelia's hand. I braced myself against the railing and helped her up. She crossed one of her legs over the rail and was ready to jump to the deck when she screamed, "Behind you!"

I turned around quickly, and Steffan was behind me. He hit me with all his strength on the forehead, and I fell down on the veranda. At that moment, Amelia jumped at him. The both rolled around in the vomit on the deck. Steffan managed to kick Amelia very hard in the stomach. She bent over in pain. Realizing that she could not fight him, she tried to run towards me. I was still sitting on the deck. Steffan ran behind her, trying to catch her.

I was only stunned, but I saw what was happening. Amelia ran past me and he was following her. I stood up and grabbed him by his shirt with both hands, and lay back on the deck. With my feet in his stomach, I catapulted him up and over the deck rail. I assumed he went into the water. But when I stood up, I saw him holding on to the railing the same way that Amelia had done before. He looked at me and started to cry like a baby. "Please, please, don't let me die," he sobbed. "I have kids waiting for me at home. Don't let me die. Help me to come back aboard."

I knew he was a rotten individual, but I could not help but feel pity for him.

I hesitated, but then I remembered my father's words to me: *If a dog bites you and you get pissed and bite him back, what does that make you? You are a dog, too.*

I gave him my hand to help him climb back over the railing and onto the deck. Before he grabbed my hand, he looked at me gratefully and said, "Thank you. Thank you!"

Amelia came back and pointed her little pistol at Steffan's head. She screamed at me, "Oh, no! No! You are not going to help this son of a bitch who tried to kill me!" I looked at her and saw tears in her eyes. "Do you know how to swim, prick? Prepare yourself to swim back to Cuba."

I said, "Listen, don't you think we should take him to the *capitán*? They will turn him in to the authorities. Don't you think this is the more honorable thing to do?"

She pointed the pistol at me. "Don't make me shoot you. This man has no honor. If we turn him in to the authorities they will probably release him in a couple of years and he will do the same thing either to me or you or a member of your family. He is like a rattlesnake. You have to cut off his head or he will come back and kill you."

I raised my arms in response to that pistol. I could see how distressed she was, and tried to calm her down. "Honey, this is your call. Don't point that pistol at me. You might shoot me accidentally, and you would later regret it. I am not your enemy. Calm down."

Steffan looked at me with a sad face. He tried to win my pity and knew he would not get any from Amelia. "Don't let this bitch intimidate you. You will have my death on your conscience for the rest of your life."

That enraged Amelia even more. She moved the pistol close to his head. "I am going to give you a choice which you did not give me. Either you let go and drop into the water, or I will shoot you. At least you will have a chance if you choose to let go now."

Steffan realized Amelia was not kidding as she began to count. "One...two...."

Steffan let go. He fell down into the dark waters, and as he fell, Amelia screamed, "Very well, prick!"

Amelia looked down for a second, saw his shoe, and became even angrier. She tossed the vomit-covered shoe overboard after Steffan. "You might need this in hell, damn you! At least you saved me a bullet!"

Then she began to cry.

I moved close to her and took the pistol out of her hand. I unloaded it and put it and the clip in my pants pocket. I hugged her, and as she hugged me back, she began to cry hysterically. I walked her carefully through the vomit to the bench. "Everything is going to be okay. It's over," I said soothingly.

A couple of men from Security showed up and asked, "Is everything okay? Some people reported they heard screaming and arguments from this deck."

"No, there are no arguments," I said calmly. "I have just been calling for help. She has been sick. Be careful, you are standing in vomit."

They backed up. They did not realize what they were standing in because it was so dark. "We will send some people from maintenance to clean this up. Is there anything we can do for you?"

"No. I am going to take her back to the cabin where she can shower and clean herself up. We are fine."

After a little while, Amelia told me she was feeling better and was ready to go back to the cabin. We started walking back down the hallway towards the cabin. Every time we passed someone, I noticed they held their noses. I guess we did not smell too well after rolling around in the vomit.

When we got back to the cabin, she said, "In reference to that job you have to do in Panama—you can count me in."

"What made you change your mind? Steffan? Are you sure you want to do this?"

"I have never been so sure about anything in my life. And, yes. That son of a bitch brought back memories of all the things my family went through in Cuba. If you want, when we finish visiting the banks in the Islands, we can take a plane to Panama. I hope you can nail those sons of bitches."

One More Attempt
Music and Lyrics by Dr. J. Antonio del Marmol

What would happen to you
If in only one day
Everything in your country had been changed
What would happen to you if you had been left alone
With no home or friends and no place to go
Bridge
One More Attempt
One More Attempt
What would happen to you If you had to run away With your broken heart And with no hope
I vanished in the night
In the ocean waters
With my friends I ran away
They came close to me...closer and closer
But I got away

Bridge
What would you do
You only have one day to live
And they tried to kill you    (Bridge continue to grand finale)
In every way, in different ways defend yourself, my friends
One More Attempt (Repeat by choral voice Bridge continue to finale)
One More Attempt, One More Attempt
GRAND FINALE.

"One More Attempt" composition by Julio Antonio

"One More Attempt" CD

# Chapter 11—The Cruise Ship

When Amelia had finished with her shower, I also took one. I had already called the captain and asked him to send a doctor. By the time I had finished showering, the doctor had already come and put a couple of stitches in Amelia's head as the wound was long and deep. The stitches should prevent future scarring.

The captain had arrived with the doctor. After I explained to him what had happened, the captain said, "The best thing is not to report this. That will save a lot of trouble and unnecessary aggravation. We will just pretend that you told us nothing except that she became ill, threw up, slipped on the vomit, and fell on the deck. She hit her head on the railing as she fell. That will explain her cut, and the one on your forehead and arm we can say happened because you tried to help her and slipped in the vomit and hurt yourself as well."

"Great, Capitan," I said. "I think that is the best. It will make it easier for everybody." I thanked him and they left the cabin.

After they left, I told Amelia I was actually hungry.

"Me, too," she said.

"Well, dinner is probably over now, but we can go and get a sandwich."

We dressed in casual clothes and left the cabin, heading down the hallway towards the cafeteria. When we got to the lobby, we ran into the same three couples who had told me where to find Amelia. They were a little tipsy and just coming from the casino. Even though Amelia had tried to disguise the cut on her forehead with makeup, she still had a black eye and a bandage. I had a small bandage on my forehead, as well. They all looked at us and then at each other. They just said hello but kept staring at my forehead and her face.

This made Amelia a little uncomfortable, and when they were gone, she said, "What's their problem? Haven't they ever seen someone with a black eye or a cut on their head?"

"No, it's more than that." I explained to her what had happened. "I'm sure they think we've been fighting. You see, honey? You should never assume anything because you will be dead wrong most of the time."

We went to the cafeteria and had a bite to eat. The next day, the ship arrived at Cayman Island. We disembarked and went into a bank in town. We asked for the manager, Charles Chastain, whom Amelia knew very well. He was a short man, blond, half bald, in his forties, with feminine mannerisms. He was aggravatingly meticulous and did not like to be rushed. We went into his office and closed ourselves in there. I took a few fifties and twenties out of my bag and gave them to him.

Mr. Chastain laid them out on his desk and examined them carefully, one by one, with a magnifying glass. Once in a while he looked at me over the top of his glasses and smiled before continuing to examine the money. He continued for so long that I began to feel uneasy, wondering what his problem was.

Amelia touched my knee and mouthed to me the words, "He likes you."

"This is very fine work," Chastain said. "Don't you think so?"

"Oh, yes," I answered. "Absolutely. We would not have brought it to you if we didn't think it was."

He took off his glasses. "By the way, what happened to you guys? You look as if you have been in a boxing match."

Amelia laughed. "If I told you I got sick, fell in my own vomit, and cut myself, and that he tried to help me and hurt himself, too, you probably wouldn't believe it. So just figure out whatever you can and believe what you want." She paused. "Are you interested in this fine work?"

"I'm very tempted to take you up on your offer," he said. "It sounds really simple and inviting, but the risks are many and the consequences of bad judgment could be equally painful."

"What risks?" Amelia asked. "There are no risks."

"This currency is the same as the currency you handle every day," I added.

"Yes," he said, temporizing, "but the eye can be fooled. Don't you think so?"

"Well then," I countered, slightly annoyed, "test it."

"Yes, that is exactly what I am going to do." He took some of the bills over to a money testing machine and fed them in. The machine flashed a green light for every bill as it passed through. "My, my. Well, that was much better than I thought. And you, Señorita Coborrubia, are connected once again to big money."

Amelia smiled. "I love money. It's so much more fun than housework."

Chastain looked at her with approval. "Just like you, I imagine. You must drive every man wild." He looked at me. "Don't you think so?"

I just nodded my head but made no reply.

Amelia said, "Making big money could not be easier. Don't talk about risks. Don't talk about anything else that is not really important. The only thing that is important here is that this is extremely good quality merchandise and whether or not you agree with our price and if you are interested in making a deal. We are in an extreme rush and we don't have time for mumbo jumbo and long negotiations."

"I have to admit," Chastain said, "I think you are right about that. Okay, I think we have a deal. However, if this money is so good, then why...well, why go through this step?"

"Good question, Mr. Chastain," I interjected. "But a company that divulges its trade secrets will not be in business for very long."

"I get your point. Just simple curiosity."

I smiled and shook my finger at him. "Remember, curiosity killed the cat."

He smiled and reclined in his chair. "Okay, but you cannot blame me for trying. Why don't you two join me for dinner tonight? It would be my pleasure to spend some time with you before you leave." He locked his eyes with mine as he spoke the last sentence.

"We would love to," Amelia replied quickly, "but our ship sails in one hour. Maybe next time we can have dinner. I promise you."

"That is not a problem. You can have dinner with me tonight and tomorrow I will send you in my private plane to catch up with the ship at whatever island it docks at tomorrow."

"I thank you very much," I said, "but we need to relax and rest tonight, as we have a very busy itinerary tomorrow."

"Okay," he said, giving up. "Next time. That's a promise? I'll show you both a good time."

We all stood up and shook hands. "Okay," I said. "Next time, I promise. We will be in touch."

I came out of the bank and was silent. Amelia noticed this and asked, "What's wrong? Everything went so well and smoothly. Why are you so quiet?"

"If he said one more time, 'Don't you think so?' I would have kicked him in the balls. Where did you get him from?"

Amelia smiled. "How could you kick his balls? Maybe he doesn't even have any?"

I began to laugh.

"Besides," she added slyly, "he only wants to show you a good time!"

"No thanks!" I shook my head strongly. Amelia covered her mouth and laughed as we walked along the narrow streets towards the ship.

An hour later, our ship was sailing again through the Caribbean Islands. For the next five days, we made contact on many different islands with many different banks. Most of the islands were under the control of a different country, but some were independent. Amelia introduced me to all the bankers. Not a single one said no to our proposal. Our last meeting took place on San Martin, which was an island held jointly by the French and the Dutch.

After we closed the deal in San Martin, we decided to take a plane to Panama, even though the ship would be stopping at three more islands and would be spending a day at each one. The last three islands were small, poor, and lacked good banking systems, so we decided to skip them. This worked well with my plans, as it gave us three days to work out our mission in Panama and return to the ship before it arrived in Miami. We would return on the same ship and would therefore not call attention to ourselves.

Captain Pascual referred me to a man named Gilberto Monzon, a Venezuela-born pilot born who grew up in the United States. "He is a true businessman" Pascual reassured me. "Very trustworthy and responsible."

Monzon chose to live with his family on the French side of San Martin because the place was so beautiful and he felt secure there. He'd had years of experience flying jets during the Vietnam War as a pilot in the U.S. Air Force. He was now in his mid-forties and earned his living flying businessmen in his private jet from San Martin to any part of the world. I arranged with Captain Pascual to board the ship at the last island just before they sailed to Miami. He smiled and reminded me, "We cannot wait for you. You have seventy-two hours."

"Don't worry," I said. "If this man doesn't fail me, I will be there."

We said goodbye to the captain and he wished us luck. A little while later, we met with Gilberto, and we flew to Panama. We arrived on

Thursday at around eleven in the morning. When we landed at the Panama airport, I arranged with Gilberto the exact time on the third day that he needed to pick us up so we would not miss the ship. We said goodbye and took a taxi to a luxurious hotel in Panama City.

When we arrived at the hotel and were in our suite, I opened my travel bag and took out my microfilm camera pins, worn on the outside of clothing, and explained to Amelia how everything worked. I prepared all the equipment, instructed her how to work all these things, and told her the plan.

We had had lunch in our room, and at about 1:45 we decided to go down to the lobby of the hotel. I wanted to make my phone call, and I did not want to make it from our room, lest someone discover where we were staying. We went down to the lobby, and I went to the public phones. I took the little note out of my pocket that the General had given to me and dialed the telephone number in it.

The phone rang a couple of times before a male voice answered. "Who is this?"

"Capitan Jorge Martinez Valdez?"

He answered in Spanish, "Yes, the same one is dressing and has his shoes on, comrade. Who is this?"

"I am Dr. Antonio Rada Montiel."

"Oh, I have been waiting for your call for several days, Doctor."

"I'm sorry. I have been completing some other business transactions."

"That's fine. We can see each other in an hour. What hotel are you staying at?"

I did not answer directly. Instead, I countered. "We can meet in the main entry to the airport. If you wish, we can go from there to anyplace you want."

"How are you dressed? That way I will be able to recognize you."

"I have on a white suit with a navy blue shirt and no tie. White hat with a navy blue bandana."

"Very well. I am wearing black pants, a white guayabera, and a white hat with a black bandana."

"All right. We'll see each other in an hour then." I hung up the phone and turned around. "Well, the fish took the bait." I looked at Amelia. "Are you ready?"

She was a little nervous, but she smiled and said, "Yes, don't worry. As long as we are dealing with men, I can put them in my pocket. I'll distract him for you. That is the reason I'm wearing this miniskirt with no undies. I'm going to get him crazy. If you see an ambulance come, it will be because one of them broke his neck trying to look at my crotch."

I laughed and touched my finger to my tongue and then to her shoulder, saying "Zizz, zizz," as if she were on fire and sizzling.

We stepped out of the lobby and told the attendant to call a taxi for us. There were already taxi cabs waiting, so he beckoned one over. I gave him a tip and told the driver to take us to the airport. When we arrived at the airport we went into the coffee shop as we were a little early. Amelia asked for an espresso, and I asked for a guanabana shake. The tropical fruit was utterly refreshing after my recent exertions.

After a while I looked at my watch. Nearly an hour had passed, and it was getting close to the time for our meeting with Captain Martinez. "Wait here," I said to Amelia. "I'll look for him at the entry and bring him back here."

I saw him before he saw me. He was wearing clothing matching the description he had given me. He was looking at his watch and all around impatiently. I walked towards him. He was a man of medium height and a little on the chubby side, with a large round head, curly black hair, and a black moustache. As I approached him he recognized me, smiled, and extended his hand. "Dr. Antonio Rada Montiel?"

"Yes," I replied, taking his hand in a strong grip. "Where do you want to talk?"

"Well, I'm traveling with my wife. She's sitting inside the coffee shop." He frowned, clearly worried about secrets being shared in front of an outsider. "She's trustworthy. Her lips are sealed, as are those of my guards. However, if you feel uncomfortable we can leave her here and go someplace else to talk privately."

"Well, comrade, the stuff we are going to be talking about, I don't think we should be talking in front of your wife. Or anyone else, as a matter of fact."

"Well, don't worry about it. Let's go inside, and I'll tell her to go and do some shopping while we talk."

"Okay, comrade," he said with a satisfied nod.

We walked into the coffee shop. As we approached the table where Amelia was sitting, Martinez's eyes bugged out. I sat down on one side and seated him directly in front of Amelia. The table top was made of glass, so he could watch her and enjoy the sight. "Capitan Martinez Valdez, my wife, Camelia." He kissed her hand and did not want to let go. He kept looking in between her legs. I concealed a smile and asked "Would you like something to eat or drink?"

"What are you drinking, Dr. Montiel?" he asked—still not taking his eyes away from the view through the tabletop.

"Guanabana shake."

"Oh, I love that! I'll have one, too."

I signaled to the waitress, and she came and took the order. A few minutes later, the shake arrived. I said to Amelia, "Honey, do you mind going shopping and leaving us for about half an hour or so? The Capitan and I have some confidential business to discuss and I don't want him to feel uncomfortable."

Before she could reply, Martinez raised his hand in the air and said, "Oh, no! You guys are married. I discuss everything with my wife. What's the point of her going away?"

"Well, you know what we discussed before…"

"No, *compañero*," he interrupted. "There is no need to mention that. I feel comfortable with your wife. It's okay, we can talk."

I noticed wryly the ineptitude of the communist system. Martinez could easily pass for a Panamanian man—until he opened his mouth. As soon as he did that, it was evident he was a typical product of the Castro communist system. The only thing he needed was a seal on his forehead reading "Castro," because the Spanish terminology they used for so many years was completely different from that used before Castro. The Cubans use *compañero*, and never use the more common *señor* used in most other countries. That made it easy for them to know when somebody did not belong. It also made identifying them outside of Cuba much easier.

Martinez looked at me nervously every once in a while, trying to make sure that I was not aware that he had a panoramic view of Amelia's crotch. He giggled and said, "This is a beautiful day. I love sitting here with you guys." He glanced away from his contemplations long enough to ask a business question. "How are you planning to get the money to me?"

I looked at him, took off my sunglasses and stared him straight in the eye. "Very simple. You give me an account number where you want the money to be transferred to, and we will deposit it there for you. If you want to be more discreet, we can suggest to you a bank in Buenos Aires where you can call and open an account over the phone. They will give you an account number and a personal code. We can deposit the money there and you can transfer it later when you feel comfortable to a more convenient place for you."

He nodded. "Okay. What are the terms of our agreement? Are they the same terms as those that I agreed to with my contact in Cuba?"

"Yes, I believe so. That is what we are going to confirm here, right now. The first thing is you have to introduce me to the rest of your group and also to Pablo Escobar. After this is accomplished, we will give you the first five hundred thousand dollars. When the first operation has been done successfully, then we will give you the other five hundred thousand."

He raised his hands high in agitation. "No, no, no! Negative, comrade." His face was long—he clearly was not happy with that. "That is not what I agreed to with our contact in Cuba."

"What was your agreement?"

"My job is only to introduce you to the rest of my group and to Escobar— nothing else. It is not my responsibility for your operation to be successful or not. I want my money immediately when I have complied with my part of the agreement as we agreed before."

I stretched out in my chair and put my hand to my chin, pretending to be worried and thinking about what he had said. I took a few seconds and then said, "But what would happen if you introduced me to your group and Escobar and then the product could not be delivered? We will be out of a million dollars to you and we will not have accomplished anything!"

This time, he was the one who reclined in his chair. He had a smile on his face as he looked through the glass tabletop at Amelia's open legs. "Comrade, we have been moving this product for over ten years from Columbia to Panama, and from Panama to the rest of the world. Don't you think that by now we know what we're doing? With all these years of experience, you can be assured that the product will be delivered on time and in the place you want with no problem." He stroked his chin—still looking through the glass top—and said, "Remember, we can do what nobody else can do because of our diplomatic immunity. We move the product in boxes disguised as books, artifacts, or whatever, and we move them from embassy to embassy in our own planes and ships. It is impossible to detect it. Nobody even dreams of what we are doing."

I smiled. "Okay, you've convinced me. When can I meet the rest of the group?"

He extended his hand. "Then the initial agreement is still on?"

"Yes." We shook hands to seal the deal. "We only have a few days. We have to move fast and utilize our time well."

"I understand, comrade. Tonight, we have a diplomatic reception at the embassy. There is going to be food and dancing. You guys are both welcome to come. It'll be a good opportunity for you to meet the rest of the group, and we'll arrange tonight when we will meet Pablo Escobar."

We shook hands. He stood up and looked at me with a very serious face. "Comrade, I am a true revolutionary. What we have been doing for the past years is not a revolution but a repulsion to my stomach. In Cuba they call us international proletariats, but actually we are the bandits of the proletariats." He put his hand on his stomach. "It makes me nauseated sometimes because we are losing our principles and morals like true revolutionaries just for a handful of dollar bills."

I smiled and said sarcastically, "If it makes you feel better, I can arrange for that million dollars to go to the United Nations to send to the children of Africa who really need it more than you."

He looked at my cynically and not so serious anymore. "What about my kids? They are also starving to death in Cuba. I have to provide for them first and to the rest of the world later."

I smiled and nodded my head. Amelia extended her hand from a seated position. He bent over and kissed her hand, all the while looking through the glass and getting a closer view in between her legs. "It is an extreme pleasure to meet you, Camelia."

"The pleasure is all mine, Capitan Martinez," she said.

He gave me a business card which read "InterCounsel" with a Cuban emblem on it. It had the address and telephone number of the embassy. "Okay, I will see you guys later this evening." He turned around and walked away.

I looked over at Amelia. "Go to the ladies' room and review the recorder and microfilm, make sure everything's okay. I'll do the same and review my stuff in the men's room. We'll meet in a little while in the lobby."

She nodded. "Okay."

Twenty minutes later, we met in the lobby. She nodded her head, indicating everything was all right. I signaled her with my hand that mine was okay, too. When she got close to me, she said, "You must be happy because the first step went very well. The plan is in progress."

I called a taxi and we left the airport. We told the driver to take us to another hotel rather than the one where we were staying, to throw off any possible surveillance. After we had spent a little time in that hotel and made sure no one was following us, we took another taxi and went back to our hotel.

We compiled all of our recordings and put the cassettes and microfilm in a little box. We took it to the main lobby and had it placed in the main safe in the hotel. We then reloaded our equipment with new tapes, this time using longer ones just in case the conversation should be an extended one. It can be very inconvenient to have to excuse oneself to go reload equipment—not to mention suspicious if it occurs too frequently.

Amelia and I showered and dressed very elegantly. We went down to the hotel bar to have a glass of wine and kill some time as it was much too early to go to the embassy. After a while, we finished our wine and it was time to go. We took a taxi to the embassy.

Meanwhile, it was about 10:30 a.m. in California. Arturo was supposed to relieve Hernesto at the warehouse in Santa Ana. Loren had also been there working all day and was extremely tired. "I'm going home to take a long bath and hit the hay," she said to the others, "I'm exhausted!"

Hernesto also left, and Arturo stayed with Romero at the warehouse. Arturo was moving some boxes of money from one place to another, and the portable phone rang. "Hello," he said. He recognized the voice of Isabel immediately.

"I miss you a lot, my daddy. I am so hot and wet I need a sponge to dry my legs."

Arturo rushed out of the warehouse and into the alley so Romero could not hear him talk on the phone. Once he was clear of the warehouse, he said, "Are you crazy, calling me here? Your husband was standing right next to me when I answered. He is going to kill both of us if he finds out what is going on!"

"I don't care. I would rather die than not be with you anymore. If you don't come right now and take me someplace where we can make love, I will tell him when he comes home. That way, he will leave me and I can be with you for the rest of my life."

Arturo grew angry. "Are you losing your mind? Come to your senses, woman! You are not only going to get yourself in trouble, you are going to get me in a lot of trouble with my friends. I promised Dr. del Marmol I would never see you again."

"To hell with Dr. del Marmol," she said aggressively. "If you don't come right now and pick me up, I will tell everything to Romero when he comes home!"

Arturo realized his hostile attitude was not getting him anywhere with

Isabel, so he changed his voice to a more humble tone and said, "Okay, honey. Let me see what I can do. Let me see how I can manage to get out of here. I will call you in a little while and I will let you know."

"No, no. Don't call because you will wake Loren up. I will wait for you outside in the driveway. Don't take too long. I love you. We are going to have a lot of fun. Hurry up!" With that, she hung up the phone.

"Wait, wait," Arturo said. "Hello! Hello?" He shook his head in distress and agony because he was not supposed to leave the warehouse, not supposed to leave Romero alone. He went back into the warehouse and asked Romero, "When do you want me to take you back home so you can rest?"

Romero was caught by surprise. He did not expect Arturo to come back so quickly. He assumed Arturo had gone to the store and normally that took a much longer time. He quickly wrapped up the hundred dollar bill plate he had been working with and shoved it into a briefcase, not wanting Arturo to see it. Arturo had so much on his mind that he did not even notice that. Romero smiled and replied, "No, I think I am going to spend most of the night here. I want to finish my work and this is going to take me a while. Why? Do you have a date tonight?"

"No, no. I just have something to do. If you want to go home early, then I can go and do what I have to do."

"Sure, sure. You have some girl waiting for you. Don't feel bad. Go ahead and enjoy yourself for the rest of the night. If I get too tired, I will just lie down there until you come back." He pointed to the little bed we had in the storage room. "I am not really tired. I want to make more progress in my work. That way, when Dr. del Marmol comes back to the warehouse, he will be surprised at what I have done."

Arturo nodded his head. "Okay, if you do that for me, I will really appreciate it. But don't tell anyone because I am not supposed to leave you alone."

Romero replied with a smile, "Go ahead. Leave. I don't need you here. There is nothing for you to do here. I won't tell anyone you left me alone here."

"Thank you. I will be back in a few hours."

"Take all the time you want. When you come back, I will be here waiting for you."

Arturo did not think twice. He opened the warehouse doors, jumped in his car, and drove towards Loren's house. When he arrived, Isabel was waiting for him in the driveway with a big smile on her face. Arturo turned off the car lights.

Isabel jumped into the car and demanded, "What took you so long?" She hugged and kissed him passionately. "I know you are not going to fail me, my little daddy," she whispered in his ear. Arturo smiled and they drove to his house.

# Chapter 12—The Cuban Drugs Enterprise

Back at the warehouse, not even ten minutes after Arturo left, a black Mitsubishi sedan signaled with its horn in front of the warehouse with a series of three double beeps: beep-beep, beep-beep, beep-beep. Two men wearing dark jogging suits were waiting in the car.

Romero pushed the button and opened the doors of the warehouse, and the black car entered. He closed the door behind them. After they greeted each other, he showed them under the big light on the table the plates he had hidden from Arturo. The men nodded their heads and smiled in agreement with each other as to the good job Romero had done.

They began to work like professionals in an assembly line. They knew exactly what they were doing. Romero was printing, one of the men was cutting, and the other man was boxing. They worked all night until nearly 5:00 a.m. They then loaded the car with the boxes of money until there was not enough room for another box.

Romero and the two men cleaned the press and made sure there was no evidence left behind. They put all the leftover pieces in a trash bag and put the bag in the car. Romero wrapped the plates carefully in a cloth and put them in one of the last boxes of money. The three got in the car and drove towards the Long Beach airport.

When they arrived at the airport, a private jet was waiting for them with the engines running. The three men and the pilot unloaded the car and put the boxes of money in the plane. They said goodbye, and one man went with the pilot while the other stayed with Romero. The pair watched the plane take off and disappear into the sky. Then they got into the car and left the airport.

Meanwhile, in Arturo's house, Arturo and Isabel took a shower and got dressed after many hours of sex. Arturo was watching the dawn, and he started to get nervous. He wanted to get Isabel back to Loren's house before she woke up. He particularly did not want Loren to see him.

133

A car was parked across the street from his house. The person inside was dressed in black, wearing dark glasses, a baseball cap, and dark gloves. He had a paper bag in the passenger seat.

Arturo and Isabel appeared at the front door. The person in the car saw them coming out. He grabbed the paper bag and began to walk towards them. Arturo was trying to close the door with the key and was holding his laptop in the other hand. It was difficult because Isabel was kissing him and giggling while she handled him. He turned to her and asked, "Would you please hold my laptop until I finish closing the door?"

"Of course, my love," she breathed. She took the laptop out of Arturo's hand and held it for him. Arturo finished locking the door. As they were walking towards the car, Arturo extended his hands to her, and she returned the laptop.

Just then, the man who had approached them shot several times through the paper bag into Arturo's body. Arturo let go of the laptop, and it seemed to Isabel that it fell in slow motion to the concrete, where it opened and broke into several pieces. Splashes of blood spurted out of Arturo's body each time he was hit by a bullet. The gunshots echoed repeatedly in her ears. As the laptop broke, she turned to see Arturo collapsing to the concrete with blood all around him.

She opened her eyes in disbelief and panic. The man held the paper bag wrapped gun—there was a black hole in the bottom of the bag where the bullets had come out. They looked at each other, and Isabel remained silent, terrified and completely in shock. She was afraid she was next. He turned around and walked to his car. This caused her at last to react. She began to scream. "No! No! Why?" She put both hands on top of her head and she gave voice to a full scream.

The man got into his car and drove away. He disappeared around the corner. Isabel got on her knees next to Arturo and tried to raise his head. He was trying to say something, but he could not. Isabel's tears ran down her face and onto Arturo's.

The black Mitsubishi seemed to appear from nowhere and parked in front of the house. Romero and the driver got out and walked towards Isabel, who was still screaming and crying. They grabbed her by the arms and tried to get her out of there. Romero said, "Be quiet! You have to get out of here. Remember, we are illegal here. You are going to get into a lot of trouble!"

Isabel tried to get loose from Romero and his companion, crying, "No! I don't want to leave him like this!"

"Do you want to go to jail?" Romero insisted. "They are not going to believe you. Maybe they will think you did it." Finally, she realized the situation, and she allowed them to practically drag her to the car, where they deposited her in the back seat.

By then, a couple of neighbors, hearing the gunshots and screaming, had opened their doors and were looking at them in curiosity. Romero saw them and told the driver, "Get out of here— quickly!" They drove away in a rush, leaving Arturo's body in a pool of blood in the driveway.

In Panama, the taxi we had taken from the hotel arrived at the Cuban Embassy. After we had identified ourselves and showed the card Martinez had given me to the guard at the front door, Martinez and three of his friends came to welcome us. One of them, who looked like a North American businessman, introduced himself and said, "Nice to meet you." He was a tall man, blond but half bald with a very distinguished look. He did not look Cuban at all. "I am General Antonio de La Guardia."

"The pleasure is mine," I said.

"Nice to meet you, General," Amelia replied.

The other man said, "I am Amado Bruno Padron.[3]" Padron was the complete opposite of La Guardia. He looked like he hadn't had a shower in a week. His manners were really poor, displaying a complete lack of class. There was also another pineapple-headed man that both of us knew: General Manuel Noriega, the ruler of Panama himself. After the introductions, he remained with our party, enjoying himself the rest of the evening.

We were invited to follow them to a reserved salon where we could have a private conversation. They ordered the servants to bring some champagne to the salon. After we sat down, they tried to make us feel comfortable by telling us that they guaranteed that whatever we bought from Escobar would reach its destination without any problems. "In ten years," La Guardia noted, "we've never had a problem with any of our shipments and the product always has reached its destination."

The product under discussion was, of course, the cocaine we intended to buy from Escobar. Amelia asked, "Excuse me, General de

---

[3] Gens. Ochoa and la Guardia, Col. Padron, and Capt. Valdez were all executed in 1989 when this operation was exposed, but that is another story.

La Guardia, but is it possible to arrange the price with you gentlemen and that way avoid the hassle of flying to Columbia?"

La Guardia smiled. "My close friends call me Tony, *señora*. But no—that is out of our hands. We have our hands full already with our deliveries. Besides, that is his merchandise, and it isn't fair for us to put a price on his merchandise.

He might like you guys and give it to you for half price. That is the kind of man he is. But it is entirely up to him to do so."

"Very well," I said. "When can we arrange this meeting? I'm on a very tight schedule."

"Tomorrow at eight-thirty in the morning," Martinez replied. "I will meet you in the airport at the same place we met today. We'll take one of our planes directly to Columbia. I have already arranged it, and Pablo Escobar will be waiting for us when we arrive."

At that moment the door to the salon opened, and a tall man with black hair, olive skin, and very thick glasses came in. Everybody stood up and greeted him respectfully. He extended his hand to me and said, "I am General Ochoa."

Before I could say anything, Martinez said to him, "Oh, General, this is Dr. Antonio Rada Montiel."

"Nice to meet you, Doctor," Ochoa said.

"The pleasure is mine," I replied. "I heard about your conquests in Ethiopia and Angola. That has made you famous all over the world."

He nodded with a sad expression on his face. "I went through a very difficult time and some personal hardships in those countries. Sometimes I prefer not to remember. Those memories haunt me everywhere I go because people remember me for that."

Everybody in the room was serious and silent. I replied, "Well, things are not always the way they are painted, and only the painter has the real knowledge of the true color of the piece. Many times it is truly sad for the painter, when he has the glory and the recognition for a painting, to accept the true motive that caused him to create that piece in the first place."

He smiled and extended his hand to me. He took a deep breath and said, "Apparently you and I have had similar experiences in our lives."

I looked straight into his eyes. "I believe that. But mine are not close to the magnitude of yours!"

"It really has been a pleasure to meet you. Whatever you and Capitan Martinez agree to, it is all right with me. Actually, he is the man in the closest contact with Escobar."

Ochoa took off his thick glasses and wiped them with a napkin that he took from the table. All of us then walked out of the salon and joined the rest of the guests. Ochoa turned to me. "May I have the pleasure of a dance with your wife?"

"Of course, sir," I said. "The honor is all mine."

He shared a couple of dances with Amelia. We stayed for a couple of hours dancing and eating with them and the rest of the guests. Finally, we decided to leave. We called a taxi and followed the same procedure as before. We went to a different hotel and had a couple of drinks. When we were sure we had not been followed, we got another taxi and went to the hotel where we were really staying.

We went to our room and reviewed our film and the recording of the happenings and the conversations at the embassy. Amelia gave me a high five when we saw how they had so obviously incriminated themselves in drug trafficking all over the world for the past ten years.

"We got those sons of bitches now!" she giggled. "There is no doubt about it!"

I shook my head slightly. "Remember, this is all hearsay. What is really going to seal this package is our meeting tomorrow with Pablo Escobar. That is actually more important than what we have accomplished so far. His confirmation will not only incriminate him but also his Cuban associates and the Cuban government."

Amelia smiled wickedly. "Okay, then I'll have to dress very sexy tomorrow. That way, I'll drive him crazy and make him so horny that he'll only be thinking of how to get close to me and will be so distracted he won't even dream of what we're really doing there."

"Whatever you do, if you wear a miniskirt, don't wear any undies! That worked really well with Martinez. His eyes almost popped out of his head every time you moved around and opened your legs."

She smiled. "I noticed his mouth started to salivate like the foaming mouth of a horny pig."

I laughed and shook my head as I grabbed up all the microfilm and microcassettes. I took them down to the lobby of the hotel and put them in the main safe.

The next day, we met Captain Martinez at eight-thirty in the morning in the airport coffee shop. He was finishing a cup of coffee and was waiting for us. He rose with a smile to greet us. "Would you like some breakfast or something to drink before we go?" he asked.

"Thank you, but no," I replied with a smile. "We have already breakfasted at the hotel."

A few minutes later, we put our travel bags on the private plane, and took off for Columbia. While we were on our way, Martinez said, "Please, let me do the talking with Pablo until he feels more comfortable with you. He has major investments in hotels and other resorts in Cuba, and he respects and admires *el Fifo*[4] very much."

I nodded. "Okay—you handle it the way you feel is best."

We landed in a private field at Pablo Escobar's hacienda a few hours later. Three Range Rover cars were waiting for us. Two of them were full of men dressed in civilian clothes with small machine guns and assault rifles. They greeted us, and Martinez said hello to everyone. He seemed to know most of them by name. They put us in the other Range Rover and escorted us to the main house, with one vehicle in front as a guide for us, and the other followed us closely.

When we arrived at his home, Pablo Escobar received us with a smile and greeted Martinez with a big hug. After we were introduced, we walked into a beautiful gazebo and sat down at a table with a big bowl of fruit and cheese, olives, crackers, and many more delectable foods on it. It looked like a buffet. Servants dressed in white brought three buckets full of ice with bottles of expensive Dom Perignon champagne. The gazebo was covered with white mosquito netting to prevent bugs and flies from getting in. It looked like an Arabian tent except it was not in the Sahara Desert, but in a beautiful green area with flowers and tropical fruit trees.

We observed men with weapons and dogs all around us protecting the area. In the short time we were there, I counted five planes that landed on the private field. The Range Rovers went back and forth to bring the occupants to the hacienda. They put these people in different areas, some on the terrace of the house, some in the guest house on the north side of the main house. The last ones that arrived they seated at a table with an umbrella not too far away from us, on the other side of the pool.

A few hours later, when we had concluded negotiations, Escobar gave me an account number at a Canadian bank in the Cayman Islands. He wrote an amount on a piece of paper and gave to me. "When this amount, which is half, is deposited, we will send the product to you." I appreciated the smoothness of his approach. By doing it this way, he

---

[4] El Fifo is the nickname for Castro used by his close inner circle.

made certain that the amounts were always kept secret from the others who were sitting there. "When you receive the shipment, verify it with Capitan Martinez and deposit the balance no more than twenty-four hours later."

We shook hands, and I said, "Very well. It will be done this way. It has really been a pleasure doing business with you, Señor Escobar. I look forward to continuing our good business transactions in the future."

"Me, too," he said. "I am looking forward to a long relationship with you guys." During our conversation, he had been looking at Amelia as if he wanted to eat her. "Why don't you guys stay with me for a couple of days? That way I can show you my hacienda. We can ride my horses, and I can show you my beautiful country."

I shook my head regretfully. "Next time it will be a pleasure. Thank you very much, but right now we are on a very tight schedule."

He shook my hand and said goodbye. Then he grabbed Amelia's hand and said, "It has really been a pleasure to meet you, Mrs. Rada."

Amelia smiled flirtatiously. During our conversation she had been exchanging sexual looks with him to the point that Escobar was turned on by her and her large breasts which were half exposed. "The pleasure was all mine. I would love to stay with you for a while next time we come, Mr. Escobar."

He smiled as he gazed at her breasts. "Please, call me Pablo."

"Okay, I'll call you Pablo. That is a beautiful name."

Escobar laughed. He was full of joy and pride.

We said goodbye and were taken back in the Range Rovers to the plane. While we were on the plane and getting close to landing in Panama a few hours later, Martinez asked me, "What do you think about Pablo Escobar?"

"Great man. He looks like a good individual."

"Oh, he is a wonderful man. Wait until you really get to know him." After we landed and were walking into the airport, he asked, "What do you think about General Ochoa?"

"He doesn't look like a bad person. He looks to me like a good man."

Martinez furrowed his eyebrows. "Well, don't trust him too much. He looks like a good person, but he's been changing a lot. He's very arrogant lately. He seems to have a chip on his shoulder and he feels he is bigger than Fidel. I believe his military conquests have gone to his head. He thinks he's better than anybody else." He touched my shoulder. "Don't even dare to tell him about our agreement, please!"

I opened my eyes wide. "Under no circumstances will I say anything to him or to anybody else. This is between us. By the way, immediately when I arrive in Miami, I will deposit the money in the account you gave me, since you've fulfilled our agreement completely and I am very satisfied." I extended my hand to him and thanked him very much. "I will call you the same way with the same code as I called you the first time to verify that you received it."

"Thank you very much. It was a pleasure to meet you."

We said goodbye and took a taxi to another hotel as usual. When we were sure we had not been followed, we took another taxi to the hotel where we were staying and packed our bags, and then went back to the airport after checking out.

Our pilot, Gilberto, was waiting for us. We took off and left Panama and headed for Barbados, where we were supposed to meet the ship. After a short flight, we arrived and boarded the ship and docked the next day in Miami.

From Miami I called California to find out how everything was going. To my surprise and shock, Hernesto told me about Arturo's assassination and Romero and Isabel's disappearance with millions of dollars from the warehouse.

"Get everybody together to help you. We need to relocate everything. Find another warehouse to rent in another city, but not too far away. I will be there tonight." I gave him the flight number and details of my arrival in Los Angeles.

"Don't worry," he assured me. "I will do everything the way you ask."

We said goodbye and I hung up the phone. Amelia was standing by my side and noticed how sad and depressed I was. "What's wrong? You should be happy. Everything went so well in Panama."

"Yes, you are right—but everything is not always as you want. Someone has killed one of my best friends," I said with tears in my eyes.

She hugged me. "I'm sorry. I'm very sorry, but it could happen to any one of us. Look how close we came to losing our own lives the other day. My sincere advice to you is to try and get out of this craziness because you are playing with death every day, and you have been cheating death every day. One day, death is going to catch up with you, and you will die violently."

I smiled sadly. "Well, we all have to die someday—if not by cancer, then by an accident or a bullet in our head. The only thing I can promise you for sure is we are all going to die eventually. Why live in fear of death?"

She shook her head. "Well, maybe you are right. What the fuck! What difference does it make?"

We left Miami. We looked at the beautiful blue sky and the gorgeous beaches as we took off. When we arrived in Los Angeles, Elizabeth and Hernesto were waiting for us at the airport. I introduced Amelia to Hernesto. She said hello to Elizabeth and gave her a card with her address in Coto de Caza in Orange County.

When we arrived at Amelia's home, Hernesto took her luggage out of the car and into her house. Hernesto's eyes were focused on Amelia's breasts. Elizabeth realized that her brother was hooked by Amelia's sex appeal and touched him with her elbow. "Watch out," she murmured. "Black widow. Big trouble."

Hernesto looked at her innocently. "What? What?" Then he smiled because he knew what his sister was implying.

Amelia hugged me emotionally and said, "Thank you." She turned to Elizabeth and said, "He saved my life."

"You saved mine, too," I said. "Thank you very much."

"No, I didn't save you. You saved me. Don't be modest."

I smiled and let it go. She put her hand on Elizabeth's shoulder and said, "Well, I brought him back in one piece. You take care of him now, okay?"

Elizabeth pretended to smile. "Sure. I'll take care of him, honey. Don't worry."

We said goodbye and headed for Fountain Valley, where they had rented another warehouse. They had already relocated all the equipment and it was functioning now in our office. Father Salomon had arrived and been working all day. He had completed the plates for the hundred dollar bills already and was about to begin printing them.

I gave him a big hug and then Hernesto began to tell me the details of what had really happened. "I found copies of the hundred dollar bills that Romero had been working with behind the press. When we compared them with the plates Father Salomon had just finished, we discovered that they were of poor quality. Yaneba had microfilms of what had happened that night after Arturo left the warehouse, and she also has the license plate number of the black Mitsubishi as well as all the details of how they took the money out of the country at the Long Beach airport."

"Very well," I said. "I will give all that information to O'Brien. They can run, but they have no place to hide."

Father Salomon said, "Well, in a few hours I will have the first bills printed for you already. How much do you want to print?"

"Run the presses until you run out of ink or paper, whichever comes first." I waited there for a while until Loren arrived, and we hugged and kissed.

"Nice to see you back in one piece," she said. "Is everything okay? How are you taking Arturo's death?" I shook my head in silence and noticed tears in her eyes. "I think I am in over my head. I never thought anyone so close to us would die."

"Listen, sweetie, you can walk out at any time." I noticed that her hands were shaking and she was extremely distressed.

"No, no. I want to finish this business because we have started it already. But after we finish, I don't think I want to be a part of what you are doing anymore."

"I really appreciate your honesty. That is perfectly okay with me. In Cuba, we have a saying: we can be together but we don't have to be glued together." We were a little distance away from the others as we talked, but Elizabeth and Hernesto realized something was not right with us.

Loren noticed we were calling attention to ourselves, and she wiped away her tears. "Let me go and help those guys and do whatever I can in there."

I picked up the phone and called Yaneba. When she answered, I said, "It's me. I believe you have a package for me."

"Hello, stranger. I have a very interesting package for you."

"Why don't you meet me at location number two in half an hour?"

"Okay, I'll be there."

I hung up and called O'Brien this time. "It's me," I said when he answered. "How are you doing?"

"I'm great, and you are going to be even greater when I give you my news!"

I smiled. "Well, I have two big ones for you, too. Let's see each other in an hour in the initial location."

We said goodbye and hung up. Father Salomon had already printed some bills, and my friends were helping him cut them. They brought some to me, and we put one under the big magnifying glass.

142

"This is superb work," Loren said. "Look at this."

We compared one of our bills with a real bill that was in circulation. Our bills were even better cut and the ink was of better quality. All four of our borders were even and uniform.

"My God, Father Salomon, you are a genius!" I exclaimed. "You have accomplished in one day what Romero could not do in a week." He smiled in satisfaction.

I said goodbye to my friends and left the warehouse to drive to Balboa Island.

# Chapter 13—The Beginning of Noriega's Downfall

When I arrived at the French café, Yaneba was already waiting for me. She hugged and kissed me, and said, "I'm so glad to see you. Are you okay?"

"Well, you know. We have to get that son of a bitch that killed Arturo."

"If I had followed him that night, he might still be alive," she said guiltily, "but I decided to go where I had been told all the time—follow the money." She handed me an envelope that contained microfilms and recordings of the details of what happened that night with Romero and his two friends.

"Thank you. It's not your fault. You can only do what you can do. You were by yourself."

"Actually, Elizabeth and Hernesto were both in Santa Barbara that night following a lead given to them by that guy, Sanchez."

I put my hand on her shoulder. "Don't blame yourself. You are not God. You cannot be everyplace and everywhere at the same time."

She looked at me in a strange way as if she wanted to tell me something. She hesitated.

"What's happening?" I asked. "What's bothering you? You know you can talk to me."

She frowned. "Why does it have to be me to tell you this?"

My eyes grew wide. "You are starting to worry me. What is going on?"

"Well, I am going to tell you the way it is. I don't want you to overreact. Maybe it's nothing. I know you are in love with this girl, Loren, and you are very happy right now. I don't want you to be unhappy. I am not jealous. I love you in a good way. Whatever makes you happy, even though it is not me, I am really happy for you."

I put both hands on her shoulders. "Sweetie, I know that. You and I have been together for a long time, and we have special feelings for each other. We are not in a relationship anymore, but no matter what I will always have a special place in my heart for you."

She smiled, and there were tears in her eyes. "Well, I saw Loren on two occasions talking to a guy, and I decided to go farther with this. I found out that guy is Sanchez. They may be friends from before or it may just be something innocent. I never saw them kissing or anything like that, or even holding hands. Did she ever mention to you that she knows Sanchez?"

"No. When did this take place?"

"While you were out of the country." I was silent for a moment and nodded my head slowly. "Do you want me to continue watching them?" she asked. "I know this must be very difficult for you, but I always want to know—especially in our kind of work. It is not only a personal feeling; it could put your life at risk."

I nodded. "Go ahead and continue what you are doing. I trust you. Please keep this between us."

She grasped my arm. "I will."

We stood up, hugged each other, and said goodbye. I got into my car and drove towards the Balboa Bay Club. When I arrived there, O'Brien was already waiting for me. I brought a few of the bills Father Salomon had printed in my pocket.

"You look very serious," O'Brien remarked as we walked along the dock. "Is anything wrong?"

"Well, I have two big surprises for you. One is very, very bad and the other is very, very good. Which one do you want to hear first?"

"Give me the bad first. That way, the good will make me forget about the bad."

We boarded my friend's beautiful yacht, where we always met together. When we were aboard, I opened the sliding glass door on the deck and went inside. I went over to the subzero refrigerator and asked him what he would like to drink.

"A cold beer will do, if you have it here." I gave him a beer and a glass, and he added, "No, the beer is enough. Put the glass back."

I grabbed a wine glass and poured myself a Zinfandel. We sat down in the back of the yacht in some very nice lawn chairs. I took a sip of my wine while he took a swig of his beer.

"Well, I will give you the bad news first. Someone assassinated my friend Arturo."

"*What!?*" he exclaimed in surprise.

"They put a bunch of bullets in his chest as he was coming out of his house."

"Oh, my God! Do you have any idea who did it?"

"Well, we don't know. It could be the Dolphin or it could be a personal vendetta because he was fucking around with Romero's wife."

O'Brien shook his head in disgust. "Why did this man get involved with a married woman? Especially with somebody who is working with us?"

"Yes, I told him that. I also told him to back off. Evidently he didn't listen to me." I gave him the envelope containing the microfilm Yaneba had just given to me. "I have not even seen this yet, but in here you will find some evidence. Arturo left Romero alone in the warehouse and Yaneba recorded everything that happened after he left. The worst scenario is that Romero disappeared with his wife and he took at least thirty million dollars with him. He took not only the hundred dollar bills that he managed to print when I was out of town but also some of the twenties and fifties that we had printed—ones you had not picked up yet."

O'Brien scratched his head worriedly. "Oh, boy. That's really bad. Those bills should not be in circulation until our operation is in effect." He squeezed at his chin in thought. "This could bring real bad consequences on what we plan to do. I hope we can stop the damage."

"Well, to me it's impossible to arrange surveillance on every man working around me. I cannot control the sexual behavior of every individual in my group."

He smiled. "Don't blame yourself, for God's sake. This had nothing to do with you."

"Well, I blame myself because I caught him in the sexual act in Loren's house, and I should have been more severe in my reprimand to him. If I had, maybe he would be alive now." I smiled sardonically. "What he did was really bad for us and our project, but in that moment and for as long as it lasted, it was probably great for them. *A un gustaso, un trancaso.*"

"What? What did you say?"

"It's a Cuban saying," I explained. "It means if you have a great time, you might have to pay the consequences later, and sometimes it is painful."

"Okay—whatever. You guys have all these sayings."

"Well, with this information on the microfilm, you may be able to locate him and his friends in Argentina and stop the damage before it happens." I pulled out the hundred dollar bills from my pocket and handed them to him.

"My God—did you guys do this? Are you sure you didn't go to the bank and pull this out of your account?"

"They just came out of the oven. They are still warm."

"Wait a minute—you said Romero is in Argentina. Who made these bills?"

"Well, that is part of the good surprise. The man who did these bills is a very good friend of mine and one of my personal contacts. But that is just between you and me. I don't want anyone to know this man even exists. I put my trust in you in this. To everyone else, these bills were done by Romero. Understand?"

"Don't worry. I give you my word. It'll be the way you want it. But are you sure he doesn't want to do this for us again in the future?"

"No," I said jokingly, "this is a one-night stand. Enjoy it because this is all you will get from him."

"Okay. That's all?"

I opened my portfolio and brought out a manila envelope full of microfilm and microcassettes. I gave it to him and said, "The first envelope has the conversation between our contact in Cuba, the General, and Capitan Jorge Martinez Valdez. Capitan Martinez agreed with the General to introduce me in Panama to all the Cuban diplomatic attachés. They are all members of the G-2, passing for diplomatic personnel in different activities. He is also supposed to introduce me to the Lord of the cartel de Medellin in Colombia."

O'Brien stood up and held up his hand, grinning from ear to ear. "Don't tell me you did this by yourself!" I grabbed another envelope from my briefcase and gave it to him. "Oh, my God. Oh, my God! Don't tell me you've brought me proof of the involvement of the Cuban government with the drug cartel!"

I took off my sunglasses, smiled, and nodded my head slowly. "Not only recordings but there is film of Cuban generals and the rest of the group from the Cuban intelligence masquerading like diplomats and accepting the responsibility of being the drug carriers for Pablo Escobar, and transporting those drugs with their diplomatic immunity in their Cuban planes all over the world. Not only that, but Manuel Noriega is there, so we can not only tie him in with Escobar but also Castro himself!"

O'Brien shook the envelopes. He hugged me and asked, "All this is here? How'd you manage to do this? This is great! Great! Now Castro cannot deny what we've already known for so long! The entire world, even our allies, didn't believe us. This is unbelievable that you did this by yourself. The old man and Addison won't believe this!"

I raised my right hand to calm him down. "Wait a minute. I didn't do this by myself. Don't tell either the old man or Addison that I did this alone because that is not fair. Amelia helped me tremendously. If I had not had her by my side, I would probably not have been able to accomplish it. She is very intelligent, and with her intelligence and her sex appeal, she distracted all these morons for me. Even Pablo Escobar wanted to take her away from me and jump in the sack with her. She made my job a lot easier. She paraded them in front of me and I was able to film them with no problem, as though I did not even exist. I taught her how the equipment worked and in only a few hours she learned how to load the film and how it all functioned—all the details. What she did in a few hours a lot of people cannot get right in months!"

O'Brien smiled. "You see, I told you that young woman was a valuable asset to us."

I grinned. "Yeah. Big ass...et!" He laughed, and I added, "By the way, remember your friend Steffan in Miami?"

"Yeah. He disappeared for years. We assumed him dead. What's up with him?"

"Well, you might remember I told you to look for him in Cuba, that he was a double agent for Castro. Evidently he resuscitated himself because he was on the cruise ship. He almost killed Amelia."

"What!" he gasped. "Steffan? Are you sure?"

"As sure as I see you right now in front of me, O'Brien."

"Oh, my God. His widow is receiving a check from the State Department because he's listed as missing in action!"

I smiled. "Well, he *is* missing in action now, but not on our side. He is on Castro's side. His ass is in the water! Amelia made him jump into the ocean right in front of my eyes."

O'Brien shook his head. "Oh, my God! I can't believe this. May he rot in hell!" He put his right hand on his chin. "This worries me. How in the hell did our enemies know that you and Amelia would be on that cruise ship? If they knew that, what else do they know? That means we've got a mole in our group."

"Not in my group," I said firmly. "Maybe in your group. Probably your informant is Romero. Probably. I assume."

"No, Romero didn't know anything about the cruise ship or anything like that."

"I believe that when you get your hands on Romero, you should squeeze him hard. Maybe you will find out that he knows more than he appears to."

"No, no, no. If you think about it, the assassination of Arturo and the intent to assassinate Amelia on the cruise ship must be related. They're tracking us and trying to stop us from what we're doing." He took another swallow of his beer thoughtfully. "Romero, I think, is a greedy son of a bitch, but I don't think he's capable or has the manpower to do something on this magnitude. This looks more like the Dolphin's hand, if you ask me, or some other Cuban agent. I think you should be extremely careful, more than ever—if the Dolphin is here as we expect, and if this is a part of his plan, we'll probably get hit again soon."

I put my hand on my chin and nodded. "Well, I will be waiting for him and I assure you he is number one on my shit list. The Dolphin doesn't qualify for the sardine can anymore. Now he is in the baby food category. I am going to grind him up and put him in a baby food liquid bottle! If he is the one who killed Arturo, he will try to kill one of us next. Let's hope it's me because I assure you it will be his last attempt."

O'Brien smiled and pulled some papers out of his briefcase. While flipping through him, he said, "Your two surprises, good and bad, were in the high category. I'm really impressed. However, my good surprise for you is in the super category! It exceeds both of your surprises, good and bad." He handed to me the documents in his hands. He reclined in his chair with a huge grin, waiting for my reaction.

My eyes grew wide in astonishment and joy. "Is this for real?"

"Yes."

I stood up, and with tears in my eyes it was I who hugged him this time. "How did you do this? How did you make this happen?"

He replied with intense satisfaction, "It wasn't easy at all, but through our good contacts with the Spanish ambassador and the international treaties that are in force right now, as well as our Interest Office in the Swedish embassy in Havana, a lot of pressure was put on the Cuban government, and we finally achieved the release of your mom and dad for a brief visit to their family: your uncles, cousins, everyone. Of course, this brief visit will become a permanent visit. We have all the paperwork in place, and as soon as they arrive, we will proclaim political asylum based on political and religious persecution in their native country of Cuba."

I was still close to him, and still teary-eyed I hugged him again. "I will never, ever be able to repay you for what you have just done for me today. You can never know or realize how much I love my mom and dad."

I hadn't talked to my dad for many years. Long before, he had called me a traitor and threw me out of the house. This was after I had told him to take our family out of Cuba as a result of what I personally heard every day that Castro was planning to do. He didn't believe me.

"I know now that he realizes the mistakes he made," I said, "and I know how bad he must feel about it. I want to hug him and tell him it's okay. I have been worried all these years that he or I might die and we would never have the opportunity to talk about it and forgive one another. I want to hug him and tell him I love him and let's put this all behind us. And now you are giving me the opportunity. This is why there is no way I will ever be able to repay you for this."

He held up the envelope with the microfilm clips in it from Panama. Grinning ear to ear, he said, "You already have! I'm very well paid."

We said goodbye, and I drove back to the new warehouse. When I arrived, I told my friends the good news about my parents' upcoming visit thanks to the intelligence community. I had been trying unsuccessfully to get them out of Cuba for many years. Finally, it looked as if we were going to accomplish it. Loren hugged me, and everyone congratulated me, wanting to know when they would arrive. I told them they would be coming into the Los Angeles airport in two days, and that I would be told the details as to the exact time and flight number later.

Loren said, "Hernesto, go to the store and buy a couple of bottles of champagne right now so we can celebrate!" She knew how much this meant to me and wanted to keep the moment that I had told them about it in our memories forever. A little while later, Hernesto returned with the champagne, and we stopped production of the money for about an hour to enjoy and cheer the moment.

We filled up the glasses and raised them up in a toast. I said, "To my mom and dad—finally, they will achieve freedom. Let's also toast to the millions of moms and dads who are still there and pray to God that one day they will accomplish the same. That they either can leave Cuba or else the Castro regime will end."

Meanwhile, in Rosario, Argentina, a short distance from Romero's house, an old van was parked in the shade under a tree. There were two men in the van, and they were observing his house. The man in the passenger seat had some small binoculars, and from time to time he used them to observe more closely what was happening at the house.

In the back of the van were two more men and a lot of audio equipment. They were listening to the conversation that was going on in the house. All four men were dressed in black overalls, and they all had black baseball caps and sunglasses.

Inside the house, Romero, with a bottle of liquor in his hand and half drunk, was screaming at his wife. He was pacing back and forth and was very upset. "I should never have taken you out of the house of prostitution! You were born to be a prostitute. In addition to that, you are a bitch!"

Isabel tried to calm him down and said softly, "Please, Romero, try to control yourself. Don't talk like that in front of the kids."

Romero screamed at the top of his lungs, "I will say whatever the fuck I want! This is my house! Don't tell me what I am or am not supposed to say! You shut up, you horny pig! You have no decency. How in the hell could you fuck that guy right in front of my face?" He was becoming more and more upset as he talked, and he grabbed a little bronze statue and hit her in the face with it.

This gave her a big cut which bled profusely. She screamed, full of panic when she saw how much blood was coming out of her wound. She started to run towards the front door of the house, trying to get away from him. Romero ran behind her, trying to stop her from reaching the door. He still had the statue in his hand.

She pulled a chair behind her, and he tripped on it and fell on the floor. This gave her time to reach the door. She opened it and screamed for help to the neighbors. Some of the neighbors were already outside because they had heard Romero's screaming. She called out to her friends, "Call the police! This man is going to kill me! Please help me!"

Her children ran out behind her, crying and screaming for her. A few ladies and several men went to Isabel and tried to help her. Evidently someone had already called the police because sirens were heard, heading in the direction of the house. Meanwhile, Romero had gotten to his feet and to the front door. Everyone looked at him in disgust, as he still had the bottle of liquor in his hand.

"You bastard!" one lady screamed at him. "Why do you treat your wife like that?"

"She is a fucking prostitute!" he answered. He waved her away and jumped into his car, tires screeching as he drove off. The front door was still open.

In the middle of all this confusion, the man who had been sitting in the passenger seat of the van slipped unnoticed into the house through a side door. He went into the master bedroom and took a little tube out of his pocket which looked like Crazy Glue. On top of the sink were two toothbrush holders shaped like rabbits. The one on the right was labeled Papa and the one on the left Mama. He took the toothbrush out of the right container and squeezed the transparent liquid onto the toothbrush. He grabbed a piece of toilet paper and wiped the excess liquid up. Then he flushed the paper down the toilet. He put the toothbrush back in the container where he had found it. When he finished, he left the house through the patio door and walked down the sidewalk on the side of the house, past all the people who were now gathered there. Some of the people were talking with the police that had arrived in response. In all the confusion, no one even noticed the man walking by.

One of the neighbors screamed, "That Romero is a very bad husband!" Another lady said, "He is a lazy bum."

One man said, "He is a really bad man and an abuser. He should be in jail!"

Another man said, "You had better be quiet because you have your own history, too."

The men in the van had already left. They were following Romero in his car. They drove for a while through a very poor and rundown area, and then finally reached an industrial area. Romero stopped in front of what looked like an abandoned factory. Some of the windows were broken, and the walls were made of aluminum that had become rusted over the years.

There was one big door that could be used for trucks and large vehicles. This door had another, smaller door cut into it for convenience and for people to enter when the big door was not needed. Romero parked his car close to this building and went to the small door. He knocked in a prearranged signal. The van parked a short distance away and observed his movements.

A man holding a machine gun hanging by a strap around his neck opened the door and greeted Romero with a smile. They both disappeared into the building, closing the door behind them. One of the men from the van stepped out and walked toward the building. He went to one of the broken side windows and began to observe what was happening inside. The other two men stayed in the van.

Inside the building, the two men who had helped Romero take the money to Long Beach approached him and greeted him. One other man was assembling newly purchased printing equipment. A tall man with wavy hair and a mustache said, "What are you doing here, Romero? We agreed that you should not come here for a while to avoid any problems."

Romero, who was more than half drunk, mumbled, "I had to come here to see what you guys were doing."

The man, realizing Romero was a little loaded, tried to calm him down. "Remember, if somebody has followed you we lose everything we have worked for. You should not come here until we know for sure that everything has quieted down. We have to let some time pass. This is too soon." He tried to take the bottle out of Romero's hands. "You are drinking too much already. We need to be able to think clearly. If we don't pay attention to what we are doing right now, everything is going to be fucked up! Then you will not be able to enjoy this money or the money we will be printing."

Romero did not want to let go of the bottle and resisted. The man stepped back and slapped him. "What's wrong with you?"

Romero shook his head. "My wife. My wife is a prostitute." He let go of the bottle.

"You can buy a thousand wives like her with all this money!" the man screamed at him as he snatched the bottle away. He pointed to the boxes they had brought from California. "We can take care of that bitch later."

Romero, not completely drunk, realized that what his friend had said was true. "Okay. Okay. You are right, my friend. I am leaving right now."

The man with the mustache screamed, "No, no! You should not drive in the condition you are in right now." He turned around and called, "Mauricio! Mauricio!" The guy in the back came toward them. "Take Romero home. Make sure he gets there safe."

"Okay, boss."

"No, no!" Romero screamed. "Not to my house. I cannot go to my house."

"Why not?" asked the man with the mustache.

"Because I hit my wife and the police are at my house waiting for me."

The man reached into his pocket and pulled out some keys. He gave them to Mauricio and said, "Take him to my house. Make sure he takes a long shower and gets sobered up. When the police leave his house, take him home."

"That is better," Romero said. "I like that."

The guy with the mustache replied, "Of course, *che*. Later, when you are back at home and things have calmed down, you will resolve everything with Isabel in bed. Fucking is how all domestic problems are resolved in every marriage."

Romero laughed like stupidly. "Of course. Of course, my friend."

"Okay, Mauricio, take Romero right now."

Mauricio asked Romero for the keys to his car and they took off. They crossed in front of the van as they left but did not notice it. The two men in the van observed them as they passed. The man who had been looking in the window of the building had seen everything that happened inside and returned to the van. He made a signal to the other men with his hand, holding up three fingers, and then walked to the side of the van and opened the sliding door to get into the back.

The men in the front seats said nothing. They got out of the van, went to the side of it, and got in. The first man was preparing himself as if for battle. He put on a ski mask, put some explosive devices in his waistband and was screwing a silencer into the front of his pistol. The other two did exactly the same. The driver got out of the back and behind the wheel and drove close to the door where

Romero had entered the building. He stopped the van, and all three got out and knocked, using the same code Romero had used earlier.

Inside the building, the man with the mustache said, "Mother whore! What the fuck does Romero want now?" Not even thinking and just assuming Romero had come back, he stopped the guy with the machine gun who normally was in charge of the door. "Let me handle this. I am going to send this son of a bitch to hell. Don't kick me in my balls anymore!"

He was angry and opened the door abruptly. *"No me rompas mas los huevos…"*

He did not finish his sentence because two soft sounds interrupted him. Two bullets hit him in the face, one in the forehead and one under his right eye. He wobbled for a moment and then fell forward. The two men grabbed him, one on each arm and slid him down quietly, pushed him to the side of the door, went inside, closing the door behind them.

The man with the machine gun was the first to notice them. He tried to raise his gun to defend himself, but there were two more soft sounds, and two holes appeared in his forehead. He fell to the ground.

The third and last man, who was working on the printing equipment, saw what happened and ran towards some metal stairs that were rotting with some steps totally missing. The assailants tried to shoot him, but it was difficult as the stairs had a railing and the bullets kept hitting it. Two of the men followed him and continued to shoot at him, and the third man ran out the door and disappeared outside.

The man who was running for his life was a little chubby and of medium height. The bullets kept coming closer and closer, and each time one hit the metal and made a distinctive sound, he panicked even more. He reached the third floor of the building and got to a window where the glass was broken. He opened it and looked for a way to save himself. He knew that once there had been ramps where they slid boxes down to load the trucks. He found a chute, jumped on it, and slid down.

The men continued to shoot at him. He could see the bullet holes in the aluminum wall as he slid down, but he felt he was getting away. When he got close to the ground, crossing the final level, he realized that he was out of their reach and soon would be at his car. Feeling more secure, he turned and gave them the finger.

When he got his feet on the ground, he reached into his pocket and got the key to his car, and ran to it. When he put the key in the door to open it, the third man came up behind the car and shot him two times straight into his heart. He fell forward onto the hood of the car. The man who shot him shook him to be sure he was dead. The man slid down, lifeless, to the ground.

The man put his pistol behind the corpse's ear and shot once more, just to be certain. The other two men came running out of the building. All three moved the bodies inside the building and began to put explosives around it. They searched the boxes of money until they found the plates. They took them out and put them in a briefcase in the van. They brought a can of gasoline from the van and spread it all over the boxes that were still full of money. They sprinkled the gasoline over the printing equipment as well. They lit a match and set it all on fire, and they got out of there.

They drove a few blocks away, and in a matter of minutes they saw the building explode into pieces. There was a huge column of smoke that went up into the sky from the building.

That same night, Romero came back to his house. The police were no longer there. Isabel was lying in bed with a big bandage on her face. The children were already asleep. He took off his clothes and got into bed. He apologized and tried to convince Isabel to make love by touching her softly. She rejected him. He insisted, and wound up forcing her to have sex with him. While he was on top of her, she looked not at him but at the ceiling. Tears were running down her cheeks. Romero began moaning as he was about to climax. She was silent. She bit her lip, and a little line of blood ran down her chin. He continued moaning.

A short distance from the house, the old van was parked and the two men in back could hear Romero's sexual moaning until he finished with a big sigh. It was already late in the evening, and after he finished his forced sex, Romero slid out of the bed. He snarled to Isabel, "You are not even any good to fuck anymore!"

Isabel ignored him, turned over, and covered herself with the sheet.

"The next time I fuck you, if you are not any better I am going to take you back to the whorehouse where I got you!" he screamed at her.

Isabel maintained her silence. Romero went to the bathroom, and after he urinated he grabbed a towel and wrapped himself in it. He went to the sink and began to wash his sweaty face with soap and water. After he dried his face, he looked at himself in the mirror. He looked at his teeth and decided to brush them. He rinsed once and when he took another sip of water he began to gargle. He could not finish. He felt a tremendous pain in his chest. He put the glass down and clutched at his heart. He spit out the water and toothpaste that was in his mouth. It went all over the mirror.

"Isabel!" he screamed in agony. "Isabel! Please help me!"

Isabel ignored him. She raised her head and then decided not to answer him. By now, the pain was so unbearable that Romero clutched at his chest with both hands. He screamed for the last time, "Isabel!" Then he collapsed on the floor, dragging the towel and the glass he had used to rinse his mouth. It fell to the floor and broke into pieces, making a lot of noise.

Isabel was still in bed and very angry at him. She heard the noise as he fell and the glass when it broke. She decided to get out of bed and go see what had happened. She wrapped herself in the sheet and walked to the bathroom. When she got close to him, she saw his eyes were bugged out. He barely whispered, "Please, forgive me." With that, he died.

She put her hand to her mouth. She looked at him for a few seconds, and then she screamed. She ran out of the bathroom, full of panic.

In the van, the two men in the back took off their earphones and knocked on the glass divider. The driver opened the curtains and the man in the back made a signal with his fingers up. He made quick circles with his hand, the signal to wrap it up and leave.

As they were driving away, once again the sound of police sirens could be heard, and the neighbors were coming out of their houses and going to Romero's.

# Chapter 14—Las Vegas Debriefing

In California, I finished drinking the champagne with my friends in celebration of the arrival of my parents. I said goodbye and went to run some errands in the city.

Loren had taken Arturo's death pretty badly. She was actually scared for her own life now. To relieve the tension, I took her out that night to a French restaurant in Newport Beach. We had a great meal and danced for a while. I tried to talk to her and make her feel better, but I realized then that she did not have the character or the nerve for these kinds of things. I wished that this operation would end quickly for our tranquility and our safety.

In the past, I had learned that you could not always depend on or trust completely a person with this type of personality. Such people are like a box of surprises— under pressure, they can react either one way or the other, and that reaction could be favorable or against you. I had been told by Father Salomon that in three or four days everything would be ready. I could not wait until those three or four days had passed. Then I could send him back to his monastery, which would relieve me of another one of my concerns.

The next morning I received a page from O'Brien. It was much earlier than he normally contacted me, and when I called him, he told me he needed to talk to me immediately. We agreed to meet in the bar at the Hilton hotel across from the Orange County airport, our location number 3.

I arrived before him. I ordered some French toast and a glass of orange juice. A little while later, he arrived and I offered him some breakfast. He accepted and ordered strawberry waffles and coffee.

He then took a little box out of his briefcase and handed it to me. "Take this into one of the booths in the bathroom. Check it out and then come back and let me know what you think."

I went to the bathroom and checked out the box. I was really surprised when I saw the contents, a money plate for some very strange

158

money I had never seen before in my life. I put everything back into the box and went back to the table. "What is this?"

He smiled mischievously, like a little kid, and said, "This is a twenty, fifty, and hundred dollar bill not yet in circulation. It'll be in circulation in approximately five years. After we finish and conclude this operation and the Zipper's been closed, all this money we are printing and putting all over the world has to be brought back and destroyed. The only way we can do this is to change the currency and bring all the old bills back and incinerate them."

I held up the box with the new plates. "You mean to tell me that this is going to replace all the bills we are printing right now?"

He reclined in his chair, nodded, and quietly said, "Yes."

I also reclined in my chair and took a sip of my orange juice. "Of course, I will not tell this to anybody. But even if I did, they would think I was a great novelist and had a great imagination, or else in the worst scenario that I was crazy."

He smiled. "Reality is grander than any fantasy the human mind could ever create."

I shook my head. I tried to digest what O'Brien had just told me. "Well, I know you did not bring me here just to show me this. What do you really want me to do with it?"

"Well, since your friend's so good at printing and graphics, the old man and Addison have asked me to talk to you about printing some of this money for future secret operations, to have it in reserve."

I remained silent, deep in thought. I stroked my chin meditatively with my left hand, my glass of orange juice still held in my right. I took a sip and thought further. I knew that this meant the operation would take longer and would get Father Salomon more deeply involved in what we were doing. Additionally, I was worried about Loren, who was on the verge of cracking.

On the other hand, I could not say no to him—this man had engineered the exit of my mother and father from Cuba! I had not felt comfortable about this operation from the beginning, and now I was feeling even worse. What else might go wrong? We had already lost Arturo, we had problems with Romero, and Amelia and I had nearly been killed in the Caribbean. All of these things crossed my mind. O'Brien kept looking at me, waiting for my answer, so I said, "This is going to be like starting again, just as I thought we were reaching the finish line. We will need paper, magnetic ink, negatives, chemicals. . . . We are only a few days away from finishing. I assume you will not want to use the originals, so that means it will take a lot more time to reproduce them."

He smiled. "You're assuming correctly. But none of this is important. The most important thing is to have the finances in place for our future operations. We've got the opportunity right now to secure that, so why not do it? All your friend has to do is give me a list of what he'll need. We'll provide him with every single thing he wants."

"Okay. Let me consult with my friend and show him these plates before I give you an answer. What I see in these new plates is that they incorporate watermarks and other details. I don't know too much about graphics, but I can see that these are going to be a hell of a lot more work to do. This bill is a lot more sophisticated and detailed."

"Of course," he said. "This is what the brains in the Treasury Department get paid for—to discourage counterfeiters from copying our currency. Of course, with the excellent printer and the fantastic graphic artist you've got, none of this is an obstacle, especially if you've got the right ingredients like the original paper, magnetic ink, and so on. You can't be stopped."

I scratched my head. "I was counting on a little vacation, but it seems to me that you want to work me to death!"

He smiled again. "We're going to be in debt to you and your group for life. This is extremely important for future operations."

"Okay. I will try to convince my friend of the extreme importance of this operation, and maybe he can stay here for a couple more weeks."

"The old man and Addison will be very happy when I tell them that everything's in process."

"Wait a minute. Nothing is in process until I call you and give you the green light because it is not up to me. This is actually a different project completely. I don't want to see anybody with a long face and disappointment if this cannot be done."

O'Brien turned a little serious then. "Well, I'll leave it in your hands. Do whatever you can do. Call me, and let me know."

"Very well. I want to make sure before I call you that my man can do this. I don't want your chemicals and ink to end up in the trash can."

I stood up to pay the bill, but O'Brien grabbed it away from me. "Oh, no—this one's on me."

"Thank you," I said with a slight smile.

160

He grinned in reply. "This is the least I can do. You never let me pay. Once I a while, I've got to take it by force from your hand. You're always in a rush to get the bill."

"I probably learned that from my father. He always told me it was better to be able to give rather than have the embarrassment to have to ask. I think I probably took that too literally."

We shook hands and said goodbye. He walked to the bar to pay the bill and I walked out of the hotel. I got in my sport Jaguar and drove towards the new warehouse in Fountain Valley. When I cruised into Costa Mesa, I stopped at one of the places where they sold tickets for major events on Newport Boulevard. I bought four tickets for the opera *Carmen*, which was playing that night in Los Angeles. After I obtained the tickets, I continued on to the new warehouse.

When I arrived and had said hello to everyone, I took Loren aside and told her I had a surprise for her, and showed her the two tickets for the opera. "Would you like to go to the opera tonight with me?"

She smiled happily, very surprised. "Oh, my God! You did that for me? Of course I'll go to the opera with you!"

"I know how much you like concerts and the opera and classical music."

"You have made my day," she said with a smile.

"Good. I am glad I can do something like that once in a while to bring happiness to you."

We walked back to the group, and she went back to bundling and wrapping the $100 bills. I got close to Father Salomon, touched him on his shoulder, and asked him to come with me for a moment. I took him to the office, opened my briefcase, and showed him the new plates for the future money that O'Brien had just given to me. I explained to him that the money we were making now would eventually have to be destroyed. This was the new money that would replace the money currently in circulation.

He looked at me in surprise. "Oh, my God!" he exclaimed. "You mean to tell me that what we are doing now is the reason the government will be changing the currency in the future?"

"Yes, absolutely. They have to bring all this money back later, slowly, to destroy it. They will then use this new money to accomplish that by replacing the money we are making now. It will be more difficult for counterfeiters to copy. As you see, everything is well-planned ahead of time. One hand cleans the other, and both clean your face. That is the way these people work. They never do just one thing only. They do multiple things at the same time."

"Why do they want to make copies of this new money which is not even in circulation yet?"

"Very simple. It is like an insurance policy for them to have money on standby for future operations."

"How long will it take for this new money to get into circulation?"

"Probably five or six."

He smiled mischievously and looked closely at the plates. "What if we print some of this new money and put it somewhere like they are doing, for our own future operations—like an insurance policy?"

I smiled and patted him on the back. "I have already been thinking of that. The question is can you duplicate these plates? If you can, then we definitely will print some and put it aside like an insurance policy for our group and in order to feed some of the hungry mouths in your monastery."

He smiled. "I like you! I always tell Father Lara you are a smart man."

"Well, do you think you can do it?" I asked once more.

He looked at me over the top of his glasses and said, "Of course I can do it, my child. With good will everything can be done."

He sat down at the desk and began to make a list. "Of course, I will need different equipment and material to do this work. I will write down what I need to do this to perfection." After he finished making his list, he gave it to me and said, "Ask them how much they want to print. According to what they tell you we will multiply it by the amount on this list. Based on what they want to print, they need to send the paper, the magnetic ink, and any other chemicals needed."

We left the office and went back to the area where the others were working. Bundles of money were sitting all over the place. They were putting them in boxes and sealing them.

Father Salomon said, "Tell your friends we are ready to ship some of these boxes already. They can send the truck for pickup tonight."

"Thank you," I replied. "I will."

Then I said goodbye to Loren and the others. After I left, I called Amelia at her medical clinic in Santa Ana and asked if she could meet me in the coffee shop of the clinic. A little while later, I arrived at the clinic, parked my car, and went to meet her. She smiled and hugged me when she saw me.

"How are you?" I asked.

"I am still sore but I am okay. How are you doing?"

"I am fine. I need a favor from you."

"For you, whatever," she smiled. "What do you need?"

I got the other two tickets for the opera out of my pocket and handed them to her. "I need you to convince Sanchez to go with you to the opera in Los Angeles tonight. Do it very casually. Do not mention my name. Tell him you have these tickets and you want him to go with you. You will see me at the opera because I will be there with a lady. Look for me during the intermission in the bar area. Bring him close to me because I want to see his reaction when I introduce the lady who will be with me to him. Her name is Loren."

Amelia nodded. "Don't worry. I will do exactly what you tell me to do. You don't have to explain anything to me. But be careful. Sanchez is not a common man. If you put him on the spot, he can react violently. I tell you this because I know him well." She put her hand on my shoulder. "I hope you won't get disappointed, sweetie because sometimes the truth can be brutal."

"I would rather know the truth no matter what," I replied, "even though sometimes the truth can break your heart in pieces."

She smiled again, nodded her head in agreement, and pointed to herself. "I am the same. I like to know the truth, too."

I thanked her, walked to my car, and called O'Brien. When he answered, I said, "Now you can tell your friends everything is in process."

"Great! Thank you very much. I know I can count on you."

"I will give you the list later of everything we will need for this new project. By the way, you can send your people to pick up the first shipment. It will be ready tonight."

On my way home, my car phone rang. A familiar voice said, "Dr. del Marmol?"

I could not place the voice, so I asked, "Who is this?"

"You forgot about me already, huh? This is your cousin, Narciso Caletano Barriety."

"Oh—I'm sorry! I did not recognize your voice. How are you doing? Are you in Vegas?"

"I'm fine," he replied. "No. I am here in Los Angeles on a business trip. Actually, I have something very important to talk about with you. How is your time today?"

"I'm fine. When do you want me to meet you?"

"Can you meet me here in an hour? I am at the Hilton Hotel on Century Boulevard in Los Angeles."

"Yeah, I am about forty-five minutes away from you. You are close to the L.A. airport. I will be there in an hour. Where in the hotel do you want me to meet you?"

"There is a little French café as you come into the lobby on your left. I will wait for you there."

"Okay," I said, "I will be there as soon as possible." We hung up, and I drove to my house to change cars. I took the red DeLorean and drove towards Los Angeles.

When I got to the Hilton, the parking attendant recognized me from several meetings there previously. He was a big black guy named Tyrone. He came close to me and said with a big grin, "Doctor, when you breed that baby, I want a puppy!"

I smiled back at him and said, "Sure! I promise you I will give you a puppy if you will keep my car around here and not put it in the underground structure, as I do not intend to be here for too long."

"No problem—I'll do that for you."

I walked into the lobby and went into the French café. I saw Caletano and Charlie at a table, as well as two other bodyguards sitting close by at another table. Charlie stood up when he saw me and extended his hand in greeting. Then he pointed to the chair he had been sitting in and asked me respectfully to sit down.

"It is a real pleasure to see you looking well, Dr. del Marmol," he said.

"The pleasure is all mine, Charlie." He then went to the other table and joined the other two bodyguards.

Caletano stood up and hugged me emotionally. "Nice to see you."

"Nice to see you, too, cousin."

"Do you want to eat or something?" he asked.

"No, but I can get some orange juice or something to drink."

The waitress came to our table, and he ordered a quiche plate surrounded by fresh fruit and an orange juice. After she brought his order and had gotten a little away from us, he said, "I think I have some very valuable information for you. It can be useful to your friends." He stroked his chin before continuing. "You know that Señor Fidel Castro likes Rottweilers. I don't know what he uses these dogs for. If it is for his personal pleasure or for one of his demonic ideas, but the truth is that once in a while he orders one of these dogs from Rottweil, Germany, where they breed these animals. As you know, they are a crazy genetic cross. This is the third dog he has ordered this year. His counter-intelligence agents, OTTO, are supposed to come next month to pick him up." He then gave me a note with all the information about the time and date they were supposed to pick up the dog from Rottweil. "I assume this information," he continued, "might be valuable to your friends, especially if this dog is for the personal care of Castro or anybody in his first ring—his close family."

"Yes," I said with a smile, "this information could be valuable. Thank you."

"You are welcome." He drank some of his orange juice and continued, "I don't know whether you know it, but one of the daughters of Fidel's brother Raul is married to one of our *paisanos* in Sicily. Through these family connections I can obtain very valuable information. I just want you to tell your friends to be careful and treat this information with respect, and don't tighten the screw too tight. We don't want to jeopardize our *paisano*."

"Don't worry about it. I will tell them to be extremely careful how they handle this information."

He nodded his head. "Thank you." He looked deeply into my eyes then. "Do you know what MQ1 is?"

I nodded. "Yes. It is the special team that works with the G-2 and is in charge of kidnapping and sometimes killing the people from Cuba that are considered traitors. One way or another, refugees have managed to escape from Cuba to many other countries in the world; but they are not safe, as the MQ1 has diplomatic immunity everywhere. They are able to trace these so-called traitors anywhere and bring them back to Cuba, where they are made an example of and are tried in public and on TV, where all can see. They are then found guilty and executed."

"We have identified four members of the MQ1 who arrived from New York in Vegas. They have been asking questions about you. Who knew you were going to be in Las Vegas? Be extremely careful, and examine very well in detail who was around you close enough to know that you were going there."

I did not reply. I was thinking seriously of what he had said.

"Remember, these people have no mercy with anyone. They are following you too closely already."

"I will take all security measures to lose them."

"Do you want me to leave Charlie and a couple of my men to make sure they don't get close enough to you to hurt you?"

I shook my head. "No, no. Thank you. I really appreciate that, cousin. I don't think that will be necessary."

He drained his glass of orange juice. "Remember, if you need me for anything, just call me."

"Thank you. I appreciate very much your information and your offer. Thank you very much." By now he had finished his food as well, and pulled out his wallet to pay. "No, no—let me."

"No. Under no circumstances," he said firmly. He pulled a $100 bill out of his wallet and said to the waitress, "Pay for everything, including my friends over there at the next table, and keep the change."

The waitress was very happy and nodded appreciatively as she said, "Thank you! Thank you, sir. Thank you very much!"

We stood up, hugged each other, and said goodbye. Charlie came close to me and gave me a hug, too. The other two men maintained their distance. All four left and went inside the hotel. I went back to the parking lot and, after giving Tyrone a generous tip, drove back to Orange County. I picked up the phone, called O'Brien, and told him I would meet him in an hour as something had come up and

I needed to talk to him immediately. Forty-five minutes later, I arrived at the French café by the Balboa ferry. It was sunset. I arrived a few minutes before he did and sat down at a patio table under an umbrella. I saw him when he arrived and watched him park his car across the street in the reserved parking area for the restaurant management.

He walked towards me with a smile on his face. "Well, you beat me this time."

"It's about time. You are always here before me."

He gestured towards the road in disgust. "The goddamn traffic on Balboa Island is like hell this time of year."

"Well," I replied, "that is exactly why we picked this place and location—because if someone is following us, it is obvious. Either they have to be in line to cross the ferry or they have to park on this narrow street. To find a parking space is like finding a needle in a haystack."

"Thank God for your connection with the owner of this café."

"Yes. I instructed my workers to drop off fifteen or twenty papers here every day for free for the customers. As you know, nothing in life is free. We are paying for our privileged parking space at this restaurant."

A cute young blond waitress with short shorts came over to us and asked O'Brien what we would like to order. O'Brien looked at her, then back at me, and said, "I know why you like this location more than any other place we meet."

The waitress understood his joke and smiled. O'Brien asked for blueberry muffins and an espresso. I asked for sangria with fruit and napoleon pastry with sugar topping. A few minutes later, when the girl brought our order, I took a miniature bottle of Grand Marnier liqueur out of my briefcase. I made the sign of the cross and said, "In the name of the Father and the Son and the Holy Spirit," and spread it over my napoleon pastry and sangria drink.

O'Brien laughed. "You and your Cuban rituals." I offered the bottle to him, but he declined. However, before I could put it away he extended his espresso and said, "What the hell. Why should you have all the fun? Go ahead and put a little bit in here."

I made the sign of the cross again. "In the name of the Father and the Son and the Holy Spirit." I poured it into his coffee until he signaled me to stop. I covered the little bottle and put it back in my briefcase, and took out the list of materials Father Salomon had given me that afternoon. I also took out the note with the details of the Rottweiler my cousin Caletano had given me. I gave him the list of materials from Father Salomon first and told him that this is what we would need to begin the job.

He took a quick look at the list. "Tomorrow, you'll have everything in the warehouse."

Then I gave him the note from Caletano. "This is very fresh information that I got this afternoon. It is about a Rottweiler dog that Castro has ordered from Germany. It looks like this could be more than a personal toy for Castro because it is not the first one that he has ordered from the same place."

O'Brien took the note in his hand and nodded his head as he bit his lower lip in thought. "This is very interesting. It's more than interesting. This is fascinating because it's extremely confidential." His eyes shone, he put both hands up high and smiled. "When I tell this to Addison," he mumbled to himself, "he's not going to believe it. This can be fantastic because we'll have a free spy with no risk inside the walls of the most intimate places of Castro and his family." He continued talking to himself, but I could not understand anything he was saying. He noticed the confusion on my face. "Oh, I'm sorry. Let me explain what's going through my mind." He took a sip of his espresso. "Probably you think I'm going crazy."

"No, I just thought you might be having an allergic reaction to Grand Marnier."

He smiled again, moved his chair closer to me and lowered his voice for the sake of discretion. "We've spent years trying to perfect something like a contact lens which through a surgical procedure could be implanted directly into the retina of the eye. This implant contains a video and audio transmitter capable of input similar to the level of the human eye and ear, and transmits via satellite like a television camera thousands of miles away. We've already tested it on dolphins, monkeys, dogs, and other animals. It's one hundred per cent reliable. Can you imagine what this means to our intelligence community? How many thousands of human lives we can save and at the same time retrieve information from any part of the world? Even from places where human beings have limited access! We can do anything with this."

I reclined in my chair and smiled. Immediately I knew what he planned to do with that dog. I took a sip of my sangria. "But this implant cannot be detected by X-rays or other optical examinations?"

"No because it's implanted directly into the retina of the eye. This discovery came through a team of research scientists funded by the federal government. They tried to discover a replacement implant for the broken retina of people who lost their eyesight in one or both eyes. Then Counterintelligence programs developed micro-cameras that could be added to the implant. Through the eyes of one person who has this implant, we can see and hear whatever he can see and hear from thousands of miles away. Remember, this whole secret program was developed and funded by the federal government with the sole purpose to protect national security in the future."

"Very well, this is great and wonderful, but how are you guys going to get your hands on that Rottweiler? I assume you need to do this surgical procedure on the dog and that you need highly qualified veterinarian surgeons. For this, you will need to take the dog away from where ever he is being held for whatever time this procedure will take. How will you do that?"

He looked at me as his idea was growing bigger in his brain. "Can you imagine what this operation will signify if we can do it successfully?"

I smiled ironically. "Why don't we put a good amount of explosives in the dog, and when he gets close to Castro in Cuba we can blow up the dog along with that son of a bitch? I don't think blowing him up will resolve the problem in Cuba and I don't like the idea of killing the poor dog, but at least he will die for a good cause. Seven hundred times you guys tried to kill Castro in the past decades and always a lot of men have died. To me, the men's lives are worth a lot more than a dog's life."

O'Brien turned serious, took another sip of his coffee, and squeezed his forehead with his left hand. "I'm sorry to correct you, my friend—it hasn't been seven hundred times. It's been nine hundred times. These are the official numbers, the ones that have been documented. You can add another one or two hundred times that are undocumented by independent groups, national and international, inside the island and outside of Cuba. They've all been frustrated for one reason or another. That son of a bitch has extraordinary luck. He's like Adolf Hitler. They're both sons of Lucifer and both protected by his two horns. They represent blood, hate, revenge, envy, and all the negatives that exist in the world."

I finished my sangria. It was delicious with my touch of Grand Marnier and my sugar napoleon. I pushed my plate away from me a little bit. "Well, you have not answered me yet how you plan to get your hands on that dog."

"Well, there are two ways to get that dog."

I cleaned my mouth with my napkin, taking away the rest of the sugar left on my lips from the napoleon. I asked again, "What are the two options you have?"

"Well, the first option is to try to buy the dog from the breeder and offer him two or three times what they're going to pay for him. We'll tell the breeder we only will have the dog for a few days with the condition they never let Castro or his agents know we had the dog before them. Then they can sell it back to Castro or whatever amount they've agreed on. This is great business for the breeder. They'll make lots of money by just letting us have the dog for a few days. The only problem we have with this is we're taking the risk of the breeder telling the Castro agents we had the dog before them. That would ruin our plan.

"The other option is maybe you come with us to Germany and you can talk to some of the agents that'll be picking up the dog. Since you're an expert in human behavior, you can tell from talking to them which of these guys would be a good candidate to defect from the Castro system. Maybe you can work a deal with one of them to let us have the dog for a few days. After we do our work with the dog, the agent can take it back to Cuba and we can arrange political asylum for him and his family. What do you think?"

"Both options are good. Both options involve risk. Which option do you prefer to try first?"

"I don't know. Let me give it some thought and consult with Addison and the old man. Later on I'll let you know. We have time, since they're not scheduled to pick up the dog until next month."

"Very well. Keep me informed on this because this dog is becoming an interesting subject."

I stood up and was about to pay the bill, but O'Brien said, "No, no—I'll take care of this. Are you in a rush?"

"Yes, it is getting dark and I have planned to go to the opera tonight in Los Angeles. I have not even taken a shower yet."

"What opera are you going to see?"

"*Carmen.*"

He stood up with a smile on his face. "That is a beautiful opera. Who's doing the role of Carmen?"

"Milena Kitic."

"Oh, she's a great mezzo soprano. You'll love her. She's really a lady with class and style. Enjoy the opera."

# Chapter 15–Verena and Leonardo

I shook hands with O'Brien and said goodbye. I took my car, got out of Balboa Island, and drove towards my house. I called Loren from the car and told her I would pick her up at her house in an hour. She told me she was ready to go right now, but I said that I was going to my house to shower first and would be there as soon as possible.

We hung up, and I called Elizabeth. When she answered the phone, she said, "Yes, I know about the opera tonight. Loren told me already. I am ready and at your house waiting for you."

"Okay, sweetie, I will see you in a little while." I hung up the phone.

As I got close to my house, the phone rang. It was Yaneba to tell me that Sanchez had met with Loren that same afternoon while I was in Los Angeles. They met in the shopping mall of South Coast Plaza in Costa Mesa. They had been together for only a few minutes and Loren had appeared very nervous and agitated. They were there for such a short time that this time Yaneba did not have time to video them or record their conversation. She said Loren was making negative gestures with her head and hands, as if she were saying no to whatever it was that Sanchez was asking her to do.

I thanked Yaneba and hung up the phone.

I got to my house, parked the car, showered, and left with Hernesto and Elizabeth to pick up Loren. After we picked her up, we continued on to Los Angeles.

Hernesto was sitting in the passenger seat, sharing some fast food with his sister. Loren was dressed beautifully in a white evening gown with one black line on the left side that went down to an opening just above her knee. She had her long hair rolled up on top of her head, and she was wearing a jeweled tiara.

"You look beautiful," I told her. "With that gown and that tiara, you look like a queen. Does that make me your king?"

She smiled and grabbed my hand. "You are my king, always. Did something happen to you? Is anything wrong?"

"No. Why do you ask?"

"Lately, I notice you are very quiet, which is unusual for you. And you are distant from me."

I smiled and touched her face. "Probably too many things going on at the same time in my head. Actually, what happened to our friend, Arturo, made me reflect about many things that before never even crossed my mind. Lately, they are running back and forth in my head like a film."

She moved closer to me and took my hand in hers. She looked straight into my eyes and said in a voice thick with emotion, "Why don't we get the hell out of this town when we finish this project we are doing now? Let's get far away from this craziness. You have a lot of money, and I have a little bit, too. Maybe we can settle someplace far away from here and have a family."

I smiled and said, "Money is not what motivates me to do what I do, sweetie. It's a lot more than money. It is deep feelings in my soul and in my heart. Perhaps it is some kind of strange attachment to those who have died already for what we believe in." I moved closer to her and kissed her gently on the lips. "Lately, what you have said has crossed my mind many times. That is one thing that my cousin in Vegas advised me to do. He said I should leave all this madness and go far away and have a family because no one person is going to be able to change this crazy world."

She liked what she heard from me and smiled, full of happiness to realize that I agreed with her up to a certain point. We arrived at the theatre and, although there were a couple of limos ahead of us, the attendants opened our doors immediately.

Hernesto called me on the limo phone and said, "I will walk with you guys into the lobby and wait for you in the bar until the opera is over. That way, I can make sure nobody gets close enough to you to hurt you."

We got out of the limo, followed by Hernesto, and Elizabeth continued driving to the parking area to park the car. We got in line to enter the theater, and in spite of the multitude of people already there, I saw Amelia and Sanchez ahead of us. They were already almost at the door to enter the lobby. Amelia saw me and our eyes met. I noticed Sanchez was also looking towards us, and I had a feeling that he had also met Loren's eyes. I reached for her hand so we would not get separated and she looked down at the floor, avoiding my eyes as if she were embarrassed over something. I did not understand why she held her head down. She had a very nervous smile on her face.

I tried to justify the incident and exonerate Loren from what I knew was obvious: she was trying to hide something. I had had too many years of experience and intense study of human behavior to not realize that something was extremely wrong. When I saw that feeling of extreme guilt reflected in Loren's face over something as insignificant as meeting someone's eyes, I knew there had to be a problem that I needed to give more attention to.

She tried to pretend nothing was wrong, but she did not have enough experience to convince anyone. She giggled and said, "Oh, I'm so happy we're going to see the opera." She squeezed my hand and smiled nervously. I smiled as well, and then the usher took us to our seats.

After we sat down, I looked at her and noticed her forehead, under her eyes, and her cheeks were quite sweaty. I took my handkerchief and gave it to her. She proceeded to wipe the sweat from her face and said, "Feels like the air conditioning is not sufficient for this many people."

I didn't feel anything was unusual. To me, the temperature was very comfortable. Evidently, her nerves were getting to her. In order to avoid arguing with her, I simply agreed casually and said, "Well, it is a little bit stuffy in here. The theater is completely full." She returned the handkerchief to me. Just then, the lights dimmed and the opera began.

During the intermission, we went out to the lobby and I noticed she was still quite nervous. As she started to head to the bathroom, I asked her, "Would you like something to drink?"

"Whatever you're having, just get two—one for me," she said hastily as she practically ran to the bathroom. She took off in such a hurry that I began to wonder if she was going to soil herself—or maybe, for some reason, she just did not want to be in the lobby. It looked as if she was trying to hide, as if she did not want to be seen by anybody.

After she left, I got into the line to buy the drinks. Elizabeth and Hernesto came up to me. Hernesto said, "Just let us know what you want to drink. We will get it for you. Go and enjoy yourself."

"Thank you," I said. "Get a couple of glasses of champagne for us and whatever you want for yourselves." I gave them a $50 bill and walked toward the ladies' bathroom to wait for Loren to come out.

A short distance away I saw Amelia and Sanchez talking together. His back was towards me, unaware of what was going on. Amelia looked directly at me, waiting for the right moment to approach me.

Hernesto and Elizabeth came up to me and gave me the two glasses of champagne. They walked a short distance away and stood there, drinking the drinks they had bought for themselves. Loren had been in the bathroom for a long time, to the point I began to worry that intermission would be over and we would not have time to drink our champagne. Just then, she came out and I handed the glass to her.

"Are you okay?" I asked her. "For a minute I thought maybe you got lost in there!"

She smiled. "You men are lucky. You just go in and out. Women have to sit down, and there's a long line in there." She took my arm and we walked back to the lobby and then to the corridor where we had to find the proper door to be able to go back to our seats. As we had planned, Amelia was waiting there, holding Sanchez by his arm and distracting him so that he would not see us coming.

When we got close to them, Amelia turned around and said in a very loud voice, "Oh, my friend! Dr. J. Anthony! How good to see you! Who is this beautiful young lady that you have with you?"

She extended her hand for me to kiss. "This is Loren," I said. "Loren, this is my good friend Amelia."

Loren extended her hand. "Nice to meet you."

"I don't know if you are aware of it," Amelia said, "but you have a real gentleman with you!"

Loren smiled timidly. "Yes, I know."

I extended my hand to Sanchez. "Hello. How are you doing?"

"Fine," he said nervously. "Thank you. How about yourself? I see you are not doing too badly!"

I smiled and looked straight into his eyes. I could see he was feeling very uncomfortable and that he was completely surprised to see us there. After I shook his hand, I turned to Loren. "I don't know if you have ever met him before, but this is Sanchez. He is Amelia's boyfriend."

They looked at each other for a few seconds. Loren said nothing. She was as pale as a ghost. Sanchez tried to handle the situation, seeing that Loren was totally incapable of dealing with it. He took her hand and said, "Nice to meet you, *señorita*. My name is Daniel Sanchez."

Loren was a little disturbed and confused, so her response was a mere mumbling, something that sounded like, "The pleasure is mine."

When Sanchez was about to kiss her hand, the bell which signaled the end of intermission rang. Loren dropped her glass of champagne, which spilled onto her dress. She quickly withdrew her hand, leaving Sanchez feeling embarrassed and leaning over in mid-air. The situation was kind of humorous. I looked at Amelia and she looked at me. We both looked at Sanchez, who looked like an idiot. Then we all three turned around and looked at Loren. I gave her my handkerchief, and she tried to wipe the champagne from her dress.

"Don't worry about it," I said. "We have to go back inside now, and we cannot bring drinks inside, anyway. In other words, your reflexes are in perfect order."

She giggled and said, "I guess the bell caught me by surprise." She was very anxious to get away. "Well, we have to go. Nice to meet you guys."

We said goodbye to them and went back to our seats. I was lost in thought for the rest of the opera. I wondered why she had lied to me. Why did she not admit that she knew Sanchez? What was she trying to hide? It was becoming more and more obvious to me that something was radically wrong.

When the opera was over, Hernesto was waiting for us in the lobby. He escorted us to the limo where Elizabeth was already waiting. "Did you guys like the opera?" Elizabeth asked.

"This lady," I replied, "Milena Kitic, is an excellent mezzo soprano. She does a great job playing Carmen. You guys should see her. Let me know if you want tickets, and I will get them for you."

"Oh, no!" Elizabeth exclaimed. "I'm sorry. I don't like opera, but if you ever get tickets for Benny More when he is in town, let me know! I will be in the first row to see him."

Hernesto burst out laughing. "You crazy woman! If anybody tells me that Benny More is in town, I will disappear from town! That poor black man has been dead for a long time. Castro killed him! They found him smoking marijuana and they arrested him. They put him in a labor camp to do extremely hard work, like digging trenches or cutting sugar cane or breaking rocks in the mines until they killed the poor man. This is what the communists in Cuba call rehabilitation farms."

Loren asked me, "Who is Benny More?"

"He was a very famous singer of country music in Cuba," I explained to her. "Everybody loved him because he was down to earth and he wrote music for the common people and for their towns. They actually killed him because he was a man of high principles and did not agree with the lack of freedom that the Castro regime imposed on Cuba. He hated Batista, the dictator before Castro—but he hated Castro even more because he became a thousand times worse than Batista was." As we were driving I patted my stomach. "Are you guys hungry? I am actually starving!" I told Elizabeth to go to Pico and Vermont to a restaurant called El Colmao. I asked Loren if she was hungry, too.

"Yeah, a little. If the food is good, I can make the sacrifice."

"These people make the best *paella valenciana*, fried plantation bananas, in all of Los Angeles," I told her.

Hernesto raised his arm and said, "Alright! All I have in my stomach today is a hamburger from McDonald's and the French fries I shared with my sister here in the front seat before you guys got in to go to the opera. With all the work and the craziness around us, sometimes we forget we need to eat."

We continued driving towards the restaurant, and I casually asked Loren, "Have you ever seen Señor Sanchez anywhere before?"

"No," she answered a little too quickly, without even thinking. "I've never seen him before in my life."

I shook my head. "I don't know why, but that guy gives me a bad feeling. There is something about him…I don't quite know what…but I don't like it."

Loren started to say something but stopped. We were pulling into the restaurant parking lot. Instead she asked, "Have you come here a lot?"

"Yes, for many years."

"This looks like a Spanish *tablao*, like a tavern in Spain. When we lived in Europe, my father took us to Spain. We had the best meals and the best times of our lives there. Spain is a beautiful country with a rich culture."

Elizabeth parked the limo and we all went into the restaurant. As we entered, Loren said, "This is very typical Spanish culture."

"Well, that is what they represent," I replied. "The original Spanish food mixed with some Cuban dishes. Kind of a combination of both."

We sat down at a large table, and a plump waitress named Candy came to help us. She was very nice and was also the daughter of the owner. "Hello, Dr. del Marmol. How are you? Long time no see. Will you have the usual to drink?"

"Yes. Do you guys want soda or juice or anything else? I have ordered a bottle of wine. It is an excellent wine from Bodegas Riojas. Blanco Brillante. It is my favorite wine."

We ordered *paella valenciana*, fried bananas, and a huge salad of avocado, onion, asparagus, and olives. I ordered a couple of side orders of *papas rellenas*— mashed potatoes with ground beef inside, made into little balls the size of tennis balls, dipped in eggs, breaded, and deep fried. Everybody was in heaven.

Hernesto said, "I have never been here before, but this place has as good or better food than any good restaurant in Miami."

After we ate and drank, we said goodbye to Candy and left her a nice tip. We took our limo and drove back to Orange County. While we were driving, we were practically silent, listening to soft instrumental music that Elizabeth was playing on a stereo cassette. The others were quiet because they were tired, I because I was thinking. I was kind of worried, and I asked myself again why Loren had lied to me. Sanchez had denied knowing Loren, too. Why? But I preferred to maintain my silence and not confront her until I saw the complete results of Yaneba's investigation, in order to be absolutely sure of what was behind all these lies. I did not want to rush into anything and make mistakes that I could not take back.

About an hour later, we arrived at my house. "Don't forget that tomorrow we have to pick up my parents from the airport at three o'clock," I told Elizabeth.

She smiled. "Forget about your mom and dad? Never! I have it written down in my book. Where shall I pick you up from?"

"From here—from the house."

"Very well."

We said goodnight to one another and went to our rooms. Loren and I went to the master bedroom, and she kissed me and rubbed my shoulder affectionately.

I kissed her back and told her I was completely exhausted.

"I am tired, too," she said.

We then went to sleep. I woke up many times throughout the night. I had several nightmares, including one where Loren was the Dolphin and was coming with a huge gun which she put right in my face to blow my brains out. The second time I fell asleep I dreamed I was going to kiss her and she turned from a dolphin into a shark. She swallowed my head in her mouth and swam away, leaving me bleeding with no head. After this nightmare, I completely woke up. It was 5:30 in the morning, and I was covered in sweat.

I looked down at Loren as she slept peacefully by my side. I realized at that moment that I could never sleep with this woman again until I had clarified what was going on. Otherwise, I knew I would drive myself crazy and would be totally exhausted from lack of sleep. Finally, around six in the morning, I passed out from fatigue and slept deeply until about 11:30 a.m.

We showered, had something to eat, and around two o'clock in the afternoon, Loren, Elizabeth, Hernesto, and I took off for the airport. I was feeling a little nervous—not only from what was going on with Loren but also because I had not seen my parents for sixteen years. Even in my clandestine trips to Cuba, I had never gotten close to them for fear of putting them in jeopardy or creating problems for them.

My parents Verena and Leonardo Del Marmol

Julio Antonio's parents

Julio Antonio at 9 years old

I had spoken with my mother occasionally on the telephone, but had never talked with my father since he kicked me out of the house when I tried to convince him that Castro and his group were all a bunch of deceivers. I knew they were going to take all the property and bank accounts from every decent person in Cuba, but he didn't want to believe me.

Loren noticed my silence and withdrawal from everyone and took my hand. "Don't worry—everything is going to be okay."

We arrived at the terminal, parked the car, and walked to the gate where the plane from Miami was to arrive. I paced back and forth and looked through the door where they were supposed to arrive. My friends looked at me and noticed my impatience.

Hernesto came over to me. "Brother, calm down. They should show up any minute. The plane has already landed."

I turned around. "I don't know how my father is going to react when he sees me. I was the first one to tell him many years ago that the political system in Cuba was no good. I don't know how he handled losing all his businesses and all the work he has done all his life—and now leaving his country behind."

"Don't worry, brother. All of us Cubans have lost something. Some minor, some major, but emotionally we all go through hell and back, and we all survive. Your father is not going to be an exception."

"Well, my uncle, his brother, was an exception. They took his pharmacy away from him, and he hung himself. He could not handle it."

Hernesto put his hand on my shoulder. "I'm sorry about that, brother. Thank God your father is not like that. They will adjust here quickly. They have you, and you will take care of them."

"Of course I will," I replied with my eyes glued to the door. The passengers were beginning to come out from the plane. After a while, the first face I saw was that of Mima—that was how we called my mother. She was really happy to be out of Cuba and to be in the USA. Behind her was my father. He did not look very happy. He was trying to control his emotions like a typical macho Cuban. At the same time he tried to force a smile when he saw me. He did not want me to feel bad.

Mima ran to hug me. She ran her fingers through my hair, her eyes filled with tears. "Your hair is too long," she said. "You need a haircut."

My eyes brimmed as I said in a voice thick with emotion, "Mima, this is the fashion here. We live in the United States now. We are not in Cuba anymore."

She pushed me away a little and looked me up and down. "My God, you have become a handsome man!"

My father was waiting patiently behind her for his turn. He wanted Mima to have her enjoyment of being reunited with her son after so many years, the joy that Castro's system had deprived so many mothers, fathers, and families in general of. She grabbed me by my arm and tried to dry her tears with her other hand. She then stepped back and drew me close to my father.

Right in front of me was the man, my own father, that I had tried to warn so many years ago to leave Cuba or else he would face the consequences. This was the same man who had reacted so violently and kicked me out of the house in defense of Castro and his regime. He was holding a small handbag in his hand which contained only the necessary personal things he was allowed to take out of Cuba. This did not include anything of value, no jewelry. He looked into my eyes, and he could no longer control his emotions. He dropped the bag and burst into tears. He stepped forward and opened his arms to me. I did the same, and we gave each other a hug to make up for the last sixteen years.

My friends were also very emotional. They all were weeping as they felt the love and tenderness of the moment—the moment that I would never forget for the rest of my life.

My father's voice was hoarse with raw emotion as he spoke into my ear. "Forgive me, my son. I don't know why I didn't listen to you when you tried to warn me."

The tears ran down my cheeks. I was feeling the pain that my father was feeling at that moment for his regrets and past mistakes. I touched his head, which had only a few hairs left. To me, this was a reflection of the suffering, sorrow, and frustration of the years he had spent in Cuba.

He backed away to look at me. "My God—I always said you grew up too fast for your age. You went from being a little boy to a grown up man right in front of my eyes, and I did not even notice." He stepped forward and hugged me again. Then he said to Hernesto, "Do you know what I used to call him when he was nine years old? The 'old man!' I could send him to do anything, and he always did it right!"

I smiled and tried to dry my tears from my face. I introduced Loren, Elizabeth, and Hernesto to them. Then I asked my father if he had any more luggage. He laughed and showed me his handbag. "This is my luggage." Then he pointed to my mom's little bag. "That is Mima's luggage. Those miserable bastards took our wedding rings, can you believe that?" I shook my head, "Unfortunately, yes, I do believe it."

By the time Elizabeth came back with the limo, my parents had been looking at everything like kids in a candy store. We walked out to the limo, got into it, and they were fascinated with the little lights in it and the bar with all the candies, nuts, and drinks. My father grabbed a couple of bags of nuts, and my mother grabbed some chocolate.

"Don't fill up on that junk," I told them. "I am going to take you to my restaurant where Manolo is making all kinds of Cuban food for you guys."

Mima laughed and said, "That is what I used to tell you before dinner when you were a child. You hid from me and ate it anyway. That is why you never ate at the table and why you used to be so skinny! Leave me alone. Let me eat my chocolate. I have not had any for sixteen years!"

Everyone laughed, and I touched her knee. "Okay, Mima. Eat whatever you want. If you don't eat dinner tonight, you will eat it tomorrow anyway."

"No," my dad said to her, "don't eat any more." He tried to take one of the chocolates out of her hand.

She refused to let him take it and laughingly said, "Leave me alone! Leave me alone!"

"Papi," I said jokingly, "be careful. Mima is going to bite you!" Everybody laughed. Elizabeth rang the phone in the limo and asked,

"Where are we going?"

"To Julio's Caribbean Grill," I replied. We arrived in Orange County an hour later. Manolo had a huge banner with balloons outside, which read *Bienvenidos Verena y Leonardo del Marmol a Su Nueva Casa en USA*: "Welcome, Verena and Leonardo del Marmol, to your new home in the USA."

Julio Antonio's restaurant, red DeLorean parked in front

# Chapter 16—Julio's Caribbean Grill

We went into the restaurant and Manolo brought out all kinds of Cuban dishes to celebrate my parents' arrival. We opened many bottles of wine and champagne. Music played and a Cuban singer performed many old songs for them. My parents were extremely happy.

After we were all a little tipsy, my mother said to me, "You should sing something for us. You are a very good singer." She turned to the others and bragged to them, "He has many records in Cuba. Have you ever heard him sing?"

Hernesto said, "No—I have never heard him sing!"

The others urged me on: "Go on—sing something for us. Your mother is asking you. You cannot say no to her!"

I was not really in the mood for singing because the doubts I had about Loren and Sanchez had me very worried, even though I was very happy about the arrival of my mom and dad. But I really had no choice, and I did not want to disappoint my mother; so I agreed to one song only.

I walked up to the musicians and gave them instructions. I sat down at the piano and started to sing one of my compositions called "El Ave Maria de Julio Antonio." I sang it once, and everyone applauded and insisted that I sing more. I played and sang another of my compositions, "El Bambino." I wanted to quit after that, but they would not let me, so I sang just one more song, a composition I called "Cuba Linda."

My mother came over to me, kissed me, and stroked my hair, clearly showing how proud of me she was. "This is my child!" she exclaimed.

"You are really good," Loren said. "You have a really nice voice. I don't understand the words, since they're in Spanish, but the music is very good and romantic, and you have a great voice!"

I stood up and let the other musicians take over. They congratulated me and told me how much they liked what I had done. I thanked everyone and told them that if they really liked the songs that they could probably find them in the record stores. Even though I had recorded them way back in 1972, they were most likely still available. I wrote the titles down on a piece of paper.

"Ave Maria" record, 1972 ARMO productions

I took my mother by the arm and walked back to our table. Some of the customers applauded as we returned. My father shook my hand and said, "That song, the Ave Maria, gives me goose bumps every time I hear it. I still have it in my memory when you wrote that song in Cuba when you were still a kid. It makes me remember Castro and his group of hypocrites and how they manipulated us to make us believe that after the revolution everyone would be equal with respect to their religion, their social rights, and their freedom of speech.

We believed we would be in a position to agree or disagree with their political ideas or whatever and not be persecuted for that. We thought we would all be able to choose what we wanted to believe in. In the end, they lied to everyone to obtain power, and everything ended up to be a complete contradiction of what they had promised and a complete fraud.

"It is unbelievable," he continued, "that you at such a young age realized what was going to happen in Cuba when we adults did not even see it coming. I remember when you played that song on our piano at home, and you drove us crazy playing it almost all day long until you finished composing it."

"Yes," I said, "that was the first song I wrote when I was a kid." Hernesto asked me, "Didn't the communists give you trouble when you played that song?"

"Oh, yeah," I laughed, "I got into a lot of trouble. I remember the first time I played it. I was in the musical conservatory. It was called the National Arts School by the communists. The director of the school asked me to play one of my compositions in front of thousands of young people who had come to Cuba for an International Modern Music Festival. It was celebrated in Havana at our school. I played my Ave Maria. Of course, they had never heard it before, and they had no idea what it was all about. When I finished playing it in front of thousands of guests, it was like I had dropped a bomb."

"There is no doubt about it," Hernesto said. "You have your heart right in the middle of your chest and giant testicles!" He made a gesture with his hands to indicate their size.

Everybody laughed. "There is no doubt about that," my father agreed. "When he convinces himself about something, nobody can change his mind!"

We heard the restaurant phone ring and a few seconds later Manolo came to our table. "Dr. del Marmol, there is a call for you. Do you want me to bring the phone to you here, or would you like to take it in the bar?"

"No, that's okay—I will go over there." I excused myself and went into the bar.

It was O'Brien. "I received your page. Is everything okay?"

"Yeah, everything is okay. There is nothing extremely important, but I got a thorn from one of your men. I need to see you as soon as possible to see if you can remove it."

"I'm in LA, and I can be in Orange County in forty-five minutes. Where do you want to meet me?"

"Meet me at my restaurant."

"Okay," he said. "I'll leave here immediately, so wait there for me. Are you happy with the arrival of your parents?"

"Oh, man! You don't know how much this means to me!"

"Of course I know. Maybe this'll bring you happiness and tranquility. Enjoy them because joy is the only genuine thing in our lives."

"Yes, I will enjoy them now that they are here by my side. Thank you very much."

We hung up. When I turned around, I saw my mother coming towards me from the ladies' bathroom. She came close to me and pulled a small envelop from her purse and gave it to me. "Sandra sent this letter to you from Cuba. She told me to give it to you personally and that you should destroy it after you read it. That way, she will not get into trouble in Cuba."

I put the letter in my pocket. She put her arm around my shoulder, and with a big smile she said, "You have to see your son, Julito. He is becoming a big man. He is already 23 years old. His personality is identical to yours. He is very lovely to his mom and to me and to everyone. Everybody loves him. They all want him around. You should be very proud." She grabbed my face. "I promised him I would give you a kiss for him. This is it." With that, she pressed her lips to my cheek firmly and for some time.

As we went back to the table, I told her, "I would like to see him at least once before I die."

"Don't talk like that," she scolded. "Of course you will see him."

We sat down at the table and my father started to yawn. I looked at my watch and saw that it was nearly 12:30 am. I knew that my mom and dad were probably tired from the trip.

"Uh, oh," I said. "My dad is yawning. That means he is ready to hit the hay."

He looked at me and smiled. "No, no—it's okay."

"You know what they say in Cuba," I said. "When you yawn it is because you are either hungry or sleepy. You can't be hungry!" I pointed at all the food on the table.

"I ate as if I had not eaten for sixty years!" my father exclaimed. "By the way, thank you very much, my son, for all this exquisite food." He raised his hand and brought Manolo over. "Thank you, too, Manolo, for this wonderful food."

"You are welcome," Manolo beamed. "You don't have to thank me."

I smiled and added, "You don't have to thank me for anything. I should be thanking you for all the stuff you did for me ever since I was a baby, not even counting probably wiping my butt!" Everyone laughed, and Mima nodded and smiled. I told Elizabeth, "Take them to my house. I have to wait for somebody here and take care of some business."

Loren leaned over to me and asked quietly, "You're not going to come with us?"

"No, honey. I have to wait here to meet someone who is coming from Los Angeles. It is very important."

She was not really happy about that, but she accepted it. "Okay. I'll tell Elizabeth to drop me off at my house."

"Okay. I'll see you tomorrow."

Everyone stood up and began to walk towards the door. Elizabeth went ahead to get the limo. When we were outside and while the others were getting into the limo, Loren came over to me and kissed me on the cheek. "Take care of yourself. I will see you tomorrow."

I kissed her back on the cheek, and she got into the limo. I hugged my father and my mother. "I will see you later."

Elizabeth said, "Do not worry. I will take good care of them, and Hernesto will be there, too. Take care of your business, and we will see you later."

I smiled at her and said to Hernesto, "They are with you, so I know they are in good hands. Take care of them, you two."

They drove away and I watched the limo until it disappeared on the Pacific Coast Highway. I went back into the restaurant and asked Manolo to give me a brandy glass with Grand Marnier, and I walked towards the stage. The musicians had already put their instruments away and were on their way out. I sat down on the piano bench and pulled out the letter from Sandra my mother had given me.

"Confidential and personal," the letter read. "For Dr. Julio Antonio del Marmol La Habana, Cuba."

*My love Julio Antonio—*

*I write these words to tell you that no matter what, I am under a lot of political pressure and I have to pretend almost 24 hours a day in order to survive that my relations with one of the high G-2 officers is real. But in reality, it is superficial. I hope you understand that even though I might be in the arms of another man, and you in the arms of another woman, our love is for eternity. In my heart I will never love anybody else like I love you. Nobody can ever kiss my lips the way you did. You made me feel that huge love that I will never find in anybody else. I believe you probably feel the same, no matter how much distance and how many political barriers separate us.*

*I want to tell you that your son is already a big man. He loves you very much. He adores you. He sleeps with your picture under his pillow. I taught him to love you, and even though you are not here, in the same way I will always love you. I want you to remember that no matter what and how much pressure this government puts on me, I will never raise a single finger to hurt you, even if it costs my own life. My heart has only one owner, and that is you. I will love you until I die.*

*Forever, Sandra.*

When I finished reading the letter, I crumpled it into a ball and dropped it on the piano. I was full of frustration, and the memories that were coming back to me made me feel very sentimental and emotional.

I flashed back to the train terminal in Cuba, before we had reached Guantanamo. I remembered her being held by the soldiers. They handcuffed her to the jeep as she struggled to escape. My friends held me back as I started to freak out. Our eyes locked, tears running down her cheeks. Kinqui reminded me that I had to let go, and I protested that she was pregnant with my child.

I dropped my head and closed my eyes. I knew the memory of that moment would remain in my head for the rest of my life. I saw the jeep full of soldiers taking her away, and the sight broke my heart.

I opened the piano and began to run my fingers over the keyboard. My feelings and my heart flew back in time to Cuba, and I felt a knot in my throat. My eyes brimmed with tears, and I thought about how strange destiny is. The only thing I had to console myself with was my son. He was a testimony of that beautiful love I had had with Sandra, love that I had been trying to replace for so many years with no luck. At least he was healthy and was growing strong with his mother by his side, and I felt that I had left a part of myself with her in that child.

I began to play the piano and the musical notes that came out of my soul through my hands were screaming of my lost love. I began to sing with the belief that we would never be together again in life. The feeling was like a torrent of water coming out of my chest. It was as if a dam that had been holding back a huge amount of water for a very long time had broken and was pouring all these feelings out of me. After I had played the piano for a while, I created a melody. I called it *Tus labios lejos de mi.* "Your lips are far away from me."

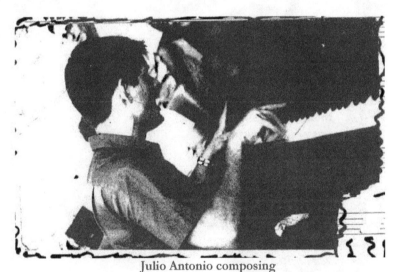

Julio Antonio composing

Your lips are far away from me
I kiss you on your lips
I give all my love only to you
You forgot our moments
You give your love for me to somebody else
I kiss you on your lips
I give all my love to you
You break in a thousand pieces
The love I give to you
You will walk around the world
And other lips will kiss you

Maybe you will call my name
And you will cry at night
I will have to tell you
If one day you want to come back
My love no longer exists
Because you took it with you
I kiss you on your lips
I love you very much
At night whether you want to or not
You will desire me
From memories I cannot live
If you are so far away from me
Finale

*Tus labios lejos de mi*
*Yo te bese en tus labios*
*Te quise mucho a ti*
*Olvidastes nuestros momentos*
*Entregastes a otro el amor que you te di*
*Yo te bese en tus labios*
*Te di todo mi amor, solo a ti*
*Y tu rompistes en mil pedazos*
*El amor que yo te di*
*Caminaras por el mundo*
*Y otros labios te besaran*
*Tu quizas pronuncies mi nombre*
*Y en las noches, tu lloraras*
*Solo me queda decirte*
*Que si alguna vez quizieras volver*
*Mi amor, mi amor ya no existe*
*Pues tu, te fuistes con el…*
*Yo te bese en tus labios*
*Te quise mucho a ti*
*Y en las noches, quieras tu o no quieras*
*Tendras deceos de mi*
*De recuerdos, yo no puedo vivir*
*Si tan lejos, estas tu de mi*
*Finale*

"Lejos de mi"--original manuscript for piano

When I finished singing the song, my hands were sweating so much that I had to use my handkerchief to dry the piano keys. My emotions must have come right through my fingers. I felt a warm hand on my shoulder close to my neck and smelled the perfume of a woman. I turned around. Yaneba was standing there with a big smile on her face. She clapped her hands together in applause and said, "Bravo! Bravo!"

From the bar, I heard Manolo and a couple other guys applauding. Manolo said, "My God, you should record that song. It gave me goose bumps. It has a lot of feeling."

"Thank you, guys," I said with a slight smile.

Yaneba sat down beside me on the piano bench. She took her right hand and with her long nails slid her hand softly over the keys of the piano. She looked at me and said, "What a beautiful song. I would give anything to be able to inspire you to compose something as lovely as that!"

"Have you been here very long?" I asked her.

"Yes, long enough to hear you sing the whole song." She had a glass of wine in her hand. She looked at the paper I had crumpled up, still lying on the piano, and glanced at the paper I had written the music on. She saw the title and understood immediately. "Bad news from Cuba?"

I shook my head. "No, not really. It is just the everyday stupid things in life from the past with no importance at all."

Yaneba shook her head in wonder. "If these stupid and unimportant things are capable of making you create such beautiful music, I don't want to see what you could create if important and great things were to happen!" She smiled then and said, "You would probably create a symphony then!"

I returned the smile. "Do you want to know the irony of what you just said? Most of the time, it is only when a person is going through the worst moment of their lives and they are experiencing a bleeding heart, their stomach is in pieces, and emotionally they are destroyed that they are able to create a masterpiece."

She covered my hand with hers and looked into my eyes. "Do you mean to tell me that every one of those beautiful love songs that we hear every day is the product of some composer expressing his or her suffering? That is really a pity because in order to be a genius and create a masterpiece, you have to be full of pain and be a miserable person."

I nodded and smiled again. "Yes, sweetie, that is the reality." She put her hand on my shoulder again and rested her head on it.

"Oh, my! I feel bad for you. You must be in a lot of pain right now."

Manolo came over. "Do you want another Grand Marnier?"

"Yes, please," I said. Yaneba realized Manolo was standing over us and felt uncomfortable with her head on my shoulder, so she straightened herself up.

"Manolo," I said, "I am waiting for someone who should be arriving shortly. Would you please either leave the door unlocked or have someone there to let him in?"

"Okay, no problem," he replied.

After Manolo refilled my glass, he returned to the bar and Yaneba told me, "By the way, I came to see you here because this afternoon I followed Sanchez all the way to the Mexican border. From Mexico, he took a plane to Panama. This got my attention, and I called our people in Panama and asked them to check out exactly what he was going to do there. They called me less than an hour ago to tell me that Sanchez did not stay there even an hour. He took another plane to Cuba."

I was very surprised. "What! What are you saying?"

"That is why I came here. I did not want to tell you this over the phone. I think you should check out this guy immediately. Something is not right about him."

I shook my head. "Well, I think certain things about him are beginning to make sense to me now." I touched her arm. "Don't worry about it, sweetie. Someone is on the way right now and should be arriving here any minute. He will be able to answer our questions about Sanchez. Thank you. You are doing a great job."

We stood up then. "By the way," I continued, "you should get out of here as soon as possible. I don't want these people to know that you even exist. Remember, your job is to video and record everything around me. It is very important to keep you floating like a ghost." I looked up toward the bar and the front door and saw one of the workers opening the door for O'Brien. "Speak of the devil—he is here already!"

Yaneba did not even turn around and look at the door. Like a professional, she smiled at me and mouthed the word "ciao" and walked towards the ladies' bathroom, which was in the opposite direction from the door. She disappeared into the dim lights of the hallway.

I walked towards the bar in order to block O'Brien's view even further. I intercepted him at the bar, and after we greeted each other, I said, "Let's go out to the reserved terraces." We sat down on one of the terraces which overlooked the ocean and the Newport Channel where the ships came in and out. I asked him if he wanted something to eat or drink.

"Oh, my God—it's too late to eat now. It's past midnight, but I'll take an espresso."

"My mother used to tell me that the stomach has no clock. Whenever you are hungry, you should eat. It's the same as whenever you want to pee, you go pee. It doesn't matter whether it's three o'clock in the afternoon or three o'clock in the morning! If you have to go, you have to go!"

He laughed and said, "You Cubans are crazy."

Manolo came out just then and heard what we had said. He also laughed. "Yes sir, indeed. It is very difficult to find a sane one!"

"Oh, I'm sorry," O'Brien apologized. "I didn't mean you, Manolo."

"That's okay. Can I bring you something to drink?"

"Yeah, I'd like an espresso."

"Do you want another Grand Marnier?" he asked me.

"Yes, please."

O'Brien held up a hand to get Manolo's attention. "Oh, could you please put a little bit of Grand Marnier in my coffee?"

"Sure," said Manolo as he went to get the drinks.

After he left, I asked O'Brien, "Do you have any idea where your special agent Daniel Sanchez is at this particular moment?"

He was caught by surprise and looked at me peculiarly. "Why do you ask me that? Did anything happen? Is anything wrong?"

"No. I just wanted to know if you knew by any chance—since he works for you and he has to report directly to you—where he is right now."

He looked like he was about to ask me what the hell I was talking about. Instead he asked, "Would you please stop beating around the bush and tell me what's going on?"

"Well, you haven't answered my question about where Sanchez is, but I think we have a double problem."

He scratched his head. "A double problem? What do you mean?"

"Yes. Either Mr. Sanchez is screwing my girlfriend Loren, or they are both double agents pretending to screw each other in order to deter us from whatever they are really doing."

He shook his head. "Are you out of your mind? Are you going crazy? What are you saying? *Sanchez?* He's one of my best men, and Loren's your girlfriend, for God's sake."

Just then, Manolo returned with our drinks. "Thank you, Manolo," I said.

"You're welcome, Doc." He put the drinks on the table and went back to the bar.

I looked around and saw the men cleaning the restaurant and putting the chairs on top of the tables so they could vacuum the carpeted areas. It was about 1:30 in the morning. From where I was sitting, I could see Yaneba coming out of the women's restroom and asking one of the men to let her out. I watched her leave.

O'Brien took a sip of his Grand Marnier espresso and said, "Sanchez is in the Caribbean Islands doing some banking transactions with some of the money we gave to him. I repeat to you—the man is absolutely trustworthy. Even so, he has limited information."

I shook my head. "Well, if this man is absolutely trustworthy, then we have an even bigger problem than I had imagined. He probably knows more than the average agent." O'Brien was a little irritated. He squeezed at his chin but did not answer me.

I leaned forward a little bit over the table. "The night Arturo was killed, Elizabeth and Hernesto were on the other side of town, close to San Bernardino, following a lead given to them by Sanchez. According to Sanchez, a group of Cuban exiles with headquarters in Santa Barbara were having a meeting to raise funds in order to make a public accusation in the United Nations, demanding the release of political prisoners in Cuba. They were also accusing Cuba of violating the human rights of those political prisoners." I grabbed my glass of Grand Marnier and took a sip. "This meeting never happened, and when Hernesto and Elizabeth got there to the address Sanchez had given them, they were told that the meeting had taken place a week earlier!"

O'Brien reclined in his seat. "So? Maybe someone had given the wrong information to Sanchez!"

"Will you allow me to finish!? There is a lot more! Yes, that is possible," I replied with an ironic smile. "But it is very coincidental that Arturo was killed that very same night. It was as if someone wanted to get them far away from him, just in case."

When I said this, O'Brien's face changed completely. He stroked his mouth in thought and before I could say anything else, he said, "I know what you're going to tell me next."

"Yes?"

"Sanchez was one of the few who knew you and Amelia would be traveling on the cruise ship to the Caribbean Islands. This is too much of a strange coincidence. You and Amelia were almost killed in the process."

I nodded and shook my finger at him. "Too much of a coincidence." I pulled the envelope out of my pocket and dropped it on the table. It contained the pictures of Loren and Sanchez talking together in different places in town.

He took it in his hands and looked at the pictures. "Have you confronted her?"

"No. By no means. But I arranged for them to meet at the opera and they both denied they had ever met previously."

He smiled as he looked up at me. "Oh, so that's actually the reason why you were rushing to go to the opera! You'd already arranged the meeting." He put the pictures down on the table and raised both hands to his head. "Man, this isn't good at all. I'm really worried."

"There is more."

He removed his hands from his head in dismay. "More?" he exclaimed.

"Yes. Since all this happened, I had one of my people follow Loren and Sanchez, and this afternoon Sanchez crossed the border to Mexico and took a plane to Panama. From Panama he took another plane to Cuba." I paused. "Did you have any knowledge of him going to Cuba? Did you send him on a special mission?"

"Hell no! What the hell does that son of a bitch have to go to Cuba for?"

"Well, there's more. My cousin in Vegas is the one who gave me the information yesterday about the Rottweiler dog in Germany. He also mentioned the hotel where we were staying in Vegas. This means the person who is giving this information to our enemies has to be very close to us to know all these little details. He apparently knows all our comings and goings. Do you think this is a coincidence also?"

"Hell no!" he said again. "Why didn't you tell me all this before now?"

"First of all, everything happened too fast. Secondly, I wanted to make sure because even at the beginning of this conversation you were defending Sanchez as if he were a member of your family. And he is like a member of your family because he is one of your team players. But the difference is that one of my team members is in question too, and she is also my girlfriend. She could be a part of this and you don't see me defending her! I am analyzing all the facts, forgetting about the emotions involved, and I am trying to determine the truth of what is going on."

He extended his hand and shook mine in apology. "I'm sorry. It doesn't make any difference how many years we spend in this business. Every time we think someone has betrayed us, or they show any indication of betrayal, our hearts are broken and we try to deny it."

"Imagine if you feel like that about Sanchez how I must feel about Loren. The most important thing right now is to try to stop the damage. We have to implement security measures to prevent any more damage from being done."

"We'll bring Sanchez in and confine him until we can determine how much damage has been done. Don't confront Loren until we do."

I smiled ironically again. "Don't worry—I have all the time in the world."

"Thank God Sanchez doesn't know where the new warehouse is located."

"Yes, that's true, but Loren knows because she's been working there every day."

Shit! *Shit!* This means you have to confront Loren immediately to find out how much she's involved with Sanchez and how much he knows."

"No, that's not necessary," I disagreed. "First of all, I will move the warehouse to another location tomorrow, and I will tell Loren that we are finished and everything is done. That way, she will automatically be isolated from everything we are doing with no link to anything. Whatever is done is done, and we cannot change it; but we can cut it off completely from here on. You take care of Sanchez. Neutralize him, isolate him, and let me know how much damage has been done. I will take care of Loren."

"Be extremely careful," he cautioned. "These people from MQ1 are very dangerous. Especially since they all have diplomatic immunity."

I brought out my nine millimeter pistol and put it on the table. I took out the clip, removed one of the bullets, and showed it to him. "See this? It doesn't know the difference between diplomatic immunity or not. They are going to take their diplomatic immunity to hell with them. The only thing that really worries me right now is my mom and my dad. I just sent them a little while ago to my house. Loren knows where my house is. The first thing I am going to do right now after you leave is call them and relocate them."

"Don't wait. Do it right now," he said.

"Thank you." I stood up and knocked on the glass window to signal Manolo to come close. "Manolo, can you bring me the telephone right now? It is an emergency, please."

Manolo realized something was wrong and brought me the phone at once. I dialed Hernesto's number, and when he answered I said, "Brother, you have to get out of the house immediately."

"What's wrong?"

"I will explain later. Take my mother and my father to location number one. I will meet you guys there."

"You know they have not even gone to sleep yet. We have been sitting here chatting about Cuba. They are waiting for you." I looked at my watch. It was 2:30 in the morning. "Do you want to talk to them?"

"Yes. Let me talk to my father. That way, it will be easier for you."

My father got on the phone. "Yes, my son? Is everything okay? Are you on your way already?"

"Yes, I am okay, but I am not on my way there. I am going to meet you guys at another house. I forgot, they are going to fumigate the house for bugs, and those chemicals are not good for you to stay there. Hernesto and Elizabeth will drive you to another place, and I will meet you there."

"Okay. I will see you in a little while."

"Let me talk to Elizabeth." When Elizabeth got on the phone, I told her, "I have already arranged everything with my father. Did Hernesto tell you?"

"Yes. We will leave the house immediately."

"Okay, we will see each other at location number one." I hung up the phone.

O'Brien looked at me impatiently. "Are they okay?" "Yes, they are leaving the house right now."

He relaxed. "Good. For a minute, I was worried." We walked out of the restaurant and said goodnight to Manolo. He closed the door behind us, and O'Brien said, "Before you close the warehouse tomorrow, bring that delivery to Amelia because she's got all the contacts in the Caribbean Islands ready."

"Very well. Whatever we have left now in storage and whatever we produce tomorrow I will bring to her personally. I will take an inventory and will tell you the amount later."

We walked into the parking lot and said goodbye. He went to his car, and I went into the management parking lot, took my XJ12 black sedan, and took off towards Corona del Mar.

# Chapter 17—The Traitors Behind Us

A little while later, I met Elizabeth, Hernesto, Yaneba, and my parents in the house in Corona del Mar. After Elizabeth and Yaneba prepared a bedroom for my parents and they had gone to bed, the rest of us sat down on the terrace. I explained to them what was going on and what I had just learned from O'Brien. I told them that this would be the last day they would be working in the Fountain Valley warehouse. I finished by telling them about Loren.

"From now on, we are not going to tell her anything about anything," I said. "She is to be kept completely isolated from our next move. She will probably show up as usual and work all day. After she leaves, we will move everything to a new location, and I will give Hernesto the address and keys later. Nobody goes to my house in Newport Beach, or even near it, until we find out what is going on." I gave the key to the mini truck to Hernesto and told him to pick it up at location number two.

We finished talking, and Hernesto said, "Well, I am leaving now. I will see you guys a little later at the warehouse."

"Say hello to Father Salomon for me," I said. "Tell him I will see him later. Put all the boxes of money in the truck and whatever you guys make later. Keep an inventory. That way I will know how much there is and I can tell O'Brien."

Hernesto left, and we all went to rest for a few hours before going to the warehouse. My mom woke me up about six hours later. The others had already gone to the warehouse, and she said, "Hey, you're sleeping too much, sleepy head."

"Mom, when I went to bed it was nearly six o'clock in the morning."

"That is not good for you. You should not go to bed so late," she scolded.

"Mom, you haven't changed. You're still my *mima*."

After I had a shower and something light to eat, I said goodbye to Mom and Dad, and I took off for the warehouse. After I said hello to everybody, I got close to Loren and asked her how she was doing.

"Fine," was all she said.

She continued working, but I noticed her mind was not on her work. It was someplace else—or perhaps it was because she felt the coldness of the others, since they had not been talking to her. I spent nearly the whole day in the warehouse. Very late in the afternoon, as we were cleaning the equipment and putting the boxes of money in the little truck, Loren asked me, "What's going on? Why are you guys cleaning everything and wrapping everything up?"

"Because today is the last day, honey," I answered. "Everything is finished. This operation is complete, everything is *finito*."

"Then I don't have to come back tomorrow?"

"Nope. Everything will be gone tonight."

"Well, probably that means I won't be seeing you again tonight, huh?"

"I'm sorry, but I will have to supervise everything because it all has to be out of here tonight. If it is not too late when I finish, I will stop by your condo."

She left at about 6:30 in the evening. I went with Hernesto in the little truck to personally deliver the boxes of money to Amelia, as previously arranged. She was waiting for me at her house. When we arrived, she opened the garage and we drove the truck into it.

Amelia was dressed very sexily as always. She was wearing a very tight T-shirt and no bra. You could see her nipples clearly as the shirt was nearly translucent. Her white shorts were so tiny that her cheeks were showing. A couple of times Hernesto nearly tripped and fell to the ground as he unloaded the truck because he could not take his eyes off her.

"Brother," I told him, "if you don't pay more attention to what you are doing, you are going to trip and leave your brains on the concrete floor!"

Amelia enjoyed the attention, but she did not pay too much attention to Hernesto. Evidently she was not attracted to him. When we finished, we went to say goodbye. She gave me a big hug. She told me she would like me to come visit her more frequently and that she would like me to come to dinner one day.

"Thank you very much, but my time is so crazy. I don't even have time to shave sometimes."

Hernesto was watching us from a short distance away. He did not take his eyes off of Amelia's body, and her bottom especially held him fascinated. She waved to Hernesto from a distance as he drove off, heading back to the warehouse.

On the way back, I took two remote controls and a set of keys from my briefcase and gave them to Hernesto. "One of these remote controls is for the driveway gate and the other is for the double garage at the house in Santa Ana, at the border of Fountain Valley and where we are right now. The address is 4222 West Regent Drive. It is a horse property, with almost an acre of land. There is a lot of space and a huge driveway. The house is in immaculate condition. It has a swimming pool and a huge Jacuzzi with a waterfall. There are fruit trees—a very nice place. Take good care of it. It has many bedrooms. Pick up Father Salomon and bring him here tonight after you guys bring all the equipment from the warehouse and put it into the garage. Try to do this discretely so that you don't attract the neighbors' attention."

"I thought we had completed the operation," Hernesto said.

"Yes, technically we have, but we have another little job to do. Keep this confidential and under no circumstances tell Loren anything about this. Father Salomon already knows what he has to do. Only you, Elizabeth, and Yaneba will help him do this work. You will be in charge of the cleanup at the warehouse. Make sure not a single paper is left behind. Everything should be sparkling clean. Turn the keys in tomorrow to the landlord."

"I understand. I will take care of everything. Don't worry about it." He paused. "What about Sanchez?"

"From now on, consider Sanchez an enemy. If by any chance you are close by him, be extremely careful. Record his conversation if he talks to you and don't give him any information about anything."

Hernesto nodded his head. "I understand perfectly."

When we got back to the warehouse, we saw the new boxes with chemicals, paper, and everything else that had been sent by O'Brien for the new project. Father Salomon came up to me and said, "Well, everything is ready. Your friends not only sent me what was on my list but they sent me much more than I had asked for. Whoever read that list knows the printing business very well because they even sent me the little things I will need to do a great job with the watermarks."

"Thank God they sent everything now. That way we can move it all today," I said.

"We are moving again?" Father Salomon asked. "I thought you just moved over here not too long ago. Is there another problem?"

I did not want him to worry too much, so I said, "Hernesto will explain everything to you. It is not a problem yet, but we want to take precautions and we will do this final operation someplace else."

"Well, well," he said, "you guys know better than me. You are in the spy business. I am in the printing business. It's just that it's going to cost us a little more time because we will have to set everything up again."

"I know, and I am sorry, but Hernesto and everybody will help you. We have to do this. It is a part of your security as well as ours." I smiled then. "Thank you for understanding."

"I know that whatever you guys do, you are doing it in the best interest of everyone."

I left the storage and drove my black Jaguar sedan towards the house in Corona del Mar. When I arrived at the house, my folks were eating a beautiful dinner that Yaneba had prepared for them. It was a Cuban dish. It smelled so good. I had been so busy with all the craziness that I had not eaten anything all day. My appetite woke up with a vengeance at that smell and the look of all the good food on the table.

We all sat down and began to eat. I told my father and my mother that whatever they needed they should ask Yaneba, Elizabeth, or Hernesto because I was out of the country most of the time and that I was very, very busy.

My father smiled. "What are we going to need? You have everything here. You have wines—boxes and boxes of wine—different juices, cold meat, fruit, and so much canned food in the closet you could stay here for months and never have to leave. What are you expecting, a war or something?"

He reached over to get a banana from the middle of the table. Yaneba told them, "I think all Cubans go through that for a few years after they have left Cuba and come to the United States. Normally that lasts for a couple of years and eventually it fades, but I think in the case of your son it will never fade. Whenever he goes for a ham, for instance, he brings back three hams!"

I smiled. "Well, guys, it is better to have it and not need it than to need it and not have it!"

My mother said, "Son, you are a little too much. I don't know if you noticed, but we are eating in the formal dining room."

"Yes, I noticed. We never eat in here. We usually eat in the dining area of the kitchen."

Mother smiled. "Yes. Well, I asked Yaneba if we could eat in here because there is so much food in there I lost my appetite. We go through so many years in Cuba with restrictions and food rationing that when we see so much food at the same time our stomachs get scared. Our brain cannot assimilate so much out of the blue."

I smiled and turned to Yaneba. "You know, sweetie, I think we should tell Hernesto to bring the little truck here tomorrow and take all that food and throw it away. That way, Mima can recover her appetite." I said it very seriously.

"Are you crazy!?" Mima screamed. "I will kill you if you throw away all these exquisite things. Don't worry about it. Don't worry about me. My stomach and my head will adjust."

Father was drinking a beer and nearly choked on it when Mima said that while brandishing a little fried banana like a sword.

After we finished dinner, Yaneba was going to clear the table, but my mother said, "Get out of here, get out of here! You already cooked the food. The dishes are my job. I will clear the table. I like washing dishes, anyway."

Yaneba smiled. "You don't have to wash the dishes, Mima," she explained. She opened the dishwasher and showed it to her. "This is our maid, Chencha. Chencha will do the dishes for us. She is better because she washes the dishes with water so hot we could not tolerate it with our hands." Mima was watching Yaneba as she opened the little container for the soap. "You see, Mima, you just put the soap in here, put all the dishes and pots and pans in here, close the door, push the button, and Chencha will do it all for you."

"Okay," Mima said. "Some other time you can teach me better. Right now, I am going to do the dishes the old way. You guys go and sit down on the terrace and look at the beautiful view of the ocean. Leonardo and I will join you in a little while."

Yaneba could not argue with Mima anymore, so she decided to let it be. Evidently they had been bonding. Yaneba had come home early to cook dinner for them. They had been talking, and Yaneba had told her about how her family had all been killed when they tried to escape from Cuba on a raft. A Cuban Air Force plane had deliberately shot them all, and she was the only survivor.

"You are the queen of the kitchen and the queen of the house," she said to Mima. "You do the dishes the way you want. If you want to learn how Chencha works I will teach you later. We have plenty of time. But right now, I am running out of time. I am going to pee in my pants if I don't run to the bathroom right now." She ran to the bathroom, followed by everybody's laughter.

A little while later, Yaneba came out of the bathroom and tried one more time to help my parents in the kitchen. They lovingly pushed her away and closed the sliding door behind her. She came out onto the terrace and sat down with me. She handed me a new envelope with more pictures. She told me these were pictures of Sanchez crossing the border to the Mexican side, and some others of him boarding the plane to Panama, in case he denied it later. Other pictures were of Loren and him talking recently.

"I am really sorry about all this," she said sincerely. "I don't want to be the one to bring all this to you. I know this is going to inflict sadness upon you. That is the last thing I want to do to you. From the bottom of my heart I hope that when you confront her about this she will have a logical explanation."

I shook my head discontentedly and said quietly, "Thank you for all of your concern, but no matter what, I really want to think the best of her, even though the facts seem to indicate the worst. More than anything, I feel responsible because I made the mistake of letting her into my private circle too quickly."

Yaneba leaned over and squeezed my shoulder. "You should not blame yourself because anybody under the same circumstances would have done the same. When you fall in love with somebody, you never think negative things about them." She smiled pleasantly. "We only think beautiful things about them and we plan ahead for the future with them, and we never consider the possibility of bad consequences they might bring to us.

"At least," she continued, "you had the opportunity to enjoy something beautiful and pure. You fell in love. Remember, if there is anything bad or negative, it is not you. It is her. You should not blame yourself for anything. She is probably the one who will be repentant in the future if all this turns out badly as a result of her behavior."

I clasped her hand and looked her straight in the eyes. "You know, you are a wonderful and great person. Before you can be a great woman or man, you have to be a great human being. If you are not, you are good for nothing, even if you are Miss or Mister Universe. Thank you very much for your kind words. You are really a great human being."

"Thank you," she said quite simply.

I opened the envelope and examined the pictures. I held up one of them and said, "I would give anything to know what they are talking about."

"So would I, but every time they get together they do it for only a few minutes, and it has been very difficult for me to install my equipment properly without calling attention to the people around. I need more time to put those long range microphones in an appropriate place."

"Don't worry about it. Just do what you can do. Keep your eye on Loren and maybe she will eventually bring to us the answer to this puzzle."

"I am. I have my eye on her like a hawk. I do have a hunch that very soon we will know what is behind all this."

My parents came out on the terrace and joined us. We chatted for a while, and my mother asked Yaneba where she had learned how to cook so well, since she had no family.

"Thank you, but I don't think I am such a great cook," Yaneba answered. "I learned from Cuban cuisine books. You can find them in any library in Miami."

"Yeah," my father agreed with Mima, "you are a good cook. I loved everything you prepared tonight."

My pager started to vibrate. It was Manolo from my restaurant. I excused myself and went inside the house, grabbed the kitchen telephone, and called Manolo.

When he answered, he did not wait for me to say anything. Instead, he immediately chimed in with, "Yes, my love. I believe I will be able to close early tonight and I can be with you. Give a kiss to my little boy, Manolito, for me." I took the phone from my ear for a moment, wondering if Manolo had been drinking too much tonight. Then I heard voices in the background; they faded away as if he was walking away from them. Evidently he went to one of those reserved areas far away from the bar. When he spoke again, he did so in a very low voice, clearly to avoid being overheard. "Don't even think of coming here to the restaurant tonight. There are four guys here asking questions about you. They look like *mafiosos* or something even worse."

"Where are they?" I asked.

"They are sitting in one of the booths on the right side of the bar. Every time Pancho takes a beer or something to them, they have ten different questions for him about you. Don't worry about it, though.

Pancho knows how to deal with these kinds of people. When you called me just now, one of them was standing very close to me, asking me for another bowl of peanuts for their table."

"Okay, thank you. Be extremely careful with these men. If they are who I think they are, they are extremely dangerous. They are professional assassins."

"Don't worry. You know I have a shotgun under the bar. With that, I can kill an army. There are only four of them."

"I am going to send Hernesto and some of my people over there, just in case. If they get too much out of line, kick them out of there and my people will help you."

"No, no, no—that is not necessary. Don't interrupt whatever you are doing. You know we have six men here who are specialists in the martial arts. Just relax. I just wanted you to know. I didn't want you to show up here and they catch you by surprise."

"Okay, call me if you have any problem with them." I hung up and immediately dialed the emergency number for O'Brien.

He picked up almost at once. "What's happening? Is anything wrong?"

"Yes, Manolo just called me from the restaurant to let me know that there are four men there asking questions about me. According to his description of them, it sounds like they are the same men from MQ1 that were asking questions about me in Vegas."

"Shit! They're in your restaurant?"

"Yep. They are in the restaurant sitting on the right of the bar in a booth and waiting for me to show up."

"Don't even think of going over there. Let me handle this in a different way. Don't send any of your people because it could endanger innocent people who just happen to be in the restaurant. Besides, it'd be bad for your business."

"Okay, handle it the way you feel is best, but remember we may not get another opportunity to catch them by surprise. If we let them get away now, the next time maybe we will be the ones surprised by them, and we could wind up with bullets in our heads."

"Okay, let's hang up right now. That way I can grab these rabbits before they run away from us."

I hung up the phone and went back out to the terrace. I told my parents, "I have to go take care of some business. You guys take care of yourselves and have a great evening."

I signaled Yaneba with a nod of my head and my eyes as I bent down to kiss my mother goodnight. Yaneba understood immediately. She stood up and excused herself as well, saying, "Well, I have to go, too. I have to go to the pharmacy to get some stuff. Do you guys need anything?"

"Yes, please," my father said. "You can bring me a little bottle of 90 proof alcohol."

I giggled. "I remember when I was a kid my father always resolved everything with alcohol. If you had a headache, put alcohol on your forehead with a little towel. If you had a scratch, put alcohol on it. If you had a rash, alcohol!"

Mother laughed, and Yaneba smiled as she said, "Okay, I will bring it for you. If I come back late, I will leave it in the first bathroom in the medicine cabinet."

"Thank you," Father said. "Thank you very much."

She stood behind him and patted his shoulder. "You're welcome. Don't worry about it."

We went inside the house and closed the sliding door behind us. As we crossed the dining room, I told her, "Those sons of bitches from MQ1 are in my restaurant waiting for me, and they are asking questions about me of all the employees there."

Yaneba grabbed me by the arm. "Remember what happened to you in Miami with Victor. Remember we found out later that Victor had been recruited by MQ1 because that is what those sons of bitches do. They recruit the unscrupulous and ambitious men. That is how they proliferate themselves and create new cells."

"What do you want me to do? Just stay here with my arms crossed? Or do you suggest I go run and hide myself?"

"No, that is not what I asked you to do," she said calmly, noticing my irritation. "I ask you only to let me handle these men professionally." She tapped her head with her index finger. "You are the leader of our group and the brain of what we do. We cannot afford to let you put yourself at risk. I am the muscle and the trigger, and you know I am an expert at changing my appearance, like a chameleon. Even if I put a bullet in the head of each one of these guys, I will do it so quietly that nobody will notice. When I go into the restaurant, I will be one person, and when I come out, I will be another one."

I smiled. "I know you are good at what you do, honey, but I don't think this will be necessary. I just spoke with O'Brien a few minutes ago and he told me he would take care of everything in a different way."

"If you believe that O'Brien can handle this then why did you leave the terrace in such a rush?"

"Well, it's always good to have a plan B just in case it does not work out the way O'Brien plans it."

She pointed her finger at me. "Okay, I got you. You had something different on your mind when you left the terrace!"

"Yes, when it comes to something as delicate as this, O'Brien's men have not always been capable of handling it well. You cannot catch anybody by surprise when you have your gun at his head ready to shoot, and then you have to call your superior to ask permission whether you can shoot or not."

She smiled. "Thank you very much. If you have to do all that, you will be dead before you can shoot your enemy."

"Okay," I said, "I will go to the warehouse to help Hernesto and the others, and I will let you handle this the way you think is best. Just be careful—make sure O'Brien does not have control over the situation before you move in."

She touched my shoulder. "Promise me you will go straight to the warehouse."

"I promise. I will see you there later." I wrote down the address of the new place and gave it to her. "This is where we will be if you do not find us at the old warehouse. This is one of my properties."

She smiled and said goodbye. She gave me a hug and kissed me on my cheek before she walked to the door of the garage. I walked out of the house through the main door because my car was parked across the street. When I sat down in my car, I saw her come out of the garage in the Range Rover. I watched her disappear in the direction of the Pacific Coast Highway. I drove to the 405 Freeway. A little while later, I arrived at the warehouse in Fountain Valley. I got out of my car inside the warehouse. I noticed it was nearly empty.

Hernesto and Father Salomon were loading the little pickup truck with some of the stuff that was left. I jokingly said to them, "The next time I have to move, I am going to call you guys. It's unbelievable how much you have moved out of here in such a short time."

Father Salomon replied, "When you really want to do something, it can be done in no time at all. Actually, all the merit goes to them because these kids won't let me do anything. Every time I try to lift something, they say it's too heavy for me, and they will do it."

Elizabeth said, "No, no—don't believe him. He has been working very hard." She pointed to him. "Father, you should not tell lies." She crossed herself. "God forgive you!"

Everybody laughed, and Hernesto said, "Look at him! See how he sweats? Do you think that someone who is doing nothing would be sweating like that?"

Father Salomon smiled. "That is because I am very healthy. Doing any little thing makes me sweat a lot."

We all smiled again and continued to load the truck until it was completely full, and then we took off for the other location. We made several trips, and a little while later the warehouse was completely empty. We began to clean the warehouse. We swept it, took all the trash, and put everything in the truck. Finally, all the trash was out of there and every trace of our operation had vanished.

# Chapter 18—The Assassins

The four men from the MQ1 were sitting in the booth in the restaurant. They were in one of the very secluded corners. The light was very dim. They had a perfect view of the whole restaurant, but it was very difficult to see them. Evidently they had picked that particular booth for those reasons.

Cuban music was being played by the band, and the soloist was singing a very famous song by Benny More, "Santa Isabel de las Lajas." Many of the patrons were already dancing. One of the men, the most attractive of the four, was eyeing a blond woman sitting alone at the bar. In the restaurant's parking lot outside and a few feet from the shelter used for the storage of the keys of the parked cars, O'Brien and two men were standing and discussing how best to handle the situation. One of the men was the chief of the Newport Beach Police Department and an old friend of O'Brien's. The other one was an agent with the Bureau of Alcohol, Tobacco, and Firearms.

O'Brien was frustrated. "I've already talked to the U.S. Federal Attorney's Office. I was told that under no circumstances can we even approach these men. If they've got diplomatic immunity, we could create an international incident. Maybe that's what these sons of bitches are looking for—they want to appear in papers all over the world as victims of local police harassment and abuse."

The police chief said, "We can't even question them under the pretense that we have a tip that they're dealing drugs in our town?"

The BATF man shrugged. "Even if we search these guys and find weapons on them, so what? All these diplomatic attachés and personal security agents have federal permits to carry firearms. That's precisely their work: to protect the security of their delegates while they're in the United States or any other country in the world where they get stationed."

"This is unbelievable!" O'Brien burst out. "We know these people are assassins, and we can't do anything about it!"

A tall Asian woman with long, straight black hair was standing not too far away and had been listening to the conversation. She walked towards them. As she crossed in front of them, heading for the door of the restaurant, they all looked at her. She was wearing a very short dress and had a vending box hanging from straps around her neck. She gave them a sexy smile and wiggled her hips seductively as she passed by. All three men were fascinated as she went through the door and into the restaurant. They shook their heads at one another and whistled.

"What a beautiful woman," O'Brien said. "She must be a mix of Chinese and European."

The police chief said, "She looks more Chinese to me than anything else."

The federal agent nodded. "She looks Chinese, but she's got some other race, like black or European, mixed in, I bet. She's perfect. She is hot!" With that, he wiped the sweat from his forehead. "Whew!" he added.

The three men smiled, and O'Brien said, "Let's place our men inside and outside the restaurant. Let's hope these guys drink too much and do something stupid. Maybe they'll give us some reason to question them. That way, even though we may not be able to arrest them, they'll notice our presence—maybe that'll disrupt their plans. There's nothing else we can do right now. Our wonderful democratic laws prohibit it—nice that we have all those freedoms even though they sometimes prevent us from doing what we think is justifiable."

They turned and began to give orders to their respective men that were waiting in the parking lot, all dressed in civilian clothes, and all ready to take action.

Inside the restaurant, the men in question ordered another round of beer. The good-looking one said something to the others and stood up. He walked directly to the bar where the blond woman was sitting. His friends observed him as he talked to her. After a few seconds, they saw her stand up and follow him onto the dance floor. Evidently they had made bets, as two of them high-fived each other while the remaining man got money out of his pocket and gave it to them.

They both counted their money with smiles, while the other one sat in the corner with a sour expression. Just then the dim light of the booth revealed the hand of the beautiful Chinese lady depositing a rose on the table for them. She asked them in Chinese-accented English, "Do you gentlemen want to buy some flowers for your girlfriends or wives? The one I just gave you is on me, even if you buy nothing."

The two men who had won the bet both smiled and looked at her in admiration. The sour-faced one pushed her aside with his hand on her waist. "You are blocking my view of the dance floor. Move! Move!" He pushed her again.

She stepped back slightly, turned towards him and there was the sound of a whistle. The man fell back and rested his head on the back of the booth, a small hole in his forehead. Before the others realized what had happened, the lady turned towards them and two more whistling sounds were heard.

One of the men was wearing prescription glasses. The right side of his glasses now had a small hole in it. The other man now sported a hole in the right side of his forehead. She arranged the bodies as if they were just resting, leaving two of them just as they had collapsed naturally in the booth. The other one, who had slumped forward, she arranged so that his head rested on his arms as if he were resting his head. She then took a bouquet of flowers out of her vendor box and placed it on the table in front of his hands to cover the blood.

The bar was completely empty as everybody was dancing. Manolo was in the back getting ice for the ice container. She left the bar at a natural pace and went into the men's restroom. She locked herself in a booth and took the vendor box from her neck and put it on top of the toilet. She was wearing a wig, which she took off and put in the box. She replaced it with another wig. She removed some tape from the corners of her eyes which had pulled them to the side to make her look Chinese. In the box were different clothes, and she changed quickly. She checked her watch several times, counting the minutes. The music was still playing and could be heard in the restroom. She put the box on the floor and used water from the toilet and a little bar of soap from the box to wash her face and remove all the makeup.

She pulled a small mirror out of the box. It had some sticky tape on the back, and she placed it on the wall in front of her to check her appearance. Her normal face was revealed in the mirror—that of Yaneba.

Yaneba put the box back on the toilet and applied new makeup, adding age and wrinkles. In a few seconds, she took a small box from inside the larger one. It was full of chewing gum of different flavors and several brands of cigarettes. She took the pistol from under the big box with the flowers and put it under the little box, which she now hung from her neck. She wrapped a thin wire around the lock on the door of the booth and left it hanging there. As she went out of the booth, she grabbed the wire and pulled it from the outside, causing the lock to close and the sign on the door of the booth to read 'occupied.' Then she hid the wire by pushing it through the crack in the door.

She walked to the big mirror in the restroom to check her makeup and dress. Then she took some prescription glasses out of her purse and put them on. She looked at her watch again and then at herself in the mirror. She had transformed herself into a Creole lady, about sixty or sixty-five years old.

As she left the restroom the music was just finishing. The people who had been dancing were all walking back towards their tables and the bar.

She went straight to the table where the three dead men were. She saw the fourth man approaching from the other side, but to her surprise he did not come to the table. He went instead to the right to the men's restroom.

She followed him until he disappeared inside the restroom. Outside the restroom she sold some cigarettes to a man and some gum to his companion. When that couple walked away, she pushed the restroom door open just a little and peeked inside. She could see the man she was following checking himself at the urinal and another man close by who was washing his hands. She closed the door and waited.

The man who was washing his hands came out of the restroom and walked towards the bar. She opened the door, peeked in again, and saw the MQ1 man washing his hands in the sink. She went into the restroom.

When the man saw her coming into the restroom and her hand under the box, he reached for his own pistol. Before he could do anything there were two whistle sounds and he fell against the wall by the sink, shot in the upper lip into his mouth and in the forehead.

She took the box from around her neck and put it on top of one of the sinks. She reached inside the coat of the man and checked both pockets. She removed his wallet and some official-looking documents. Then she quickly grabbed the man by his arms and dragged him into one of the booths. She raised the lid with her foot and dropped him on the toilet. Once again she wrapped a little wire around the lock on the booth door and locked it from the outside.

She quickly grabbed some paper towels and wiped up the blood on the floor. Just as she was finishing, a man walked into the restroom. He was taken aback by the presence of an old lady in the men's restroom, but she calmed him by saying, "Go ahead. Go ahead." She

214

dropped the last of the bloody papers in the trash can. "You are in the right place. My grandson is in one of the booths. He is sick and he vomited here before he could make it to the toilet."

The man was very uncertain and undecided as to whether he should leave and hold it for a while or if he should just go on in. Meanwhile, Yaneba continued to clean up the top of trash can and dropped several clean pieces of paper on top of it to cover up the blood and the bloody paper.

Then she opened the door and left the restroom. She took the hallway to the front door.

O'Brien and the other two law enforcement men had finished talking to their men and giving them instructions as to what they were supposed to do, and they came into the restaurant. The poorly dressed Creole lady passed by them.

Manolo came over to them and said discreetly to O'Brien, "Something is wrong with those men. Remember the men we were talking about before?"

"Yes," replied O'Brien, "what about them?"

"Something is very wrong. Pancho went to their table to ask them if they wanted more beer, and nobody responded. Then I went to check, and I saw something sticky all over the table. I don't know if it is vomit because they are drunk, but it looks to me like blood. I touched one of them several times, and he didn't move. I tried to wake him up, but with no luck."

O'Brien looked at the other two men and said, "Oh, shit."

They all looked at each other and then rushed into the bar to see what was happening. Outside the restaurant, the old Creole lady got into a taxi and left the place.

When O'Brien and his colleagues got close to the table inside, they realized all three men were dead. "Don't worry about it," O'Brien assured Manolo. "We'll take care of this. Don't let anybody know what's going on."

"Do you want me to close the bar?" Manolo asked.

"No, just keep everything going like normal."

The blond lady at the bar came over to them. "Is everything okay?"

The Chief of Police took her by the arm and walked her away. "Oh, yeah. Can I buy you a drink?"

"Where's the other man?" O'Brien asked Manolo. "There are supposed to be four of them. Where's the other one?"

"I don't know," Manolo answered. "The last time I saw him, he was dancing with that blond lady."

O'Brien looked at the flowers on the table. "Hmm. Where is that Chinese lady who was selling flowers?"

"I don't know. I never saw her before. This is the first time she ever came here."

"Okay. Just go back to the bar. We'll handle it from here."

Manolo walked to the bar and told Pancho, "Whatever the lady and the gentleman drink, it is on the house."

As the Chief and the lady thanked Manolo, O'Brien walked over. "The gentleman who was dancing with you a little while ago," he asked her, "do you know where he went?"

From her unfocused stare, she was clearly a little tipsy. "I don't know. I must have bad breath or something. He said he was going to the restroom, but he never came back."

"Oh, no," the police chief assured her, "you have very sweet breath."

"I don't know," she disagreed. "He disappeared."

O'Brien put his hand on the policeman's shoulder. "Why don't you stay with the lady? We'll be back in a minute. We're going to check on something. Would you excuse us?"

They left and went towards the men's restroom. When they went in, O'Brien noticed the little wire in the crack of the door on one of the booths. He grabbed a pen from his pocket and put it in the crack. He pulled on the wire, opened the door, and saw the big box of flowers on top of the toilet.

He moved things around in the box with the pen and discovered the wig, makeup, and the little miniskirt the Chinese lady was wearing when she went into the restaurant. The federal man was behind him, watching everything he was doing. "She's not only beautiful," O'Brien said in admiration, "she's also smart. Deadly smart!"

The walked out of that booth and checked several others. They all opened and were clear. When they got to the last booth, they noticed it also was locked. O'Brien used the pen again and pulled out the wire like before. The door opened.

"Bingo!" he exclaimed. The fourth man was sprawled on the toilet, bleeding from his two wounds. O'Brien turned around and asked the BATF agent, "Do you want your men to take care of this, or do you want me to handle it?"

The man smiled. "You guys are better than us at this. You'd better handle it." O'Brien left the booth and closed the door again. He left the wire out, and went to the other booth and did the same. "Do you want me to close the men's restroom?"

"No," O'Brien replied, "under no circumstances. Let's keep things as they are. Just stay here while I talk to my men outside. No one will use those booths, anyway—they're locked."

O'Brien left the restroom and went outside while the federal man stayed there. A few minutes later, O'Brien's men came with a cart that looked like one that hotels use to pick up dirty laundry. One of the men put a sign outside the restroom door that read, "Wet floor. Closed for fifteen minutes for cleaning." A few minutes later, they came out. There was a van waiting for them outside. They rolled the cart into the van. Other men came and closed off the bar area and the two doors that connected the bar to the rest of the restaurant and dance area. They left one man on each side to tell anyone who asked that someone had gotten drunk, thrown up, and that the bar would reopen as soon as the mess was cleaned up.

Outside, O'Brien, the Chief of Police, and the BATF agent were talking. "Evidently, somebody is a step ahead of us, and they took a big headache out of our hands," O'Brien said. "Remember what we discussed before. This is considered classified on the basis of national security."

The Chief said, "All three men have guns with silencers. Just one of them doesn't have any ID on him. I'd love to hear what the Cuban embassy tells the FBI when you put that in your report—that every single man here was carrying a gun with silencers. They're totally illegal in this country."

"What report?" O'Brien raised his arm in disgust. "The Cuban government will always deny everything. This isn't going to be an exception. They'll say the CIA put those silencers in the hands of their diplomatic agents in order to incriminate them. That's why we don't even bother to report cases like this sometimes. It only complicates matters more." He smiled cynically. "Castro is a saint and the salvation of the poor," he added sarcastically. "We are the villains."

Everyone laughed. The van that contained the dead bodies they had taken from the restaurant was leaving the parking lot. There was one car in front of it and another one behind it, escorting the van. Three of O'Brien's men drove up in another car to pick him up. He said goodbye to his colleagues, got into the car, and followed the van and the other cars.

Meanwhile, all the equipment and materials from the other warehouse had been relocated to the garage of the house in Santa Ana. Everything was ready to begin printing. We decided to take a break, and I took Father Salomon and the others into the house to show them the patio, swimming pool, and other amenities. I opened a bottle of wine and, after everyone had a glass, I showed them how everything worked. I told them that if a neighbor asked them any questions, they should say they were family and that I was away on a trip.

This house was the only property in my name and was my primary residence. It was located in a middle class neighborhood because if any problems arose it would look like I did not make a lot of money. From the outside, it did not look like much, but it had nearly an acre of land, and the house had a beautiful interior. It had marble floors, cathedral ceilings, a fireplace in each of the six bedrooms, and a huge fireplace between the living and dining rooms. It had a huge swimming pool, a large Jacuzzi, a wet bar, and a meditation pool with a waterfall.

We sat down in the pool area, drank our wine, and enjoyed the scenery. I opened another bottle of wine when we had finished the first one. Just then, my pager started to vibrate—it was O'Brien. I excused myself and went up to the front of the house to my car, parked under a huge weeping willow tree in the center of the driveway. I called O'Brien from the car phone.

"We just had a very bad incident at your restaurant," he told me. "I don't think you have to worry about the MQ1 men anymore. They're all dead."

"Well, you guys are really efficient. Thank you very much."

"You don't have to thank me," said O'Brien. "We didn't do anything."

"You guys didn't do anything? Who did it, then?"

"You mean to tell me you people had nothing to do with this?"

"At this moment, I have no knowledge of our taking any action on this," I said.

"Hm. This is strange. Then who does that Asian woman work for? She came into the restaurant and almost under our very noses sent all four men to hell—then disappeared like smoke!"

I smiled at that.

"Do you have any idea who this person could be?" he asked me.

"No, I don't have any idea, but I will let you know if something comes up."

"If something comes up, say thank you very much for our side. She did a very clean and professional job. It's one less headache for us. Are you ready for the other job?"

"Yes, we are ready."

"When are you going to start?"

"Probably tonight. Everything is ready to go."

"Okay. Arrange everything as if you weren't going to be here because it's possible that you and I may have to take a trip to Europe for a couple of days."

"Very well—I will arrange everything as if I were not going to be here. All you need to do is to tell me where you want it delivered when it is done."

"I'll give you the details tomorrow when we get together."

We said goodnight and I hung up the phone. Before I got out of my car, I saw the headlights of a car arriving at the main gate of the house. I grabbed a remote control from my glove compartment and walked down the driveway towards the gate. When I got close to the gate, I recognized the Range Rover and Yaneba. I opened the gate, and she drove in and parked on the other side of the driveway under the willow tree.

She had a satisfied smile on her face as she gave me a big hug. She whispered in my ear, "You have no more problems. You can come back to your house any time you want." She handed me an envelope. "This contains important documents that I took from the MQ1 team leader. I have very interesting incriminatory evidence and no doubts that Sanchez is working with these people—like Sanchez's phone number, bank transfers from the Cuban government to his account in Madrid, Spain, and so on."

"Thank you very much. A job well done."

She smiled again. "I did exactly what you told me. I waited until I saw the frustration of O'Brien and the other agents due to the impossibility of doing anything through legal channels due to the diplomatic immunity of those men. So I took action and put bullets through their heads before they put bullets in ours. They were too close to us to ignore and let them go."

I raised the envelope and touched her shoulder with it. "Thank you—thank you very much, again."

"You don't have to thank me. That is my job. I am in charge of your security and the security of the others."

"When I say thank you, I say it because you give me personal tranquility. I am not worried about myself or my friends. I can take care of myself, and so can my friends—to have you here, watching our backs is a great asset for us. I do worry, however, about the security of my mother and father. Now I will sleep more peacefully."

"You don't have to worry about your mom and dad," she replied. "I will keep my eyes on them."

"You see? That is why I thank you. But I am not going to return to my house yet. I have to sit back and wait and see how things develop with Loren. I will act according to her next move. I will wait until O'Brien brings Sanchez in, and then I will probably know what Loren has to do with all this."

"Good idea," she agreed.

"But sometimes we plan things one way, and we have to do it another. Let's see how things develop in the next few hours."

Father Salomon, Elizabeth, and Hernesto came out from the patio because they had heard Yaneba's car come in. They were curious as to what was happening. After Yaneba said hello to everyone, Father Salomon said, "Let's go to work because by the end of the week I want to be back at my monastery."

Elizabeth pouted as she jokingly said, "Oh, Father Salomon doesn't want to be with us anymore!"

"No, no—it's not that," he reassured her. "I have spent so much time with you already. When I first came I was under the impression it would be for only a few days. I need to get back to my monastery."

"Yes, Father, I understand," I apologized. "You are probably homesick by now."

"Don't worry—I will probably be back home by the weekend if we maintain a good pace in our work."

"I already have everything arranged. Jacobo will take you back as soon as you finish."

Father Salomon clapped his hands. "Let's go to work, then!"

"I will stay with you guys until midnight," Yaneba said. "That way, I can help you to get everything done more quickly."

We all went into the house and then into the garage. Father Salomon gave instructions to everyone as to what they needed to do. Then I took an envelope out of my briefcase, walked over to him, and handed it to him. "In this envelope are the account numbers where I want you to deposit all the money that is left from the previous operation. Also, there are detailed instructions how to handle the money you are printing now. The keys for the safety security boxes are in the envelope, too. After you deliver the amount required of us to O'Brien, all the rest you divide in packages and put in those boxes. I have already talked to the branch managers of these banks, and everything is arranged. Your name is in the books of those banks as well as mine. All you need to do is identify yourself. The reason I did this is just in case something happens to me, I know you will find a good use for that money in the future."

He put his hand on my shoulder. "Thank you for your confidence in me."

I smiled. "If I cannot trust you, who can I trust?"

"When everything is finished and I am ready to go, if you are not back from your trip, what do you want me to do with the keys?"

"Give the keys to Yaneba. She will give them to my father."

"Okay—I will do everything the way you ask."

"One more thing," I added. "When you guys enter or exit the garage, never do it through the big door. Always do it through the house. That way, if any curious neighbor happens to be near the gates, they will not be able to see what we are doing in here. As soon as you finish, Hernesto has instructions to remove all the equipment and sell it to a second-hand dealer. He will leave this garage as clean as a whistle."

"Hernesto is going to take care of everything, right?" Father Salomon asked.

"Yes, you don't have to worry about anything."

He gave me a hug. "Well, if I don't see you again, good luck to you. Come to visit me at the monastery."

"Of course I will, but I am sure I will see you again before I leave."

I said goodbye to everyone and drove to Corona del Mar. After I had been driving for a while, my phone rang. It was Loren.

"Hello, stranger," she said. "Where are you?"

"I am on my way home."

"Why don't you stop by? I need to talk to you. You're close, anyway."

I remained silent.

"I stopped by your house a little while ago," she went on, "and there was no one there."

"I told you I would be working until late tonight."

"Yes, I know," she said, "but I wanted to surprise you. I thought maybe I might catch you at your house at dinnertime, but there was nobody there. Everything was dark. Since you have to cross by here on the way to your house, why don't you stop at my condo for at least ten or fifteen minutes? I need to talk to you about something really important."

"Okay, I will stop by for a few minutes." I did not plan to confront her yet, and I didn't want to go to her house. One thing could lead to another, and I might get angry and emotional, and spill my guts. But, since she insisted so much and said she had something important to tell me, I still wanted to give her the benefit of the doubt. It just might happen that she would open up and tell me the answer to why she was involved with Sanchez and to what point or degree. As soon as I hung up I called O'Brien's emergency number.

# Chapter 19—Broken Heart

O'Brien answered at once and asked if anything had happened or if something was wrong.

"Take it easy," I said. "Everything is okay. I am on my way to Loren's house right now. She says she has something important to tell me. I want to know if you have any news about Sanchez and if I can confront her about him now."

"No, there are no new developments yet, but we've cut all connections with him everywhere. We don't know what damage he's done in the past, but we do know that he can't do any in the future. Handle Loren the best way you can, and try to get as much information out of her as possible. After what happened today, I don't think we have to worry about it. At least not for the next few weeks, until the enemy reorganizes themselves."

"By the way," I said, "I have in my hands the documents of one of the MQ1 men. They are really compromising to Sanchez. They contain his telephone number and the other documents that show his implication with these people without a doubt. I will give this to you tomorrow."

"Aha! So it *was* one of your people who did this job!"

"Yes," I said. "They just informed me a little while ago. They observed you for a little while, saw your frustration, and used their best judgment in order to prevent innocent lives from being lost at the hands of those assassins. We already know they took the life of Arturo, and they decided not to take a chance with the legal system."

"Okay," said O'Brien. "I'll see you tomorrow at 12:30, location two. We can talk freely tomorrow. Even though this line's secure, we shouldn't take a chance."

"I understand. I will see you tomorrow."

We said goodbye and hung up, and I arrived at Loren's condo a few minutes later. She opened the door and gave me a hug. She had a glass of wine in her hand. She noticed I was not very responsive and was even a little cold. She offered me something to eat or drink, and I declined. At that moment, I did not feel I could trust her to even drink or eat anything from her hands. "I have already eaten dinner," I politely refused.

"How are your parents?"

"They are fine."

"Where are they?"

"At home."

We walked through the house and sat down in the living room on the sofa. I did not sit too close to her. "No," she said. "I went to your house and rang the bell for a long time. Nobody answered."

"I had to move them to another house in a rush, as an emergency arose."

She remained silent as if she were thinking. I also remained silent. Finally, she asked, "Is something bad going on? Is something wrong?"

"Well, as of earlier this evening, everything was great. My friends just informed me a few minutes ago that some assassins who were sent by Castro to kill me—and heaven knows who else—have been killed in my restaurant. They are most likely the same ones who killed our friend, Arturo. Justice always prevails. They are probably in the morgue right now with little tags on their big toes. I don't know if they even qualify for that. They may just be buried in some unknown place in the desert."

Loren looked at me wide-eyed. She was extremely nervous and agitated but said nothing.

I looked directly into her eyes and said, "Do you have any idea who those men were?"

She stood up and reacted violently. "Me!" she screamed. "Why do you ask me? How would I know anything about someone who wanted to kill you?"

I remained silent. She was pacing back and forth, while I leaned back on the sofa and crossed my legs.

"Do you think I had anything to do with these men!?" she screamed again.

I smiled sardonically. "I never said you had anything to do with these people, but we know that your friend Sanchez knew a lot about them because we found evidence on one of the bodies that incriminated him."

"My friend Sanchez?" she repeated. "Who told you he was my friend? I only saw that man once in my life—the night you introduced him to me at the opera!" She came close to me, shaking her hand in my face. "Why are you calling this man my friend?"

She was looked as if she were about to lose it. "Why do you keep smiling that cynical smile as if you were enjoying making me suffer, when the reason I asked you to come over here was to tell you something beautiful and pure? I'm pregnant!"

I uncrossed my legs and sat on the edge of the sofa. I put both hands on my knees and shook my head at her. I told myself this had to be another lie. The blood rushed to my face. I was indignant. But I took a deep breath and tried to control my emotion. I said nothing. She began to cry and walked to the wall near the bar that divided the kitchen from the living room. She leaned her face against it and wept.

I think she was expecting me to console her, as I had always done in the past when she cried. I just remained on the sofa in silence. She continued to cry for a while until she realized I was not going to stand up and comfort her. I shifted on the sofa, which caused her to turn around to see what I was doing. I signaled with my index finger, indicating I wanted her to come to me. I patted the seat next to me where she had been sitting before.

She evidently thought I meant to make peace with her. Dragging her feet, she walked slowly over to me and sat down by my side. I waited for a few minutes until she calmed down. I just kept looking around silently at the walls and the ceiling until I felt she had control of herself.

Then I decided to give her one last chance to tell me the truth. I said in a kind voice, "Sweetie, are you sure you never saw Daniel Sanchez before I introduced you to him at the opera? Think carefully because maybe you met him someplace before for some reason and you have forgotten. This is very important."

She turned and looked at me. She kissed her fingers and said, "I swear to you I never saw that man in my life."

I looked at her for a few seconds. I tightened my jaw and thought that it was definitely time to confront her. I pulled an envelope from a pocket inside my suit. I opened the envelope and took out the pictures. I spread them on the small glass table in front of the sofa.

She saw the pictures of the two of them in different places. She became livid, changed colors, and reacted immediately. She screamed at me, "What the hell gave you the right to spy on me?"

Pretending to be mad, she tried to stand up, but I reached out and grabbed her by both of her arms. I put my face so close to hers that I felt her breath on my cheeks. I said softly but very firmly, "Don't fuck with me anymore. Start to tell me the truth now. My friends already believe you are an accomplice with Sanchez in the murder of Arturo. You know what this can signify for you. My friends don't believe in the legal system and wasting time in the courts with trials. They believe more in the law of the jungle: the strongest ones survive. They also believe in divine justice—an eye for an eye and a tooth for a tooth. Believe me, I don't want you to get hurt! Stop lying! Tell me the truth, or you are on your own. The only reason you are still alive is because you have a relationship with me. Either you tell me the truth or you can go to hell!"

I released her arms and got up. I went into the kitchen and refilled the glass of wine that she had been drinking when I first arrived at her place. I brought it back to her. She was still sitting on the sofa, crying again—this time, however, she was sincere. I realized now that she was really scared. I handed her the glass. "Drink this; it will make you feel better." She grabbed the glass and took a sip. I sat down on the other side of the sofa, as far from her as possible.

"Daniel Sanchez is a marked man," I told her. "Whenever he comes back to this country, he will either be killed or arrested, tried as a traitor to this country, and will spend the rest of his miserable life in jail. I don't know what he holds over you, but he cannot harm you anymore. I don't know what your association with him is, but if you don't tell me, then I cannot help you."

Loren began to cry even harder. She realized she could no longer hide anything from me. She continued to cry for a few minutes and then began to control herself. She put her left hand on her forehead and squeezed. She sipped her wine, trying to clear her throat.

"I know Daniel Sanchez from a few years back," she began. "He approached me in the bank where I was working and asked me if I would like to make some extra money on the side. I met with him, and he told me he worked for United States Intelligence. He said he needed a woman with a good appearance like me to distract his clients from him and to open merchant accounts in the commercial banks for ghost companies— companies that did not really exist. From these accounts he pulled out hundreds of thousands of dollars, and he gave me ten percent of the profit."

"Where did the money come from?"

She paused. "He provided me with a computer printout of hundreds of thousands of credit card numbers and the identity of the owners. He never showed his face to any of the institutions where we opened the accounts. I did it all. When I wanted to get out of this operation because I knew that eventually it would get me in a lot of trouble, he blackmailed me. He said that if I did not continue working with him he had copies of all the documents and applications to the merchant account with the banks, and it was all in my handwriting. Even though the accounts were opened under an assumed name, my handwriting was on all of them. He threatened me, saying he would send all these documents to the FBI, together with an anonymous letter giving out my real name and identity. That way, they could arrest me, prosecute me, and throw me in jail for the rest of my life."

I looked at her with pity and at the same time a knot in my stomach. What kind of person was this that I had involved myself with?

"Are you really that dumb, or do you just pretend to be a dumb blond?" I demanded. "Didn't you know that if he did that to you, you are entitled to defend yourself? You could talk to the FBI or the DA and tell them that you made a stupid mistake by associating yourself with him, and he was actually the leader behind the whole operation. You did not realize what you were doing until you actually got involved. When you realized what was really going on, you tried to get out, and that is why he turned you in. Then you would probably only have gotten a slap on your hand."

She began to cry again. "I don't know anything about how the law works," she sobbed, "and he scared the hell out of me."

"What happened with the pact we made in Vegas when you toasted to friendship, loyalty, and sincerity until death do us part? Did you forget all that already? Did you forget it so soon?"

"No, I did not forget!" she screamed at me. "That's why when he called me and we met, I told him I did not want to associate with him anymore. He scared the hell out of me! He said I was going to end up dead with a hole in my head!"

I stood up. "Is that the reason you were fucking him and giving him information about me and my friends that almost cost the lives of Amelia and me in the Caribbean? What you told him facilitated the death of Arturo!"

"No!" she screamed again. "No! I had nothing to do with Arturo's death. He never got any information from me at all. He wanted me to show him the location of the warehouse. I never did that, and I never mentioned your trip to the Caribbean. If you remember, you never told me where you were going. He must have gotten that information from somebody else, but not from me."

She put her glass on top of the bar, looked at me, and spoke sarcastically. "Let me tell you, Daniel Sanchez is a homosexual and a pedophile. He does not like adults. He likes children no more than fourteen years old. I don't think a woman like me attracts him in any way." She touched herself from top to bottom and added, "I don't think I look like a fourteen-year-old boy!" She poured herself a little more wine. "I know I've been stupid and lying to you out of fear. I am really sorry for that. I won't blame you if you don't want to be with me anymore. I understand completely. But if you can find it in your heart to forgive me, I promise I will never lie to you again."

I sat down in one of her big lounge chairs and sighed. I lay back and shook my head from one side to the other. "I don't know how much truth is in all that you are telling me. I only know this has damaged your credibility in my mind completely. The most important thing between human beings, especially a couple, is trust. When you shatter that in any relationship, you damage forever the roots of that love and friendship. Even if one day I heal and learn to forgive you, the ghost of those lies will live forever in my mind. Our relationship is over because a few minutes ago you looked directly into my eyes and swore you had never met him before. Now, after I proved it to you and you are caught red-handed, you admit your relationship with him and your social and criminal activities. At least, if you had admitted this to me earlier, when I first asked you and was still hoping you would come clean, there would have been a chance for us. It would have made a big difference."

I looked at her with no mercy and only recrimination in my eyes. She began to cry again. I placed both of my hands on my face, furrowed my brow, and said, "I owe Mr. Laden a big apology because he tried to warn me about you. I would not listen to him."

When I said that, she began to cry even harder. "Forgive me," she sobbed. "I am really in love with you. I love you with all my heart. I will make it up to you if you can just forgive this horrible thing. I know I've been stupid, but I don't think I want to live without you by my side. You have given so much to me, and I shit all over you. I cannot live with my conscience."

"Don't worry about the material things. You don't owe me anything. You can keep all, and in reference to the pregnancy you told me about, I don't even know if that is true. Maybe you are just making it up in order to make me feel bad and have pity for you. Even if you are pregnant, I don't want anything to do with it. I am not ready for a son or daughter right now. Even if I was, I would not want one with you! You have broken my heart in pieces. Do whatever you want with your pregnancy. I want nothing to do with it.

"For the past week," I went on relentlessly, "I have only had a few hours of sleep every night. I see the sunrise every morning because I am awake and thinking why or if you have been lying to me. As far as I am concerned, our love relationship is finished right here and now. I will leave for a trip in a few days. When I come back, we should sit down and talk more calmly and see if we can save something of our friendship at least."

I stood up and went to the door to leave. At the door, she wiped her eyes and said calmly, "With all my heart, I will always regret not being sincere and telling you what went on between me and Sanchez. I will have this guilt on my conscience for the rest of my life."

I opened the door and looked her straight in the eyes. "At least I can walk out of here knowing you have told me the whole truth now. Is there anything else I should know before I leave?"

She sobbed a little and said, "I swear to you, I have told you everything." She started to cross herself but stopped when she remembered a little while before she had done the same thing when she had sworn in vain about Sanchez.

I smiled and nodded my head. "You see? That is why we cannot lie. We damage our credibility with others, and our credibility is part of our dignity."

She began to cry again. At that moment, I knew she felt horrible and guilty. I felt in my heart the full desire to hug her, kiss her, and tell her to forget all about this and make a new start. However, I turned around, closed the door behind me, and left her crying.

As I walked to my car, I realized for the first time in my life that our pride and dignity are more powerful than the strongest love you can feel for someone. The innocence in our heart is gone when they betray us. No matter how strong that love was, and how much you want to forgive them, when someone breaks your heart the doubt you have about them is like a cancer. It will always be there, eating away, piece by piece, until that love is completely destroyed.

I got into my car, and the tears rolled down my face before I had even started the engine. I had been holding them back for too long. I asked myself how much truth was in Loren's words. Just then, Mr. Laden's advice came back to me. He had told me she was a compulsive liar. I was feeling terribly guilty because, if she were really pregnant, how could I ever know for sure that the child was mine? In order to make myself feel better, I decided she had probably invented the pregnancy idea just to smooth the tension between us. I shook my head and tried to forget about the whole thing. I started the car and drove to Corona del Mar.

I arrived at my house to find my parents already sleeping. I went to the bar and poured myself a brandy glass of Grand Marnier. I filled up the glass because I wanted to get wasted, release the tension, and be able to sleep. I went out the sliding door onto the terrace that overlooked the ocean. I watched the waves crashing against the rocks for a while. I sat down on the sofa swing, took a tablet and a pen, and began to write. I poured out onto the paper what my heart was feeling at that moment:

*My Lost Love*
*I have been in love with you but you broke my heart*
*I have been in love with the idea of being in love with you*
*I see you like a drop of rain, a drop of crystal clear water*
*Pure and perfect rolling into the lips of a red rose on a spring night*
*When I miss you I feel thirst for the love of nature*
*And the pure love of God, too powerful sometimes*
*I have forever been thankful to God for you and for your love*
*The most great and wonderful love of my life*
*You have been the most unique gift God brought into my life*
*You are the drop of rain in the spring night*
*The crystal clear and pure water like a waterfall in my life*
*You have been the essence of my life but also you broke my heart*
*You are the beautiful and warm rain on a spring night*
*Quenching the thirst of the rose that I am holding for you in my heart*
*And I am like that rose on the spring night and you were truly*
*The greatest love of my life I say this with great pain in my heart*

I drank almost all my Grand Marnier and, between the warm breeze from the ocean and the liquor, I passed out on the swinging sofa. After a few hours, something woke me up. I opened my eyes and saw Yaneba's smiling face. She was holding a little grass foxtail, which she had passed over my cheek, tickling me.

"I think you should go inside," she said. "We're expecting rain tonight. I don't think you would like to wake up all wet!"

I sat up and shook my head as I came to full wakefulness. She sat down beside me. "Rain here! Didn't you ever hear that song—'It never rains in Southern California'?"

"Yes, I have heard that song. I have also heard that when it rains in Southern California it pours! Mud slides and craziness happens when it rains. If you stay here and sleep for romanticism or laziness you will wake up in the morning wet as if you had been sleeping with a baby." This time it was I who smiled. She took the poem I had written in her hands and asked, "May I read it?"

"Yes."

"Did you speak with Loren?"

"Yes, I did."

"Good or bad news?"

"We broke up. She lied to my face. She denied everything. She swore to God what she said to me was true until I showed her the pictures. Then and only then did she admit that she had been lying. She told me a Walt Disney story that I did not know if I could believe or not. She was trying to justify why she had lied in the first place. I don't think I can ever trust her or believe in her again."

Yaneba put her hand on my shoulder in sympathy. "What a pity. Your heart must be broken. That is why you are drinking, right?" She pointed to the glass which had a little Grand Marnier left in it.

I grabbed the glass and finished it. "Yes—broken-hearted and disappointed."

Yaneba looked at the poem again and asked, "Who inspired you to make such a beautiful poem? Probably her, right?"

I replied with a sad expression on my face, "I don't think I made it to anybody. I made it to my pain." I shook my head. "Well, maybe to her because she is the one who gave me that pain. Really, the object is love and disappointment. They look as if they are a married couple, and they walk through life holding hands like they are one." My eyes brimmed with unshed tears. Yaneba turned around and hugged me. She looked into my face, saw the tears, and wiped them away with her fingers. She hugged me again compassionately and gave me a kiss on my cheek.

"Come on. Let's go to bed. Don't drink any more. That is not going to help you. It will make you feel miserable in the morning."

We stood up and I could tell I was a little tipsy. She helped me walk into the house and said, "Okay, you have to go to sleep and rest."

We went into the kitchen and she poured a glass of milk for me. She warmed it for a few minutes in the microwave and gave it to me. "Drink this. It will help you to sleep better." She hugged me again, and after I drank the milk she asked, "Are you okay now?"

231

"Sure, I feel better."

She went to her room and I went to mine. When I got to my room, I brushed my teeth and took off my clothes. It was a warm night, so I went to bed wearing only my underwear. About half an hour later, I heard a noise at my bedroom door. I put my hand under the pillow where I kept my pistol and slowly sat up in the bed to see who was there.

"It's okay—it's me," Yaneba said. "Did I wake you up?"

"No. I cannot sleep. I have not slept for a week."

She was wearing only a bathrobe. I saw her silhouette in the doorway. "If you want me to, I can massage you and that way maybe you can relax and go to sleep."

"Okay."

She closed the door behind her and locked it. She dropped her bathrobe to the floor, and I saw her naked silhouette. She came close to the bed. "Are you sure you want my company?"

I smiled and moved to the opposite side of the bed, leaving space for her to get in beside me. "No. It's okay. You can lie down by me. It's okay."

She lay down beside me and began to massage my neck and back. It felt very good, comfortable and warm. After a while, she turned me over and began to massage my chest and arms. Her touches began to be more explicit, and I grew sexually aroused. She noticed my arousal, hugged me, squeezed her breasts against my bare chest, and kissed me tenderly on my neck. She moved back slightly and began to kiss my lips. Our kisses were soft at first, but quickly became passionate, longing kisses.

We made love for at least two hours—possibly more. When we finished, we lay back in the bed, looking at each other and talking. She fondled my face and asked, "Do you feel better?"

"Yes, for the first time this week I think I will be able to sleep until late." She started to get out of bed. "Where are you going?"

She put on her bathrobe. "Goodnight, love." She kissed me on my check and continued, "I have to go to my room to sleep. I don't want your mom and dad to get the wrong impression of me." She smiled. "You have to remember, the customs are different in Cuba from the customs here. Out of respect to them, we need to maintain that image in front of them."

"Okay. I understand."

She rubbed my shoulder. "Besides, you have lots to do tomorrow and so do I. We need some sleep." She kissed me on my lips and left the room.

# Chapter 20—Tanga Negra

In the morning, we both got up very late. It was almost 11:30 am, and Hernesto and Elizabeth were already awake with Father Salomon. We all sat down and had brunch because it was nearly lunch time. After we ate, we said goodbye to Mom and Dad, and we left in different directions. They went to my house in Santa Ana to work on the new project, and I went to the Balboa Bay Club to meet O'Brien.

A little while later, O'Brien and I were sitting in the back of the yacht, watching the other boats cross by. I asked him if he wanted something to drink. "If you've got a cold beer, I'll take one."

I went to the refrigerator, opened it, and said, "Do you like black ladies?"

"I love black ladies!"

"That's good because you are going to have a black lady model."

"Oh, my God—today's my lucky day!"

I brought him a tall beer glass with a Mexican beer called Negra Modelo. He laughed and poured the beer into the glass. "Do you have some lime?"

"Of course. Here it is. If you don't have lime, it is like not having icing on the cake."

I opened one for myself, and we sat down and enjoyed the beer. I opened my briefcase and took out a manila envelope. I gave it to him.

"In that envelope you will find pictures of Sanchez taking a plane to Panama and later from Panama taking a plane to Cuba," I said. "Also, you will find official Cuban government papers from one of the agents in MQ1, identifying him as one of theirs. And you will find a telephone book belonging to an MQ1 agent with all of Sanchez's telephone numbers, both private and official. In addition, there are some documents from a bank in Spain that show deposits of money from the Cuban government and withdrawals by Daniel Sanchez. In other words, there is no doubt at all: he is a double agent."

O'Brien took the envelope, looked at all the papers, and put them back. "You don't have to worry about Daniel Sanchez anymore. He was arrested last night when he tried to get into the States at the Miami airport from Panama. He's confessed to everything. I talked to Addison first thing this morning. He gave me all the details of what's going on with Sanchez in Miami."

I reclined in my chair and drank a little beer. "Well, is this good news or what? I just wonder how much damage this son of a bitch has already done."

"A lot. He's been passing information to our enemies for almost a year. He confessed that it all started last year. He went to Cuba on a special mission to arrange asylum for one of Castro's big military figures. When Sanchez got to Cuba, however, that man had already been arrested and, under torture, had told Cuban Intelligence about him. When he arrived, they were waiting for him. They accommodated him in one of their special suites which they have in nearly every five star hotel in Havana. These suites are outfitted with audio and video recorders. They record every prominent figure that visits Cuba and use the recordings to blackmail them later on. They already knew about Sanchez's sexual deviation. They provided two little boys for him and filmed him doing despicable sexual acts with the children. Later on, they arrested Sanchez, of course, because that's illegal everywhere in the world.

"Then the Cuban Intelligence people played the film to Sanchez and told him not only would he have to spend several years in jail in Cuba, but they would release the film to every single tabloid in the world and reveal his identity as a CIA agent. They told him they would send a special copy of the film to his wife. That way, his wife and children could enjoy it."

I shook my head. "My God. These people are capable of anything."

O'Brien took a sip of his beer. "Yes. Yes, sir. This is how they got him to work for them. He became a double agent for the OTTO agency— Cuban Counter Intelligence."

"That is the only fear I have of these people to win over us. They are willing to do anything—even exterminate an entire population to accomplish what they want. They have no books, no rules, and no congress to tell them that they cannot do this or they cannot do that. But also, they do not have God on their side because they don't believe in Him. I believe that is our greatest advantage because we believe in God and I know He is on our side."

O'Brien shook his head and said, "Amen. No matter how much we bend the rules and we do crazy things sometimes, we always do it with the well-being of the majority of people in mind. We don't do anything with malicious intentions. We don't want to hurt people or deprive them of a good way of life."

"Well, what you have just told me about Sanchez and his addiction to sex with little boys is nothing new. That is exactly what Loren told me last night. No matter what, I still don't give Loren too much credibility. However, since you tell me this too, at least I know that one thing she told me was true."

"We questioned him about Loren. She was another victim of his. He was doing some personal illegal activities, and he blackmailed her into helping him." O'Brien squeezed his forehead. "What irony—the blackmailer ended up being blackmailed himself."

I nodded my head. "Well, that is another verification. That is exactly what she told me."

O'Brien reclined in his chair and took another sip of his beer. "Well, what're you going to do with her?"

"Nothing. For the moment. But our relationship is over."

O'Brien looked sad. "I'm sorry, my friend. I know you were really gung-ho for this woman."

I shook my head and bit my lip a little bit. "Well, it just happened. Shit happens."

O'Brien opened his briefcase and took out a large envelope which he handed to me. "Inside you will find all the details about our operation in Spain. Your contact in Spain is named Secilia. She is a very pretty Spanish blonde with blue eyes and a beautiful shape." He smiled wickedly. "But don't get involved!"

I smiled and shook my head. "I don't think I will get involved for a very long time."

"Hah! Whatever! Anyway, she will be waiting for you in Madrid. They've already arranged suites for you in a five-star hotel. The name of the hotel is Miguel Angel. This hotel is used by the Cuban Counter Intelligence like a mailbox. Follow the instructions of our plan the best you can. If necessary, however, improvise like you always do. This man from OTTO has probably been expecting us. Be aware of this, and they will not be able to surprise you. This operation will be called Tanga Negra. Not even our intelligence forces have any knowledge of this. This is completely classified and only a handful of people know what we are going to do. Let's hope you'll be successful and we'll get that Rottweiler in Castro's first ring. Then we'll be laughing as we watch Castro taking a dump in his private bathroom with the Rottweiler coming to smell his shit!"

We both laughed, and I said, "You are bad, man!"

"Don't worry. I'll be there, close to you guys, just in case. If anything goes wrong, I'll use all of my power to get you out of Spain safely."

When are we supposed to leave?"

"Day after tomorrow. They're waiting for you in Madrid. All the instructions are in that envelope," he added, pointing to the envelope in my hand.

We stood up then, and I said, "Okay. We will see each other in a few days. I will leave Hernesto in charge of whatever is left to complete the Zipper."

"Good luck to you."

I smiled and said jokingly, "Don't spend all the money we made in one place. Leave something for the Cuban freedom fighters."

He smiled, and we shook hands and left in different directions. I went to my car and called Dr. Martin Perez, the head of the relocation of the freedom fighters in Los Angeles. I told him that I needed to speak with him urgently. I had a job to do and needed his help. We agreed to meet that same night at 8:00 at the Cuban restaurant El Colmao.

I then drove to the house in Santa Ana, greeted everybody, and went up to Father Salomon to see the new bills they had printed. The money looked strange to me, like foreign money, so different was it from the bills that we were used to seeing. I appreciated the quality, even the water mark. Father Salomon had been doing an excellent job with this new money. I said to him, "Congratulations. I think that when my friends see this, they will be completely satisfied."

Father Salomon smiled, satisfied himself. I went to the trunk of my car and pulled out two large suitcases. I told Hernesto to fill them up with the $10,000 bundles that were already packaged and prepared. When the suitcases were filled, we put them back in the trunk of the Jaguar. I gave them final instructions and said goodbye to them. I told them Hernesto would be in charge, as I had to leave the country for a few days. I hugged Elizabeth and Father Salomon, and I told Hernesto to keep his eye on everything.

I drove to Fashion Island in Newport Beach to the office of Dr. Triana, my psychologist and freedom fighter associate—and a personal friend. After I parked my car in the underground parking of the building, I took both suitcases out of the trunk. I walked towards the elevators. A few minutes later, I arrived in her office and walked up to the receptionist. Dr. Triana was holding a folder in her hand and giving her instructions. When she saw me, she stopped talking and began to walk towards me, a joyful expression on her face. I put both suitcases on the floor, and we hugged.

"Are you going on a trip?" she asked me.

I smiled slightly and glanced at the receptionist. Dr. Triana understood the look and said, "Come on. Let's go to my office."

In her office, I put down the suitcases. We sat down and she showed me the diamond ring she was wearing it proudly. "I was just joking with you when I said bring me a little diamond ring from Vegas!" she said. "You must have been a big winner in Vegas, huh?"

I smiled. "What's the matter? You don't like it? It's too little for you?"

"Too *little*?" she exclaimed. "If this is little, I don't want to see what big is!" She held the ring up to the light, as if she really enjoyed watching it sparkle.

"Well, as long as you like it, then that's what it's all about. It is a pleasure for me to be able to bring you some enjoyment. You deserve a lot more than that."

She smiled again. "Thank you very much. You should not have spent so much. But I like generous people because they have good hearts."

"Well, perhaps that is one of the things in my genes. I have to thank my grandpa for it because I hate selfish people, too. I receive more joy when I give than when I receive."

She reclined in her chair. "Me, too. By the way, you look good physically, but I can see your mind is not all here. Are you worried about something? What's the matter? Tell me."

"Nothing escapes you psychologists. You catch every single detail in my demeanor. You know me too well."

She smiled again. "I hope it's nothing really bad."

"No, it's nothing too important. I just made another mistake in my love life. I thought I had found my soul mate, someone equal to the only love of my life that I left behind in Cuba. But it turned out to be a big fraud."

She shook her head. "I always told you to take your time before you open your heart completely to somebody. You have to protect yourself and not give your love and trust to anyone until you know they deserve it."

"Yes, you are one hundred percent right. But shouldn't it be the other way around? Shouldn't we love and trust everyone until they give us a reason not to? Then you can withdraw your trust and your love if they don't deserve it."

She smiled again and nodded. "Yes, yes. That is the way it should be in a perfect world—a world full of honest and dignified people like you. But, sadly, this world that you imagine does not exist. In the world we live in, we have to take all precautions so that we don't get hurt."

I shook my head. "What a pity, eh? We have to live constantly on guard for fear we might get hurt."

Triana looked at me with a sad expression on her face. "You know better than anybody because in your line of work you have to be on guard twenty-four hours a day."

"Precisely—that is why we look for somebody in our personal and private lives that we can trust. It can be a great relief for all the tension we have. I know it might be unrealistic to find someone that you can trust completely with no reservations."

She smiled. "Well, you can trust me. I hope you know that."

"Of course, of course. But I am referring to an intimate relationship."

She looked at me wickedly. "Well, that is not a big problem."

She crossed her legs, exposing her beautiful thighs a little bit, which were tanned by the sun. This caught my attention for a minute, but I was not sure if she were just joking or if she were propositioning me. We had known each other for many years, and we had worked together many times for the freedom fighters, but I had never looked at her as a romantic prospect. I had always thought of her as a friend.

I was surprised to realize I felt a physical attraction to her. Triana was petite and slim, but well proportioned. She had large and expressive eyes. Her long, wavy hair made her look like an Egyptian princess. She had good and refined manners. But we had been friends for too long, so I controlled myself for fear of ruining our friendship. I stopped looking at her legs, concentrated on her eyes, and changed the conversation topic.

"Well, the reason I came to see you is because I have a couple of favors to ask of you."

She smiled again and said, "What can I do for you?"

"I want you to hold these two suitcases for me. If possible, I need you to take them to your vacation home in Puerto Rico and put them in a secure place there far away from here."

"May I ask you what those suitcases contain, or is that classified information?"

"No, it's not classified, but it is absolutely confidential. Nobody should know they even exist."

"No problem. Nobody will know I have those suitcases with me. What about their contents? You don't have to tell me if you don't want to."

"Money. Lots of money. For the future. But with no value at this moment. It will probably be valuable a few years from now."

She looked at me a little confused, clearly not understanding what I was talking about. Nevertheless, she said, "Don't worry. I will put them in a secure place. When you need to retrieve them, just let me know."

"Don't worry, I will explain in more detail later in our trip."

She grew even more confused. "Trip? Are we going somewhere?"

"Yes, that is the other favor I want to ask of you. I want you to come with me to Madrid, Spain, because I have to do a job there that is extremely delicate and confidential. I will need all your psychological expertise to do it successfully."

"When do you want me to leave for Madrid, and who else will come with us?"

"Well, everything is arranged to leave the day after tomorrow. Only you and Dr. Martin will come with me. Of course, that is if you have no problem coming with me on such short notice."

She reclined in her chair. "Huh! You never give me enough time to prepare a decent bag. Why do you guys always do everything in a rush?"

I smiled and replied, "Remember, we live in the fast lane."

I remained silent for a few minutes, waiting for her answer.

She crossed her legs again in the opposite way, catching my attention.

*Either she is horny or I am*, I thought. She noticed I was looking at her legs and smiled, but did not change position. She knew she had my attention. She rubbed her leg with her hand, causing me to pay even more attention to her. "Okay," she said at last. You can count on me. I will cancel my appointments for the rest of the week."

"Thank you for your support on such short notice. I am sorry, but you know how things are. We will go to Spain from Mexico as we have always done in the past."

"Yes, we never go to another country directly from the United States," she said, understanding. "Do you have any idea how long we will be out of the country?"

"No more than four or five days," I replied.

"Very well. I will use this trip to complete some personal errands in Europe."

"Thank you again. Later on, I will give you more details and brief you on the plan."

We stood up and she took a few steps toward me. She hugged me and said, "Thank you again for the beautiful present you sent me." She gently waved the ring in the air. She gave me a kiss, which I think was intended for my cheek but just then I moved my head and it landed close to my lips.

We looked at each other for a second, and I felt a tickle in my stomach. I intended at that moment to kiss her on her lips passionately but then restrained myself. She remained motionless in front of me, and I did not know whether she expected me to kiss her or not.

So I just said goodbye and left the office with a quick farewell to the receptionist on my way out.

I drove to the house in Corona del Mar, where my parents were staying. My mother received me with joy. She was in the kitchen frying plantation bananas. She had both ripe bananas and green ones. They smelled so good I could not contain myself. I put a few of each type on a plate.

"Where is Papi?" I asked her.

She pointed to the terrace that overlooked the ocean. "He is over there."

I looked outside and saw him reading a book and sitting on the swinging sofa. I took my plate of bananas and walked out onto the terrace. When he saw me, a big smile came to his face.

"What are you reading?" I asked him. "Do you want some fried bananas?" I offered the plate to him and he grabbed one. I put the plate on the little table in front of the swing. He raised the book to show me what he was reading—*Cuba Ruleta Rusa de America*. I smiled. "Oh, you are reading my book. How do you like it?"

"Very good book. Congratulations. I hope that everyone who reads this book takes your past experiences seriously and does not make the same mistakes we all made in Cuba. It is very painful when someone uses you like a fool to get in power and then when they don't need you anymore, they kick you in the butt."

My father had tears in his eyes. I put my arm around his shoulder and said, "You have to forget the past and those bad experiences because that remorse will kill you. You have to let new experiences make you happy and not feel any more guilt. Remember, you are not the only one Castro and his people made a fool of. They made fools of millions of people. That is why Miami has millions of immigrants. Still they are making fools of very intelligent and famous people. They believe in their promises to help the poor and bring equality for all. Famous actors, directors, movie stars, doctors, and attorneys go to Cuba today and offer their work for free to Castro's system, completely blinded by the propaganda they spread all over the world about the free medical attention and other wonderful things Castro does for Cuba. It is all a fraud."

My father looked at me with a sad face and teary eyes. "How could we have been so stupid? How can these people today still be so stupid?"

"Not stupid. We are all good people. Passionate people, who want to be the remedy for all the injustice and sickness in the world."

My father turned to me, hugged me, and said, "I want you to know that whatever happens, no matter how crazy it is, I will always be proud of you. I will never doubt whatever you tell me again. I wish I had listened to you when you were a little boy and you tried to warn me what those traitors were doing to our country. That is the reason I look at you now as a grown up man, and I say you have an extraordinary vision of the future. You should write more of these books. I hope people will read them and listen to you."

"Thank you, Dad," I said, noticing how emotional he was getting. "If my book makes you sad and brings back bad memories, I don't want you to continue reading it."

He moved back a little in the swing and wiped his eyes. "Well, it's too late. I have read it all already." He shook the book in the air in front of me. "That is why I told you it is a good book. I have already read it. I think it is a great contribution to the new generation."

I smiled and said, "Let's hope so."

Mima opened the sliding door and came out onto the terrace. "Why don't you come inside and sit down and eat? I have made a great *arroz con pollo a la chorrera*. You guys are going to lick your fingers."

I looked at my watch and saw that it was already six in the afternoon. I said to my mother, "Save me a plate. I will eat it later. I have to run now and take a shower because I have an important meeting at eight in Los Angeles. If I don't get ready quickly, I will be late."

My mother smiled. "Don't worry—I will save a plate for you. I will put it in the refrigerator."

I gave her a kiss. "Thank you, Mima." I gave my father a pat on the shoulder and said to him, "See you later. Don't be sad. Be happy. Don't think of the bad things that happened in Cuba anymore."

He smiled and nodded his head. "Okay."

I took a shower, changed clothes, and drove to Los Angeles. When I arrived at the El Colmao, Dr. Martin Perez was already waiting for me. We greeted each other with a big hug. Before we even sat down, he said with a smiling face, "Whenever anyone mentions you at one of our social events or at a meeting of the freedom fighters, I always tell them that I was the first one to meet you when you came here from Miami many years ago—that I am the one who relocated you."

"Yes, you were. I appreciated that very much. You were the one."

We sat down, and he said, "You know, all my friends look at you very highly because of all the things you have done for our cause. Sometimes, I see doubt on their faces when I tell them I have known you for so long."

I smiled. "Well, if you need any confirmation on my part, just dial my number. I will be glad to substantiate what you say."

He made a big gesture with his hand. "No, no—it's okay. If people don't believe what you say, don't waste your time trying to convince them because they will always find a reason to doubt you."

After we had eaten, I explained to him that I needed him to go to Spain with me. He felt very honored and grateful that I had selected him for such a great and delicate operation, and he accepted cheerfully. When I had given him all the details, we said goodbye, and I drove back to Orange County.

# Chapter 21—The Contradictions and My Guilt

When I arrived in Orange County I received a call from O'Brien. "How would you like to have lunch with the old man at the Bonaventure Hotel? He has to be in LA to attend to some things, and he himself asked Addison and me to ask you—he wants to personally congratulate you for a job well done."

"This is a great honor for me!" I said in complete surprise.

"Well, this is a perfect time because the day after tomorrow you'll be leaving town."

"Yeah. Good timing. Let's meet tomorrow morning at ten at location two."

"That works for me. See you then!"

As soon as we hung up, I called Yaneba. I told her I needed to meet her in one hour at location number three and to bring Elizabeth with her.

An hour later, we met at the Baskin-Robbins ice cream parlor on Harbor Boulevard in Costa Mesa. When I arrived, Yaneba and Elizabeth were already waiting for me in the parking lot. We walked into the parlor together, ordered some ice cream, and sat down at a small table by the window.

"Did something bad happen?" Yaneba asked curiously.

"No. Something good happened. O'Brien just called me not too long ago to inform me that the old man wants to meet with me for lunch tomorrow at the Bonaventure Hotel. We will be leaving from Newport Beach tomorrow morning at ten. According to O'Brien, he wants to congratulate me personally for the work we have done on the Zipper operation."

Elizabeth smiled and patted me on the shoulder. "Will you please do something for me?"

"Sure—what is it?"

"I want you to congratulate him for his work being well done. Tell him that in my personal view, he will go down in history as one of the best leaders we have ever had."

I smiled. "I will tell him. He will probably be delighted to hear that." Yaneba asked, "Do you want us to record and film that meeting?"

Elizabeth did not wait for an answer. "Of course," she blurted out. "This is a golden opportunity for us to make sure that if something goes wrong they cannot pull the rug out from under our feet and leave us hanging in the air all by ourselves."

I nodded and bit my lip. "I understand your feelings, but I have a very, very bad feeling about recording him. He not only is a really good guy but he has supported us all the way. However, I know that we cannot let this opportunity pass because we could regret it later if something goes wrong. They would have to live up to their commitment and not wash their hands of us."

"Yes," Yaneba agreed, "in the past they have left some of their people holding the bag with their dirty laundry."

"Well," I said, "we should not talk anymore. This is your job. But please be careful." I took the spoon out of my ice cream, which was a combination of toasted almond and pistachio with caramel topping and fresh strawberries. "Remember, that place will be full of security men tomorrow. I don't want them to find you guys there under any circumstance and the whole thing end in an embarrassment for all of us."

Yaneba smiled. "Sweetie, you have forgotten. We are professionals. We will go there prepared. We will use the butterfly transmitters. Just be certain than none of the security guards tries to kill the lovely butterflies in the planter or by the window."

I frowned and looked at her. I took off my sunglasses. "Of course you are professionals. But knowing you guys, that is not the only thing you will try to do. Do whatever is possible to accomplish this, but do not compromise your security!"

Elizabeth said, "Don't worry. We won't. However, we have to accomplish this because this is more powerful than any recording or video we have from O'Brien, his boss, or anybody else."

"Alright, I trust you guys," I said. We finished our ice cream. Yaneba said, "Do you realize that we have to leave immediately to accomplish this by tomorrow? We have to set up our equipment in strategic places in two different locations. That way, we have backups to the butterfly, and if one of us is caught, the other can finish the job."

"Alright," I said. "Good luck to you guys." I hugged Elizabeth, and Yaneba gave me a very strong hug.

"Don't worry," she said. "We are not going to fail. Tomorrow you will have another reel in your security box to add to your film collection."

I smiled and touched her face. "Okay, tigers—go and get it." They both laughed, and we left the Baskin-Robbins in different directions.

I got up very early the next morning. After I showered and had a light breakfast, I drove to the Balboa Bay Club to meet O'Brien.

I picked him up, and we drove a few hours to the Bonaventure Hotel in Los Angeles. The old man received us with a pleasant smile and great cordiality. After he gave O'Brien a hug, he turned, hugged me and took my hand in a firm handshake. I noticed a small, lovely butterfly sunning itself in the window and felt again that quiet guilt over what we had to do.

"I'm really proud of you and your boys," he said. "Because of the things you did, we might be able to change the face of our world. We may be able to make a better world for future generations."

We sat down and talked for a little while. He respectfully told the security men who were in the room to go outside and leave us alone. We discussed several things, one of which was the Rottweiler project and the great advantages it could bring to us. When we finished talking, we had lunch.

While we were eating, I began to feel more comfortable and said, "Sir, I have a friend and associate who asked me to tell you something. She knew I was coming to meet you today."

He smiled. "What did she ask you to tell me?"

"Well, she said to me that in her opinion you will go down in history as one of the best leaders we have ever had, with no exception."

"What is the name of your friend?"

"Elizabeth."

"Does she work for your group?"

"Yes, she is one of the most trustworthy and valuable members on my team."

He smiled with satisfaction. He walked over to the bed, opened his briefcase, and took out a small picture. He sat down and wrote something on the back of the photo. When he finished, he handed it to me. "Give this to your friend Elizabeth, and tell her I really hold in high regard those beautiful words she asked you to tell me. They mean a lot to me, especially coming from a freedom fighter like her."

246

I took the photo in my hands. It was a picture of him sitting by a fireplace with a brown and white cocker spaniel sitting in his lap. I smiled. "This picture is going to make her very, very happy. But more than the picture, this gesture, you sending it to her, sir, will make her ecstatic."

He smiled and said, "Don."

I did not understand, confused because of my accent. I thought he said 'wrong,' so I asked, "What?"

"Don," he repeated. "Call me Don. That is what my closest friends call me."

"Thank you very much," I said, deeply honored. "You are a great man."

We stood up, and I felt deeply guilty that my colleagues were recording him. He gave both O'Brien and me a big hug. We said goodbye to him, left the hotel, and drove back to Orange County. After I dropped O'Brien at the Balboa Bay Club, I called Elizabeth and told her I had a little present for her from the old man—a picture. She was excited to hear this, and we agreed to meet in location number two on Balboa Island in half an hour.

We met in the French café by the Balboa ferry. The women had already arrived and were waiting for me with smiles on their faces. Each one had a glass of wine.

"You guys look happy," I said by way of greeting. "Did everything go well?"

Yaneba gave me an okay sign with her hand and winked. "It went great!" She handed to me a manila envelope. "We left copies in safe places. We just brought this one to you for your enjoyment."

I gave Elizabeth the picture that the old man wanted her to have. She took it and smiled. "I saw it already on the video." Her face clouded slightly. "I share your feelings of guilt for filming and recording him because he really is a nice man." She took a sip of wine. "We have to be extremely careful with this. We did not do it with the intention of harming anyone, especially the old man. We did it to protect ourselves, but my guilt brings to my mind the possibility. What if this ended up in the wrong hands? Can you imagine the scandal? It would be worse than Watergate."

"Did you guys secure the copies in the safe security box?" I asked.

"Yes, we did," Elizabeth affirmed.

"Then there is nothing to worry about. After I review this, I will put it in a secure place, also. Should we ever have to use this, the people we release it to will be under pressure to make certain none of it gets out to the public." We talked for a while, and then I said, "Well, I won't see you guys for a few days because I am leaving tomorrow. Keep your eyes on everything—especially my mom and dad."

They assured me they would. We said goodbye and left in different directions. I called Triana from my car.

"Are you ready for the trip tomorrow," I asked, and added with a teasing tone, "or are you still packing?"

"I finished packing a long time ago!" she exclaimed in mock indignation. "I'm ready to go anytime you want."

"Okay, I will pick you up in the morning. However, I want to talk to you tonight if possible, to brief you on the plan. Do you want to meet me in any particular place?"

"Why don't you come to my house in Laguna Beach? I think you will feel more secure."

"That is fine with me. I'm in Newport Beach right now. I'm going to stop at the gas station, so I should be there in twenty to twenty-five minutes."

"Okay, I will wait for you."

I put gas in the car at a convenience store on the Pacific Coast Highway. Before leaving, I entered the store and looked for a decent bottle of wine. I found one that was close to decent, bought it, and drove to Triana's home. It was a beautiful house in the hills overlooking the ocean. I pulled into her driveway, grabbed the bottle of wine, and rang her doorbell.

She opened the door with a big smile on her face. She was wearing a bathrobe that was nearly translucent, and wearing nothing under it. *Uh, oh!* I thought to myself. *This egg wants salt.*

I gave her the bottle of wine, and she exclaimed, "Oh, thank you! You didn't need to do this."

I smiled. "My mother taught me when I was a little kid that I should never go to anyone's house empty-handed. That is the reason stingy people in Cuba meet in corner cafes and coffee shops."

She laughed and moved aside only a little in order to give me just enough room to pass by her and enter the house. She closed the door behind me and put the bottle of wine on one of the shelves in the entry hall. She opened her arms to hug me. As she did so, I could feel her hard, pointed breasts rub against my chest. I found this and her near-nakedness intensely arousing. I had been thinking of her all day because of the incident in her office earlier when she had crossed her legs so seductively. She did not kiss me on my cheek as she normally did. She kissed me on my neck, which gave me goose bumps.

As I held her in my arms, I smelled a familiar fragrance. "What perfume are you wearing?"

She smiled at that. "You don't recognize your own fragrance."

"What? My cologne?"

"Yes, this is your cologne, my love. Monsieur de Givenchy. I like it, and I ordered it from Paris because I couldn't find it here in the States."

I smiled. She grabbed my hand and led me further inside. "Let's go to the bar. What do you want to drink?"

"A glass of wine is fine."

She raised a bottle of Chardonnay in the air. "Is this okay with you?"

I nodded my head. "Sure." I had never seen that kind of wine before, but I trusted her good taste.

She took a couple of wine glasses from the freezer and filled them both. She handed one to me and raised the other. "Cheers! Here's to a lasting and indestructible friendship!"

After I drank from my glass, I nodded. "This is a very good wine."

"Once every few months, I take a trip to San Francisco, and I use the opportunity to enjoy tasting wine, to get away from the stress. This is one of my discoveries. It is a great wine and I love to share it with my friends. Of course, sometimes by the end of the trip I have tasted too many wines and am almost drunk. My palate gets screwed up, and sometimes I bring home a case of wine that I cannot even use for cooking, and I wind up pouring it out in my garden!"

"Why did you buy that cologne? Do you like men's cologne?"

She smiled. "No. I like the way that cologne smells on you. Of course, on my skin it doesn't smell the same. Sometimes, before I go to sleep, I squirt it in my bed and fantasize that you are lying in bed with me." She came around the bar and grabbed my hand. "Come on. Let me show you my new and beautiful bed. I redecorated the master bedroom."

As we walked into the bedroom, she said, "By the way, I don't know why they don't import your cologne. You can find any other cologne from Givenchy, but not Monsieur."

"It's very simple," I replied. "On my last trip to Paris, many years ago, I told Mr. Givenchy not to send that particular cologne to the USA. I don't want any other man to smell like me."

She burst out laughing and gave me a little pat on the shoulder. "What if I smell like you? You don't like that, either?"

"Well, that is different. You are a woman. I don't want any other *man* to smell like me. I don't want any competition." I smiled and took another sip of my wine.

We were already in the doorway of the master bedroom. It was dimly lit, and there were candles all around. I noticed that as we had been walking down the hallway towards the bedroom, she had been turning off all the lights, as if she did not intend to go back for a while. "I hate bright lights," she said. "There is nothing more beautiful and romantic than dim and soft light."

"Me, too," I agreed. "I believe that bright light is really scandalous and jarring, and soft light is sensual and romantic."

She glanced at me brightly. "Oh, I like that!"

We walked into the bedroom, and when we were close to the bed she let go of my hand. She sat down on the edge of the bed and opened her legs a little bit. Then she crossed them every bit as seductively as she had in her office.

She could clearly see my excitement, and so opened her bathrobe to expose her breasts completely. She poured a little bit of wine on her chest and allowed it to roll down to her belly and crotch. She beckoned to me and said, "Don't you want to know how Monsieur de Givenchy smells in my feminine parts?"

I said nothing but smiled. I put my glass of wine on the little table by the bed and got down on my knees in front of her. She bent forward to kiss me, and we kissed passionately for a little while. Then she reclined a bit, opened her legs, and I could smell my cologne wafting up from her. I gave her oral pleasure, and then moved up to have splendid intercourse with her. After a few hours, we were completely exhausted.

We both took a shower and finished our wine. I sat down on a little bench in the bathroom, and while she dried her hair with a towel, she said, "You have no idea how long I have wanted to make love with you."

"But you never gave me any indication before," I protested mildly. "Not until you gave me a little hint in your office, I had no idea."

"I was terrified that I would ruin a beautiful friendship."

I kissed her on her lips tenderly. "Sweetie, our friendship will never be ruined—not by sex or anything else in the world that happens."

"Well," she asked me impishly, "what about it? Did you enjoy having sex with me?"

"Of course. Couldn't you tell? Men are not like women. We cannot fake it. You know when we don't like it! Actually, all day today I was thinking of your beautiful, tanned legs. You looked to me as if you had come from a tropical island and had been wearing nothing but berries and leaves, like Adam and Eve. That was my fantasy."

"Well, maybe I can make your fantasy come true. Let's go to the kitchen. I have a lot of berries in the refrigerator. No leaves, though."

We walked into the kitchen. She put some ice cream in a bowl and surrounded it with berries and fresh fruit that she had in the refrigerator.

"Do you have any Grand Marnier?"

"Of course I have, love." She poured it on top of the ice cream and fruit. We both ate in the kitchen from the dish. It was delicious. We sat down for nearly an hour, and I finally explained to her our plan for Spain. After a while, I got dressed and she walked me to the front door.

"Could you stay with me?" she asked.

"I'm sorry, but I have to go home and pack."

"A-ha! You don't have your suitcase ready yet? And you talk about a woman taking forever to prepare for a trip!"

"Sweetie, sometimes we are so busy we have to prioritize. I know it will only take me fifteen or twenty minutes to pack what I need." We kissed each other at the door in farewell, and I told her I would see her in the morning.

I drove to my house on Lido Island in Newport Beach. Most of my clothes were there, as well as my suitcases. I decided to stay there that night, since it was late and there was no longer any danger from Sanchez or Loren.

The next day, Triana, Dr. Martin, and I left California for Mexico and from there we went on to Spain. When we arrived at the airport in Madrid, our contact, Secilia, was waiting for us. She and I introduced ourselves, verified our identities to both our satisfaction, and then I introduced her to my friends. "This is Dr. Martin and Dr. Triana."

The pretty Spanish girl smiled and said, "Wow! We have three doctors in the house! We won't have any problems if someone gets sick!"

We all laughed and followed her to her car. She took us to the Miguel Angel Hotel, where there were already three suites reserved for us. We all sat down in my suite and discussed the plan for a couple of hours. Each of us would be operating on his or her own. Even though we were coordinating our movements, others could finish the job if one of us had a problem.

We all three agreed to meet in the restaurant that night. That way, if anyone saw us talking together, we could say we were all tourists traveling in Spain and had just met in the hotel. This would completely throw off any possibility of suspicion that we were a team working for a particular intelligence group. We knew that this particular hotel had been used by Cuban Counter Intelligence for many years like a mail box to drop off and pick up things. We also knew that we had to walk on glass and be extremely careful because any one person in the hotel could be one of them.

Secilia was indeed a pretty blond with big blue eyes like the ocean. She was from Seville. She explained to us that her team had already prepared the Rottweiler, Tanga Negra. She would personally bring the dog that night from La Costa Brava to our hotel in Madrid. The surgery had already been performed on the dog and the implant was successful. Everything had been done in Sweden by a special team of veterinary surgeons in a top-secret and classified environment.

Our part of the plan was for our team to be in charge of the exchange of dogs. The exchange could take place as soon as the next evening, depending on how soon the OTTO agents arrived in Madrid from Germany with dog number one. Our job would consist of exchanging Tanga Negra with dog number one. If all went according to plan, everything should go smoothly, providing nothing unexpected happened that would force us to improvise.

We were all hoping that would not happen.

Our suites were all lined up with one vacant one in the middle, the one the OTTO agents were supposed to use. Our intelligence had arranged it like that to facilitate our work. In every one of our suites, our intelligence had prearranged for an empty cart like those used by room service to be in the closet. It was covered by a white table cloth that went nearly to the floor. We were supposed to use those carts in order to bring Tanga Negra into the hotel so that nobody would see her, and to remove the other dog when the job was done.

Secilia informed us that in the past when this had been done by the OTTO agents, they had brought the dogs from Germany to Spain. After they had registered them, they took them to different countries in the belief that by doing this they completely lost the trail and confused anyone who wanted to know where the dogs had gone. Later on, they would take the dogs to Castro in Cuba.

We did not know whether the dictator had used the dogs for his own pleasure or to make a special pet. We hoped it was not for any kind of diabolic ritual, but we knew that it cost him between $8,000 to $10,000 for each dog. After we had exchanged ideas and discussed all the details of the plan, Secilia left my suite. Before she left, she told me to be in my suite between 10:00 and 10:30. She said she would call me before she brought the dog in.

Dr. Martin was the first to leave my suite, followed shortly after by Dr. Triana. We all went in different directions to the restaurant. We sat at different tables, but close to each other. After a while, Triana dropped her fork.

I picked it up and said to her, "You cannot use that anymore. It is full of bacteria." I called a waiter over to get her a clean one.

"Are you a doctor?" she asked.

"Yes, I am."

"What a coincidence. So am I. What kind of doctor are you?"

"I have a PhD in genetics," I said.

"Oh. I am a psychologist."

Dr. Martin was close to us and chimed in. "I am a doctor, too! What is there—a medical convention in this hotel?"

The waitress brought our food to our tables and overheard our conversation, as we had planned.

"What kind of doctor are you?" I asked Martin.

"I am an orthopedic surgeon."

I smiled and said to Triana, "Well, that's good to know. If any of us breaks a bone, you will be there to assist us."

Triana replied, "If either of you guys gets distressed, feel free to call me, even though I am on vacation."

I raised my glass to them. "Cheers to you guys. *Bon appétit.*"

We proceeded to eat the delicious food we had all ordered.

Even though I finished my meal at approximately the same time as Triana's, I ordered a Grand Marnier to kill some time. This way, we left the restaurant one by one. I was the last one to leave.

# Chapter 22—OTTO and Tanga Negra

When I arrived at my suite, I waited for Secilia to call. I looked at my watch. It was 10:30 p.m. I was getting impatient because she had told me she would be calling at about that time. Finally, the telephone rang, and it was Secilia.

"Is everything okay there?" she asked in a Spanish accent.

"Yes, everything is fine. I was starting to worry because you had not called. I have been watching the empty suite between us, and no one has arrived yet."

"You don't have to worry about it. As soon as they arrive, my people from the front desk in the hotel will let me know. They will call me."

"Okay. Good to know."

"Call room service and order some food. Champagne, fruit, or whatever comes to your mind. That way, they will need to use a cart."

"Okay—I understand."

"We will be there in twenty minutes."

"Very well," I said and hung up the phone.

About twenty minutes later, somebody knocked on my door. "Who is it?" I called.

"Room service," a feminine voice answered.

I looked through the eyehole of the door and saw Secilia dressed in a hotel uniform. I opened the door immediately.

"Hello, sir," she said with a smile as she pushed the cart into my suite.

I closed the door behind her at once. She rolled the cart to the center of the small living room in the suite and raised the table cloth that covered the cart. Under the cart I could see a cage such as the one we used to transport animals on planes and cars. It was wooden with wires around it and a handle on the top.

"Can you please help me?" she asked with a smile on her face. "This dog is very young but very heavy."

I helped her raise the cage and take it out of the bottom of the cart. Between the wires I could see the beautiful Rottweiler. We took the cage into the bedroom and put it close to the bed on the carpet. I put my hand around the wire, and this beautiful dog tried to lick my hand in a very affectionate gesture.

"Is he aggressive or is he nice?" I asked Secilia.

She smiled, opened the door of the cage, reached her hand inside, and petted the dog, though she did not let it come out of the cage. The dog welcomed her affection and licked her hand. "This dog is lovely. It does not have an aggressive hair on its body."

"Very good because if it is not friendly it could make our work very difficult."

Secilia continued to pet the dog. "Come on, get close. It will be good for you to get to know the dog and for it to know you."

I extended my hand and allowed it to lick my hand. I petted it on its head and ears. Its fur was so soft and seemed to like me even more than Secilia. "Is it a male or female?" I asked.

Secilia giggled. "If you had to bet your life on it, what would you say?"

I smiled and looked at her. "You are a gambler, hey?"

"Isn't every day of our lives a gamble?"

"Well, up to a point, you are right. I have to tell you that you are gambling at the wrong table."

"Come on. Take your best guess."

"Absolutely a female."

Her mouth dropped open and she put her hand to her lips. "How did you know? Did somebody tell you?"

"No. I had no idea."

"It is not possible for you to know! She was supposed to be a male because Castro ordered a male. At the last minute, after we had already done all the surgery on a male dog and had him ready to go, he changed his mind and ordered a female. Then we had to pick Tanga Negra and do the whole operation again. We did not even know if we could do it in such a short time!"

I smiled again. "The reason I told you that is because the females are very friendly and sweet. They are friendlier with men because they smell our testosterone, and the male dogs are extremely temperamental and aggressive. Of course, there are genetic exceptions. This is something I know a little bit about because I studied animal genetics.

That is why I told you before that you were betting on the wrong table."

She laughed. "That must be very interesting. What is the reason the male is more aggressive and temperamental?"

"Exactly the same thing that makes us men more aggressive and temperamental. My mother used to tell me that if a woman was in politics and in power, we would never have wars. If a war did start, they would be dropping flowers and water balloons on each other."

She smiled. "Wow. You are on our side, honey. Your mom did a great job with you."

"Well, we are different, but we should respect each other. I have a high regard for women. If it were not for you, none of us would be around and the world would cease to exist."

"Well, well, well—we need more gentlemen like you here in Spain."

"Thank you."

"But you still did not tell me why the male Rottweiler is more aggressive than the female."

"The principal factor is the testosterone in the male," I explained. "The female does not have that. Another factor is heredity from the father and mother when the genetic cross takes place."

She smiled, and patted me on the shoulder after she closed the door of the cage. "You have taught me something today. However, I advise you not to let her out of the cage unless she is howling. That is her signal that she wants to go to the bathroom. When you take her to the bathroom, put her back in the cage once she finishes her business. Even though she is big, she is still a puppy, and we don't want her to do any damage to the carpet or curtains here in the hotel. This would not only create a problem for us but also arouse suspicion."

"Don't worry about it. I know how to handle an animal like this, and I will only release her from the cage when I can be close enough to supervise her."

We went back to the small living room, and she took a medium-sized bag of dog food from the bottom of the cart. "Just in case our plan takes a little more time than we expect, I have brought enough food for her for a week. Only feed her two times a day—once in the morning and again in the afternoon." She realized I was making a face because I did not need her to lecture me on how many times a day to feed a dog. "I'm sorry. You know how to handle her. You are the expert, you know better."

We took out the empty room service cart which had been left in the closet for that purpose. As she rolled the empty cart towards the door, she said, "Say hello to your friends, and tell them not to worry about when the OTTO agents arrive. We will let you know. That way, they can relax in peace." She left the suite.

I picked up the phone and called Triana and then Martin. I told them the dog was in my room and they should come over to see it. I stated that the door would not be locked, and they were not to knock; they should simply enter.

Triana was the first to arrive. I took her into the bedroom and showed her our beautiful Tanga Negra, which I had already released from the cage. Triana began to play with her.

"Oh, my God!" she exclaimed. "She is a doll. What a pity that we have to send her to that son of a bitch. Is there any way we can keep this dog?"

Dr. Martin arrived and came into the bedroom. The dog jumped on him and he petted her. She rolled on the floor on the carpet. She was so happy to be released from that cage. Heaven only knew how long she had been in it. We came out of the bedroom and went into the living room. I started to feed her, and she loved it.

"Is there any way we can keep this dog?" Dr. Martin also asked. "Can't you clone it for us?"

I put my finger to my lips. "Shh! You guys had better keep your mouths shut. Someone is hearing and watching through the eyes and ears of this dog right now. Just remember the purpose of Tanga Negra. Remember what she was prepared for."

Dr. Martin smiled nervously. He had evidently forgotten that small detail. He tried to cover it by saying, "I didn't say anything bad. All I said was I would love to take it home."

Triana understood my joke. She backed me up and helped me continue teasing Martin. She looked in his eyes seriously. "Are you sure that is all you said?"

Martin was quiet and thought for a minute. We both looked very serious. He looked like a kid who had been caught with his hands in the cookie jar. "What did I say? That's all I said, guys."

We could not hold back any longer and burst out laughing. "Come on, man" I said. "We were only joking with you. Whoever is watching and listening to us right now is on our side. They are probably bursting out laughing right now."

Martin smiled. "Shit, you guys. Don't do that to me! It's funny, but for a minute my memory went completely blank. I could not remember if I had said something out of line a few minutes before. You scared the shit out of me!"

We both smiled. He grabbed the dog by the collar. "Come on, honey. Let's go back to the room." He opened the door to the bedroom and put the dog back in her cage. When he came back, he said, "We have a lot of work to do, and I don't like being watched when I am working."

We got a suitcase out of the closet and put it on the coffee table in the living room. We began to take all our equipment out of the suitcase. We took out a very sophisticated silent drill which had many different sized bits, a couple of earphones, and a high-tech stethoscope that could be used to hear through the walls.

We also took out one small gas cylinder like one that was used for nerve gas. The difference was that this gas was not lethal. Instead, if it were inhaled by a person, he would sleep for several hours. It acted like an anesthetic.

We also took a couple of bottles of antidotes, just in case someone tried to poison us or to neutralize us with certain bacteria. Finally, we removed a box containing two thin cable camera lenses with a tiny monitor and another box containing several different motion sensors.

We went to the door which divided my suite from the one that was to be occupied by the OTTO men later on. I put the stethoscope in my ear and they remained quiet while I listened for a few minutes at the door to be sure there was no one on the other side. When I determined that the suite was empty, we put on overalls with big, long zippers, gloves, and shower caps to avoid leaving any DNA evidence. I took a set of master keys from a tiny package in the suitcase. I tried several until one of them opened both locks. We went into the suite and checked everything. I left Martin and Triana working in the suite. They were placing motion sensors—one under the carpet of the front door and another in the frame of the mattress of the sofa bed in the living room. They also put one in each frame of the two beds in the bedroom.

Once they had placed these sensors, they came back to my suite and connected a very thin cable under the carpet right next to the baseboard. They ran it all the way to the coffee table and plugged it into the main box, which had four red lights, four green lights, and a little antenna.

Meanwhile, I drilled three small holes—one in the living room directly above a decorative picture and the other two inside the air conditioner vent in the bedroom. In the living room, I connected a small camera. In the bedroom, I placed another small camera in one of the holes. In the other hole, I threaded an IV line that connected my suite to the gas cylinder which I had hidden behind the sofa.

If anyone walked into my suite, they would not see anything unusual. We put the monitor into the suitcase.

I plugged the cameras into my small monitor, and they were working perfectly. Triana and Martin tested the motion sensors. Triana walked through the front door, and the little red light in the sensor box began to flash. She repeated the same test on every other sensor with the same result. They went back to the other suite to double check that everything was properly hidden.

Finally, we put a splitter on the thin cable that was connected to the front door in the other suite and ran it all the way to my bedroom. We connected the other end to a small pager. If someone were to open the door while I was sleeping, the pager would wake me up.

After we finished and made sure everything looked exactly the same as it had when we had first entered the room, we left and double locked the door again. When all three of us were in my suite, we took off the overalls, the shower caps, and the gloves, and we wrapped them in the same plastic bag they had been in.

"From now on, we cannot leave my suite alone," I told them. "We will disconnect the equipment whenever someone is coming to clean the suite. Otherwise, one of us has to stay here at all times. Even when we go to eat, we will take turns."

They nodded, and I looked at my watch. It was already past midnight, so I said goodnight to Triana, who was the first to leave. About ten or fifteen minutes later, Martin and I said goodnight, and he left. I lay in bed with no worries. I knew that some of the guys on Secilia's team were working in the hotel, and they would notify me if the OTTO agents arrived. I fell asleep, and a little while later, the phone rang. I jumped up and grabbed the phone. Before anybody said anything, I asked, "Are they here already?"

Triana's voice answered, "No, it's me. I cannot sleep. Are you sleeping already? Did I wake you up?"

"Don't worry about it. I was just beginning to fall asleep. When you called, I thought it might be Secilia. I thought the OTTO agents were here already."

"Did you take the dog to the bathroom before you went to sleep?"

"Oh, no—I forgot."

"You should do that now because if she wants to go later, you will have to get up in the middle of the night."

"Yes, you are right," I answered. "Secilia told me that she howls when she has to go. I don't want her to wake up everybody in the hotel."

"If you want, I will come over there and help you," Triana offered.

"Okay, I will open the door for you. When you come, you won't need to knock. Just walk in."

I jumped out of bed and went to the door and unlocked it. Then I went back to the bedroom to let the dog out of the cage. A few minutes later, as I was walking her to the bathroom, I heard the front door open and close. I stood still until I saw Triana walking in. She joined me, and we both walked into the bathroom with the dog.

"Hold her by the collar," she told me. She began to unroll a bunch of toilet paper and covered the floor with it. I watched Triana do this, and so did Tanga Negra. Then the dog sat down by my side as if she were waiting. "Let go," Triana said. "There is plenty of paper on the floor."

I let go of the collar and Tanga Negra immediately opened her hind legs and urinated on the paper. After she smelled it a couple of times, she crouched and defecated as well.

"This is a great dog!" I exclaimed. Triana and I looked at each other and smiled. I petted the dog and said, "Good dog. Good dog." She wagged her stumpy tail in response. Triana said something in German. I did not understand what she said, but the dog got more excited.

"What did you say?" I asked her.

Triana looked at me and smiled. "Good dog, in German." Evidently, Tanga Negra understood German because she continued to wag her tail.

I picked up all the paper and flushed it down the toilet. After I washed my hands, we put Tanga Negra back in her cage and went to bed. We were extremely tired from the trip and from having gotten up so early that morning. We cuddled each other and fell into a deep sleep. A few hours later, the pager began to beep, waking me up.

I rushed to turn it off. Triana woke up as well and sat up in bed. I sat next to her and place my finger on my lips to tell her to remain silent. I grabbed a little flashlight which was on the table by the bed and pointed it at my watch to read the time. It was 4:30 a.m. I put the watch on and jumped out of bed. I put on my pants but not my shoes. I walked silently to the living room, followed by Triana. All four red lights on the motion sensor box were blinking. I turned on the monitor and saw a man resting on the sofa in the other suite. On the other camera, we saw two men lying in the two beds with their clothes still on. With the camera, I zoomed to the living room and saw nothing else.

Then I zoomed in with the camera in the bedroom; close to the bathroom door I could see a cage identical to the one that Tanga Negra was in.

I looked at Triana, who was standing behind me getting dressed and pointed to the monitor. I signaled her to keep quiet and then gave her a thumbs up sign. The dog was there.

"Shall I call Dr. Martin?" she whispered.

I shook my head no. I had been thinking that we should knock them out with the gas before we did anything. It was possible that they might have technology as good as or better than ours, as they had unlimited funds, and I did not want to take a chance on their discovering us.

I hurried to the gas cylinder and opened it halfway. The man that was on the sofa in living room got up and went to the bathroom. When he finished, he walked out without even washing his hands.

"What a pig!" I muttered under my breath.

He crossed by the other two men and said to them, "I am completely exhausted. Don't bother me and don't wake me up until late in the morning." He continued walking to the living room sofa and closed the bedroom door behind him. The other two men remained in the same position. As he walked towards the door which connected their suite to mine, he looked up.

I had my eyes glued to the monitor. "Oh shit!" I said softly.

After he had looked at the door for a minute, he went to the front door and did the same. I tried to zoom and follow him to ascertain what he was looking for. The room was somewhat dark, and although our cameras were infrared, I could not see anything abnormal on or around the doors.

Triana and I looked at each other. I shook my head and whispered, "Shit. Heaven knows what kind of booby trap these guys may have put in those doors. That is why it is so extremely important to know ahead when they are coming in. That way, we could have watched them."

The man from OTTO went back to the sofa and lay back down. He wrapped himself in a blanket and turned off the lamp. I looked at my watch and saw that the gas had been running for about thirty minutes. I reached for the faucet on the cylinder and opened it all the way. It was about five o'clock in the morning.

Triana and I continued watching the monitor for another fifteen minutes until we saw the man on the sofa drop his hand to the side as if he were dead. Then I grabbed the phone and dialed the number of their suite. It rang several times, and none of the men gave any indication that they heard the phone. Then I told Triana to get Martin.

I began to dress, putting on the same clothes I had worn when we were bugging the other suite—overalls, shower cap, and gloves, but this time I picked up gas masks as well. "You pack and tell Martin to pack," I told Triana, "and be ready to leave as soon as we finish our job here. We are going to have to improvise because their arriving without our knowledge has completely thrown off our plans. Thanks to Secilia, we might be taking a very high and unnecessary risk by entering their suite now."

"Calm down," she said. "Don't worry. I know you will think of something. We can do this. Everything will go well. I did not really like the initial plan."

I smiled. "Thank you for your support. Now, go and get Martin. We have to do this as soon as possible and try to get out of here in one piece."

I dialed a pager number and hung up. A few minutes later, Triana came back with Martin. We all looked at the monitor for nearly twenty minutes, trying to figure out what that guy had been looking for on the doors, but none of us could see anything. "I don't like this at all," I told them. "There is no doubt in my mind that he was checking for something. It could be a booby trap. We could open the door and be blown to pieces."

"You know what?" Martin said. "We could abort the operation."

"No," I said.

Just then, the phone rang.

Triana was close to the phone so she answered it. "Yes. Oh, he is here. Wait a minute." He handed the phone to me. "It is Secilia."

"Hello," I said.

"Did you page me?" she asked.

"Yes."

"What happened?" she asked with some anxiety in her voice.

"Well, the birds are in the nest and they caught us by surprise. You friends did not call us."

"Oh, shit! I'm sorry! I don't know how that happened."

"Well, you tell your friends that I will not depend on them to watch my back. We have a big problem and now we have to improvise. Our initial plan is obsolete. Don't worry about it, though—we will figure out something."

"I'm sorry," she said again. "I will be there in twenty-five minutes."

"Bring a vacuum cleaner."

"What?"

"Just in case we are all blown to pieces, you can vacuum us up."

"You are joking, right?"

"No, I am not. They came in and caught us off guard. I have been watching one of the men looking at both doors. I don't know what he is looking for, so there could be a booby trap there."

"Listen to me very carefully," she said. "Abort the operation. I will take the responsibility."

"Okay," I said, "don't bring the vacuum cleaner then."

"Don't do anything," she said seriously. "I am on my way. Let's discuss it when I get there. I am sorry."

I hung up the phone and said to my friends, "Help me to get the mattress off the bed."

We took the mattress to the door that divided the two suites.

"Put on your masks, then stay on the other side and hold the mattress," I told them.

We put on our heavy gas masks and our breathing echoed in our ears. I grabbed the keys and opened the two locks. I opened the door extremely slowly. I did not hear any electronic signal, buzzing, or beeping—nothing. When the door was completely open, I pointed my flashlight at the floor and saw a broken toothpick in front of my feet. I bent over and picked it up. I wiped the sweat off my forehead and walked into the suite and to the entry door. I saw there was another toothpick, identical to the first one. I left that one alone. I turned around and went back into my suite to show the broken toothpick to the others.

They both nodded their heads, and Triana exclaimed, "Thank God! It is only that." I helped them put the mattress back on the bed.

"Okay," I said. "Are you guys ready? Let's make the exchange." Martin went in to my bedroom, took Tanga Negra out of her cage, and brought her close to us. We went back into the other suite and into the living room. I checked the pulse of the man on the sofa, and he was okay. I let go of his arm and it dropped down as if he were dead. "Did you put the mark on Tanga Negra?" I asked Martin.

"Oh, shit! I forgot with all this commotion!"

"No problem," Triana said. She went back to my suite and got a little bottle of peach colored nail polish from the suitcase. It was nearly the same color as the dog's natural nail. When she returned, I held my flashlight for her while she painted the last nail on the left front paw of the dog. When she finished, she closed the bottle and we went into the bedroom where the other two men were laying and where the other dog was. As soon as we opened the door, the dog began to bark. She was so loud and aggressive that the cage shook. We froze for a minute, looking at the men on the beds, but they did not move. I told Martin to take Tanga Negra to the bathroom and close the door. Tanga Negra completely ignored the other dog. She walked past as if she were the only dog there.

I checked the pulses of the two men, and they were okay—just completely unconscious. The other dog continued barking. Triana went up to the dog and tried to calm her down, but she bared her teeth very aggressively and growled. I moved close to Triana and said, "Oh, shit. I think we have another problem."

Triana said something in German in a very strong and commanding voice. The dog became quiet immediately. Triana repeated it again, and the dog began to whine. Whatever she said sounded like a German soldier from the movies ordering prisoners to their deaths. She opened the cage and took the dog out. She grabbed her by the collar and repeated the same words but with a slightly less angry tone, and walked out of the room with the dog, who followed her obediently without resistance.

After Triana left the room, I opened the bathroom door and signaled Martin to come out. We put Tanga Negra in the cage. I petted her before I closed the door, and Martin and I said goodbye to her. We then got out of the room and closed the door behind us. I felt terrible that we had to leave such a beautiful and kind animal in there.

When we got back to the living room, Triana came to meet us and said, "Dog number 1 is in the cage."

"What did you tell that dog? She almost peed and nearly cried in there."

She smiled. "The only thing I said was 'bad dog—you are really a bad dog.'"

"Really? That is all you said?"

"Yes, that is all I said."

"Well, it worked. She must be a really intelligent animal."

"Well, what do you expect to do with the toothpick problem?" Martin asked me.

"Nothing. There is nothing we can do. There is only one solution. We have to get out of the front door. Before we do that, you guys have to disconnect all the wires and cover all the little holes. After we finish that, we will leave from the front door. While you are doing that, I will prepare our exit."

They began to disconnect everything, making sure that all was the same as when we had first entered the suite. I went to the front door, unlocked it, and removed the toothpick. I took the toothpick with me to my suite and double locked the divider door from the other side. I left my suite from the front door and entered the other suite from its front door. I put the toothpick in the divider door.

Martin and Triana signaled that everything was in order. We went out the front door, locked it, and went back to our suite from the front door. We took the cage with the dog in it and put it under the service cart. We took off the overalls, shower caps, gloves, and masks, and returned them to their plastic bags. We all sat down on the sofa and took a deep breath. We opened the bottle of champagne that I had ordered earlier and each had a glass of it.

"Well," I said, "it was not a perfect job, but under the circumstances it was the best we could do."

"They are going to squeeze their brains trying to figure out how in the hell someone came through that front door without breaking the security chain," Martin said. "Let's hope that when they realize there is nothing missing and the dog is still there, that for fear of looking stupid to their superiors they won't even report this incident."

Triana took a sip from her glass. "Remember, they were really tired when they came in. They will probably blame each other. 'Who was the one who closed the door?' 'Who was the last one in that was supposed to secure the door?'"

"That is very unlikely," Martin disagreed. "Normally you remember recent events. Your memory keeps the last thing that happened or the last words you say for a while."

Triana smiled. "Really? Is that why you acted like a child with your hands in the cookie jar a little while ago? For a moment, you didn't even remember whether you had said something embarrassing or not. Remember, honey—I am a psychologist."

Martin looked at me for help.

"I'm sorry, brother," I said. "She has a point. We come into our house with the key to the front door in our hand, and we swear we put them on the kitchen counter like we always do. Then we go to the bathroom and take a leak. Then we go looking for the keys and we cannot find them. We go crazy. After looking twenty times in the same place, we remember we went to take a leak, and so just for the heck of it, we say, let's go check in the bathroom. And there they are. On the sink. In other words, my friend, the doubt will be in their minds forever. They don't know for sure whether they locked the door and forgot to put the chain on or not. That is the reason I decided to use the front door. They had no reason to use the other door to our suite. That is why I put the toothpick in the divider door—to clear ourselves of any suspicion."

Just then, someone knocked on the front door of our suite. I stood up to go answer it, but Triana said, "I'll get it." She went to the door and returned a few seconds later with Secilia. She was still extremely apologetic over what had just happened. She saw the bottle of champagne that we were drinking.

"Are you celebrating?" she asked. "I see you are all in one piece."

I lifted the tablecloth from the service cart. "Surprise!"

"That is Tanga Negra. What is the surprise?"

"No," I corrected her. "That is Number 1. Tanga Negra is over there."

"What? Are you guys crazy?"

Martin said, "No. We just like to finish what we started, even though sometimes people make it more difficult for us."

She apologized again, but I told her it was okay. She handed me our tickets for the plane and said, "In the lobby there are some people waiting for you. They will take you to the airport. Like you asked, Dr. Martin's ticket is to Rome, and Triana's ticket is to Paris. Your ticket is to Mexico. It has really been a pleasure to meet you."

"Wait a minute," I said. "What do you guys intend to do with this dog?"

Triana offered her a glass of champagne. "Why don't you drink a glass of champagne with us before you leave?"

She hesitated and Martin took her hand as he practically pulled her down to sit beside him. "Heaven knows when we will see each other again," he said. "Why don't you celebrate a little bit with us?"

She smiled. "Okay." She took the glass that Triana had offered to her and raised it up. "*Salud.*"

We all raised our glasses and responded, "*Salud.*"

I looked at her sadly. "You have not told me yet what you intend to do with this dog."

"I have orders to destroy her because that way there will be no proof that she ever existed."

"I don't know why, but that is what I figured you would do. Is there any other alternative? It is a pity to destroy such a beautiful and intelligent animal."

Secilia looked sad. "Please believe me; it is difficult for me to do this. I love animals, but those are my orders and I have to comply with them. I don't want to create trouble. I have to do things the way they are planned."

"Like the way we had planned to exchange the dogs? You and Triana were supposed to distract two of the OTTO men downstairs, while we—"

She did not let me finish. With a big smile on her face, she said in her Spanish accent, "Okay. Okay. I get your point. I have apologized to you probably twenty times by now. I am sorry again that my team screwed up. If you really want this gorgeous and intelligent dog, I will close my eyes and instead of shipping her to be destroyed I will ship her to Mexico or wherever you want, providing you don't mind closing your eyes and lips about this little incident that happened here. It would not make my team look good."

I smiled and looked at my friends. They both nodded, so I asked Secilia, "What do you want me to say?"

"That everything went well and according to plan. You don't have to mention that you had to improvise at all, and we will all be happy."

Tanga Negra with little girl

I pulled a little book out of my pocket and wrote down my complete name and other information. I told her I would pick up the dog at the airport at my final destination in Baja California, Mexico.

"Thank you very much," she said.

"Thank you, also," I replied. "Make sure you put in your report that everything went according to plan. Everything we are talking about here is off the record. That way, there will be no contradiction in my report."

She smiled. "Yes, sir. As I said to you before, we need more gentlemen like you here in Madrid."

Triana glanced at her and smiled. She looked at me and slowly shook her head as if to say she thought I was making a conquest here.

"Do you have any children?" Secilia asked me.

"Yes. I have one big boy who is nearly twenty-three years old now. He is with his mother in Cuba. I have seen him many times, but I cannot go near him. Every time I go to Cuba, I go illegally, and I cannot compromise his safety."

"What a pity," she said. "This dog would be a great present for a child. When I brought Tanga Negra to the hotel, I stopped at my house for a little while. I let her out in our patio, and my little girl loved her. She is only three years old. I went to the bathroom and left her playing with Tanga Negra for a few minutes. When I came back out, they were sitting side by side. They looked so cute that I took a picture of them."

She took a picture out of her wallet and handed it to me. I looked at the picture—the little girl was beautiful. She was blond with blue eyes like her mother. She looked like an angel. She was sitting next to Tanga Negra, who looked big and mean with her huge head, but also relaxed and kind as she was looking into the camera. They looked adorable together, and I had to smile.

I shook my head and handed the picture to Triana. "Look at this— isn't this a picture that could be put in a gallery? Beauty and the beast; Secilia, you have a beautiful little girl, God bless her."

"Thank you very much," Secilia answered.

Triana held the picture up high. "You are right. This picture is adorable! Tanga Negra looks like a powerful monster, and she looks like an innocent beauty." She put her hand to her mouth. "Oh, my God—I want a little girl like that. You make me jealous!"

She gave the picture to Dr. Martin, who was anxious to see it by now. "What a couple of creatures! This is proof that love and innocence is more powerful than anything else. The beauty and innocence of your little girl made this macho-looking dog look like a pussy cat, kind and soft!"

We all laughed, and Martin handed the photo back to Secilia. "They are both right, and did not exaggerate—you have a beautiful girl."

Secilia smiled proudly. "Thank you very much. You guys are very nice. It has been a pleasure working with you." She opened her purse, pulled out three business cards, and handed them to each one of us. "I am not accustomed to doing this with people I work with because it is against our regulations. But since we are off the record here and I like you all very much, I want you guys to be my friends in the future. Whenever you come back to Madrid, you will have my personal number. Feel free to call me. That way, we can enhance our friendship and share a little bit of our free time."

We all thanked her very much for her trust in us, and we told her the feeling was mutual. We likewise gave her our numbers in the States. Martin added, "Don't worry about your team. We all screw up once in a while."

We said goodbye to one another, hugged each other, and followed her to the door. She was rolling the room service cart with the dog inside.

When she went out, she turned to us and said, "Ciao, guys." She disappeared down the hallway.

We all got our luggage and went down to the lobby, where two men approached us and identified themselves as friends of Secilia's. They took our luggage out of our hands and walked us out of the hotel. A third man was waiting in the driver's seat of a car that was parked in front of the hotel with the engine running. When he saw us coming, he jumped out of the car and helped the other two men put our luggage in the trunk. We got into the car and left for the airport.

When we arrived at the airport, the driver helped us with our luggage. We said goodbye to each other and left in different directions. We were hoping Tanga Negra would arrive at her destination in Cuba and that our mission would be successful and produce great results.

# Chapter 23—Baja California

When I arrived in Tijuana many hours later, I went to claim my luggage and my dog. I named her Roca Negra in honor of Tanga Negra. When I signed the papers required to get her out of customs, one of the agents handed me an envelope, stating that he had instructions to give it to me personally. I opened it and, to my surprise, there was a copy of the photograph of Secilia's daughter and Tanga Negra. On the back of the picture, Secilia had written, *Good luck. This picture is a souvenir for you. Preserve it as a memory of the time we spent together and the beginning of a great friendship. Ciao, Secilia.*

When I finished reading her note and put the picture back in the envelope, I felt a hand on my shoulder. I jumped, and when I spun around, I saw O'Brien standing there behind me.

"Don't do that to me, man!" I exclaimed. "Do you want to kill me ahead of time?"

He said nothing but smiled.

I continued, "It's nice to see you, Mr. Ghost. I didn't see you at all in Madrid. Have you guys invented something to make yourselves invisible?"

"Maybe you're joking," he replied, "but that is what I was—an invisible man. I was there all the time, watching your back. Did everything go according to plan?" He had a knowing look, as if he felt he knew something I did not know.

I smiled and nodded my head. "Yes, almost. You know nothing goes exactly as planned. In the end, the important thing is that the work is done with no problems and nobody was hurt. That is my main concern."

At that moment, the customs agents brought the cage with the dog. One of them said, "Here she is, your Roca Negra. She's a beautiful dog. She must have cost you a fortune."

"No," I replied with a smile, "she was a present from a friend."

O'Brien looked first at the dog, then at me. We both smiled. "Roca Negra, eh?" he said. "I see you have a new friend."

We walked out to get the luggage and he asked me again, "Are you sure there's nothing you want to tell me?"

We picked up the luggage, and I remained silent. We walked towards the parking lot. I was pushing the luggage cart with the cage on it. I did not like the way he had been questioning me.

"Do you think it's a smart move to keep that dog with you?" he asked me again. "You're not planning to take it across the border into the States with you, are you?"

"No," I said abruptly, "I am not planning to take it to the States. I plan to leave her here on a ranch that I have in Baja. Is that okay with you? Why don't you stop the bullshit and ask me directly what you want to ask me—or tell me directly what you want to tell me. Stop beating around the bush."

We arrived at my yellow Land Rover jeep. I turned around and faced him, clearly annoyed. He smiled and put his hand on my shoulder. "For God's sake, chill out! I was just teasing you. You Cubans are like water and Alka Seltzer—you cannot be brought together. You're effervescent."

"No," I responded, "we are a straight people and we don't like it if someone tries to hang a tail on our ass. If you want to ask me something, ask me directly and I will give you a direct answer. For God's sake, you and I have known each other for twenty years. If you don't know me by now, you never will."

"I'm sorry. I just wanted to give you a little hard time because I knew you didn't expect me to see you with that dog."

"I know that eventually I will tell you everything—when we are talking off the record. Especially when it would compromise my word with others, I will keep my lips sealed. I will not tell that to anybody."

"Calm down! I know you're a man with great pride and moral convictions. I was just playing with you. Actually, I'm extremely proud of your work in Madrid. The people you took with you were great professionals like the ones you always select to work with you."

My face remained serious in spite of his joking. "But..." I gestured to him to continue with what he had to tell me the problem was, as I knew that was coming after all these compliments.

"Oh, man," he smiled. "You got me. You read me too well. I know that you had to improvise there because I received my own report in addition to the one your friend Secilia submitted. What she reported was a half-assed report in order to save her ass."

I glanced at him. "Help me to put my luggage and my dog in the jeep. Off the record..." I looked at him intently and repeated with emphasis, "Off the record...," and waited for his response. He was silent, so I repeated again, "Off the record...."

The Yellow Land Rover

"Okay—off the record."

"I will tell you what really happened there. But this has to remain between you and me, is that clear?"

"Have I ever let you down?"

"No, not yet—but there is always a first time."

He shook his head in disbelief.

"Well, come with me to my house here in Baja. We can have a couple of Negras Modelos, and I will explain everything to you over that."

"Oh, no—inland in Mexico? I have to be back in the States tonight."

"I promise you that you will be back in the States tonight. Let's go and have dinner at a beautiful restaurant. I promise you will be surprised. We will drink that beer at my house, leave my dog at the ranch, walk on the beach, and tonight we will be back in the States."

"Alright. I'm going to trust you."

We put the luggage and the dog in the jeep and left the airport. On our way to Ensenada, he said to me, "You know what? You're a great man and a fantastic friend. You have many good qualities, but one of them—to protect others when they make mistakes—does not take into consideration the consequences this can bring to the others. And to you. One day, this could bring you great trouble. I hope that one day it doesn't cost you your life."

I smiled in understanding. He was talking about the screw ups made by Secilia's team in Madrid. I replied, "Remember, the rules are square like a box. Sometimes when you are unfolding that box, there are more than four corners. What does that tell you? You cannot always follow the rules the way they are."

O'Brien smiled slyly. "I know you enjoy breaking the rules, and in that way we're very much alike. But we can only break the rules in extreme circumstances, when there is no other alternative. Every time we break a rule, we expose ourselves and risk losing everything we've worked for in our lives. We should ask ourselves, is it worth it to take the chance?"

I smiled again. "What exactly is bugging you? What do you have on your mind? You have told me so many times that you guys are like Father God and you can see and hear everything—so many times that I have started to believe it."

He did not reply but kept silent. He merely looked through the window at the scenery from the toll road in the high mountains, with the ocean below between Tijuana and Ensenada. After he enjoyed the scenery for a few seconds, he turned to me. "God, this is beautiful. I haven't seen anything like it except in Greece, and I've been all over the world!"

"Yes, indeed," I said, "it is beautiful."

"Let me answer your question. Number one, I have to congratulate you and your team for the great work you did in Madrid, especially under the circumstances. It was great the way you improvised when things didn't go according to plan."

I smiled and shook my head. "But?"

He smiled back. "No buts. I only worry about you because you do things without thinking of your own safety." He paused. "Remember our creed: when we're in doubt, we stop. We do not proceed. That's the reason we adhere to the option. The option is to abort when there's too much danger and the risk is too high. You do things differently. You walk into the casino with all your money on one number. If you win, it's beautiful; but if you lose, you're stuck with no money for the rest of your vacation. In our business, you lose your life."

I smiled again because I knew where he was coming from and I knew that he was truly worried about me. At least, that is what I felt at that moment.

"I know that what we did in Madrid was taking a big risk," I said. "Right then, I considered it necessary because we probably would not have had another opportunity like that again, as Castro may not have ordered another dog in the future. It's true, I took a risk—but I took it only for myself. I protected my friends as best I could. That way, if I had died, they could have continued, finished the job, and my life would not have been sacrificed in vain. Maybe for you guys this is difficult to understand. I know that. You guys do not live under the humiliation and persecution and psychological pressure which are prevalent under the political system of Castro because you have never lived in Cuba or any other place in those circumstances."

"I understand. Even though you think I can't feel your frustration, I do understand."

I shook my head. "Let me tell you—the worst hours of my youth were when I began to doubt the existence of God because of the horrible things I saw under that political system. It practically destroyed me to the point I sometimes felt life was not worth living. Maybe to you guys, it was like playing cat and mouse, just a political game. BWut for us it was much deeper than that."

O'Brien looked at me sadly and with sincere compassion in his face. He analyzed what I had said for a few seconds. Then he put his hand on my shoulder. "I know you guys think we can't comprehend how you feel because we've never lived in your shoes. But I've got a good imagination, and I can guarantee you that I would've been very pissed off if a son of a bitch like Castro had been in power for thirty years in my country. If a man's promised social benefits and reforms for the poor under the façade of being a benefactor to the people, then instead took all the wealth from everyone to keep for himself and his close friends and family, then I'd really have been frustrated, just as you are right now."

"Yes, almost thirty years of frustration. That is a long time."

He shook his head. "God only knows how many more years he'll be in power."

I smiled. "Let's hope that what we are doing will help, and that it will not be too much longer. We should be optimistic."

O'Brien smiled as well. "That's what I like about you—you're an emotional optimist."

A few hours later, we arrived at Ensenada, and I took O'Brien to a French restaurant, El Rey Sol. We ordered an exquisite meal and relaxed while listening to a pianist playing old melodies. O'Brien reclined in his chair, drinking his wine and enjoying his food. "There's something I have to say about you. You know how to live very well. How'd you ever find this fantastic place in the middle of nowhere?"

"Very simple. With friends. My publisher and the distributor of my first book, *Cuba, Russian Roulette of America*, brought me here because he was a very proud Mexican man. He wanted to show me this wonderful restaurant and the great places that exist in Mexico. Even though he lived in Long Beach, he had a vacation home here on the beach. He is the one who introduced me to this exquisite place."

"Very good book. I read it translated into English. Fantastic! It took a lot of balls for you to write that book, with your family still in Cuba at the time. The way you guys escaped from Cuba was unbelievable! They should make a movie about it."

"Thank you. I'm glad you liked it."

We finished eating, and they brought a rolling cart full of pastries to our table. I pointed at various pastries, and said, "I'll take one of those, one of those, one of those, and one of those."

"My God!" O'Brien exclaimed. "How many are you going to eat?"

"Whatever I don't eat, you will probably eat later. I am going to take them home in a box."

He pointed to two of the pastries as he began to eat them. "Oh, my God! This is delicious. What do they put inside these things?"

"Some have almond crème with cognac, some have different nuts with Grand Marnier. Aren't they exquisite?"

"Yes, and the service is outstanding."

Just then, the waiter came with a little brush and a silver plate, and brushed the crumbs off the white tablecloth onto the little plate. "Not even in Europe have I been in a place that is as refined as this one," he added.

"Yes, my friend Enrique has excellent taste. This is actually one of my favorite restaurants here in Baja. There are quite a few good ones, but this is the best."

"Well, you've got good taste, too, because you continue to come here, and lucky me because you brought me here today."

"I have been coming here nearly ten years already."

"How come you never brought me here before, man?"

"Well, if you remember, I have tried many times. But you are one of those gringos that doesn't want to cross the border into Mexico unless it is absolutely necessary, and you always told me that you did not feel comfortable in Mexico."

He looked at me in resignation. "You're right. It's my fault."

"Well, I hope this excellent place and atmosphere changes your mind and you feel a little more comfortable. In the future, maybe you will visit me here more frequently. Remember, there are *bandidos* everywhere in the world, but Pancho Villa died many years ago. You don't have to worry about him anymore."

He smiled and nodded. "I never imagined in my wildest dreams that I would find a place like this so close to the border."

We finished our pastries. He ordered an apricot cordial, and I ordered a pineapple cordial. O'Brien liked his very much, and I said, "That is made in Mexico, too."

He smiled again. "If I didn't know better, I'd think you were Mexican!" he teased.

"Every country has its good and its bad, but this is a truly beautiful country."

I paid the bill and we continued on our trip down south in Baja. A few hours later, we arrived at my house on the beach. We opened the gates and pulled into the garage. We took the dog out of the Land Rover and went for a walk on the beach. We walked and played with the dog for about half an hour before we decided to go back home. On the way back, we ran into my neighbors, Jack and Tina. They were a pleasant couple who were permanently retired in Mexico and had been great friends of mine for many years. They kept an eye on my house when I was not there, and if I was gone for a long time, they paid my electric and water bills and took care of little problems for me. I was very grateful to them for being such good neighbors.

They both said hello. Jack hugged me and told me they had heard us coming in but saw I had a visitor, and so decided not to bother me. Tina hugged me. "God," she said, "it's been a long time since you were here. Where have you been?"

"Honey," I replied, "all over the world."

"I paid all your bills. The receipts are in your mailbox."

"Thank you very much. Do I need to give you some money?"

"No," she said. "There is still some left from what you gave me. It should last for another month or two. Don't worry about it."

I turned around. "This is my good friend, O'Brien. If he ever comes here by himself, let him into the house. He is one of the few that I trust completely."

O'Brien smiled and shook hands with them. "Nice to meet you. It's really a pleasure."

"Is this your first time coming to Baja?" Jack asked.

"No," O'Brien replied. "I've been in Baja before, but further south."

"How do you like it here?" Tina asked.

O'Brien grinned. "This is paradise."

Jack and Tina smiled. Jack asked, "Why don't you guys come over later and we'll have something to eat or drink together?"

"Thank you very much," O'Brien replied. "You're very kind, but we have to go back as soon as possible. I have to go back to the States tonight."

"Why?" Tina asked. "You just got here. Why do you have to go back so quickly?"

I smiled and pointed to Roca Negra, who had been sitting patiently by us. "She is the only reason we came. We are going to leave her at my ranch so my workers there can take care of her. Just do not have the time to take care of her properly in the USA."

"Such a beautiful dog," Tina said admiringly. She came closer and petted her. "Where did you buy her?" O'Brien and I looked at each other and smiled. Tina, who was a very perceptive person, realized there was something going on about that dog. "I'm sorry if I'm being indiscreet," she apologized.

"Oh, no," I replied. "By no means. She's a present from O'Brien."

Tina looked at O'Brien. "Well, I'll bet she cost you a lot of money. She looks like a very refined and well-bred dog."

O'Brien smiled again. "Yeah, it's an AKC. But I cannot do enough for my friend, J. Anthony, even keeping my mouth shut when I probably shouldn't. I owe him a lot and this is a very tiny present compared to all he's done for me in the past."

Tina smiled suspiciously. She knew there was more to the story than what we were actually saying, but she kept silent. She only said, "I know what you mean. I like him very much, too."

We said goodbye and continued to walk towards the house. On the way back home, I asked O'Brien, "What do you want to do with the first boxes of hundred dollar bills we printed in the beginning with the little flaw of the hair touching Franklin's collar?"

"Burn everything."

"Oh, my God!" I exclaimed. "That will take at least a week. There are millions of dollars there. Is there any alternative? Can you guys take it and shred it someplace?"

"No. It's too risky to be moving it from one place to another."

"Okay. When I get back, I will tell Hernesto and the others to burn everything."

Deck of Julio Antonio's house in Baja

"By the way," he said as he pulled an envelope from his sport jacket and handed it to me, "this is a ticket for you to go to the Caribbean Islands. Addison and I think you should take three or four months of vacation out of the U.S. You deserve it anyway, plus we think it'll be a good safety precaution."

**View from the house in Baja**

"Thank you very much. It has been quite a while since I visited my house in San Martin. Whenever you want, you know you are welcome to visit me there. You could spend a little vacation with me."

"Thank you very much," he replied, "but I don't think I'll be able to do that for a while. In any case, if I can escape from here, I'll take you up on your offer, even if it's only for a few days."

"No problem—come anytime. We can drink a Negra Modelo with lime."

He smiled, and we arrived at my house. We sat down on the terrace for a little while. I made a couple of rum and Cokes, and we relaxed and looked at the ocean. Later on, we took the dog to the ranch, where I introduced O'Brien to Ruben, the man in charge there. I told Ruben to give special attention to Roca Negra because she was a special dog that I intended to breed later. Ruben took the dog, and we both petted her before he took her away with him.

O'Brien was fascinated with the ranch and all the beautiful animals we had there—horses, cows, goats, sheep, chickens, and a lot of pigs. We took the Land Rover and drove around. I gave him a tour of the ranch. I showed him the coaches from the 18th century that we took to town and rode around in on warm summer nights. "Oh, man!" he exclaimed. "I have to come back here. I cannot die without eating one of those suckling pigs, roasted Cuban style with black beans, white rice, and bananas!"

"I thought you were not comfortable in Mexico!" I teased him. "Sounds like you are getting more and more comfortable every minute!"

"My friend, you are capable of changing anyone's opinion. It's a pity Castro doesn't give you the opportunity to spend time with him. Maybe if you had some dialog with him for a day or two, you could change the destiny of Cuba!"

I laughed. "I think you give me too much credit."

He smiled and said, "I'm only talking from my own experience. Thank you for a fantastic time. You actually forced me to spend time with you. Thank you very much for bringing me to your house and your beautiful ranch, not counting that exquisite meal in that restaurant in Ensenada. What was the name?"

"El Rey Sol."

"Al Rey Sol," he repeated with a North American accent.

I smiled and explained to him that El Rey Sol was King Louis the XIV of France and that they named the restaurant after him because he was very happy and had a great personality. "I personally met the owners of the restaurant many years ago," I told him. "*La señora* Pepita and one of her sons, Sr. Joun-Loup Bitterlin."

He smiled. "I won't even try to repeat that name."

I smiled and we continued our trip. A few hours later, we crossed the border and stopped at a gas station to fill up my Land Rover. After that, we continued our trip to Orange County. We arrived in Newport Beach, and I said to O'Brien, "Well, I have brought you back home and the evening is still young."

He looked at his watch and noted it was 2 a.m. "Well, it's not that young anymore. But that's okay because I had a terrific time."

"Why don't you stay at my house?"

"No, for your security and mine it's better if you leave me at the Sheraton Hotel by the airport."

I took him to the Sheraton, and after I helped him with his luggage, he said, "Thank you very much for everything."

"You are welcome. Thanks to you for your support and your silence about what happened in Madrid because I gave my word to Secilia that I would not tell anyone what happened."

"You have nothing to worry about. It'll stay as you promised."

I said goodbye to him and took off for my house on Lido Island.

# Chapter 24—Amelia the Freelancer

The next day I slept late. When I awoke, it was nearly 11:30 a.m. I ate a light breakfast and checked my messages on the answering machine in the house. There were several messages from Amelia, and the last message was marked urgent. This caught my attention, so I went to the phone and dialed her number.

"Hello," she answered. "Who is this?"

"It is me," I replied. "How are you doing?"

"Thank God!" she blurted out. "Where have you been? I have been trying to reach you for several days."

"I have been out of the country. What is going on? You sound disturbed."

She was silent for a few seconds. "No, I am fine. Where are you at this moment?"

"In my house."

"Can you meet me immediately? I need to talk to you about something very important."

"Can you wait for an hour? I just got up and need to take a shower and get myself together. I don't want to scare you."

"Sure, sure," she said. I could tell from her voice that she wasn't smiling at my joke. She was usually very happy and a great sense of humor.

"Where do you want me to meet you?" I asked. "At your clinic or at your house?"

"No, neither one. Meet me at the French café right across the street from the South Coast Plaza shopping mall."

"Okay, I will be there in an hour." I hung up the phone, shaved, and took a shower. When I was ready, I took my red DeLorean and drove to our meeting place. When I arrived at the café, she was already waiting for me under an umbrella table in the front patio by the garden close by the parking lot.

I parked my car and went to her. She stood up and gave me a strong hug. "Wow, you smell so good!"

"I just took a shower."

"It is not soap that I smell. It is that expensive cologne that you use. Every time you are around me and I smell it, it arouses me sexually. Does your cologne have hormones?"

I smiled. "No, the hormones are mine. They are mixed with the cologne you like so much."

"Do you want to eat something?"

"No, thanks. I just had breakfast."

She looked at her watch. It was 12:30. She looked at me. "You just got up. You just had breakfast. What a good life you are living!"

"Don't believe everything that looks beautiful to you because in reality, life nothing is the way it appears to be. I did not go to bed until nearly three a.m., after a long, long trip."

Amelia took a sip of her coffee from the cup in front of her and wore a sad expression. "That is precisely what I want to talk about with you. A few days ago—last week, to be more exact—we closed all the transactions and money exchange in the Caribbean Islands to bring O'Brien and Addison the summary of all the account numbers and the rest of the information. We agreed to meet at eight-thirty in the evening in the bar of the Hilton Hotel by the L.A. airport on Century Boulevard. I left early to avoid the evening traffic, and got there two hours early. I sat down on the back side of the bar.

"When I arrived, it was happy hour. I ordered a glass of wine. The place was packed with people. O'Brien and Addison came in early also, and I started to stand up to say hello to them. They didn't notice me because it was dark and there were so many people. Before I could stand up, I noticed Charlie the Cleaner was with them. That man gives me the creeps, so I did not stand up. I sat back down and turned away from them. You won't believe it, but they sat down almost back to back with me. I didn't even turn around." She put her fingers to her lips and shook her head. "I did not like the conversation they had at all, especially Addison. They were talking about you and your group."

I was surprised. "About me? Are you sure."

She looked around to make sure nobody was listening to what she was about to tell me. "Yes. About you. I heard your name, Dr. del Marmol, very clearly several times. Have you been recording some of your conversation when you have meetings with these people?"

"Where the hell do you get that from?" I tried to pretend I had no idea what she was talking about.

"That is one of the things Addison told O'Brien several times. O'Brien said no, no, no. Addison told O'Brien that you were becoming a really serious problem for them, and if something went wrong, you could be very dangerous for everyone in general."

A waitress came to our table. We kept silent. She asked us if we would like to order something to eat or drink. "Yes, please," I said. "Bring me a shot of Grand Marnier."

After the waitress left, Amelia looked at me directly. "Isn't it a bit early for that?"

I stroked my chin with my fingers. "Well, it helps to tranquilize my stomach. Right now I am really pissed off."

We maintained silence for a few seconds, and then Amelia asked me, "Your trip that took you out of the country was to Spain, right?"

"How did you know that? That was supposed to be classified!"

"Because that is one of the things Addison told O'Brien. He said to do something when you come back from Spain, but I could not hear what that something was because someone screamed right beside me for a glass of wine precisely when he said that. I only heard, 'when you come back from Spain.'"

I stayed quiet, thinking. The waitress came back with my Grand Marnier. I took a sip and looked Amelia straight in the eyes. "Why do you tell me all this? You are exposing yourself to trouble."

She looked at me gratefully. "Have you forgotten already in such a short time that I owe you my life?" She took a sip of her coffee. "That debt you can never pay for, and besides, I know you are a gentleman and you will use this information for your benefit and will not reveal it to anybody."

"Thank you very much. I really appreciate this, but you don't owe me anything. I did in that moment what I was supposed to do."

She reclined in her chair and smiled. "And I am doing in this moment what I am supposed to do. I am bringing to you the chords for the guitar. You put those chords together and see what kind of music you get out of it."

I stared at her in deadly earnest. "I am going to entrust you with something. Yes, I have been doing some recording of whatever I consider important conversations. The only purpose is to protect my people and me because I don't want to end up like one of my best friends in Miami, whom they sent to fix a propeller in a ship because he is a professional scuba diver. The ship turned out to be loaded with drugs for a secret operation.

"Something went wrong, and the local authorities arrested the people on the ship. They got my friend, too, because he was repairing the propeller. The men on the ship were released slowly, one by one, with different plea bargaining, but my friend is still in jail today after six years! He is the only one who was a Cuban freedom fighter, and everybody from the intelligence community has been ignoring him in order not to create a problem for themselves."

I sat back in my seat. "I guarantee you that will never happen to me or to one of my friends if I can avoid it. I have known Addison for many years, but we have never had too much contact, as I usually deal with O'Brien. That is the only thing that really surprises me. We have just been together for so many hours on a long trip. Why did not not just ask me directly?"

Amelia made a face and shook her head. "Why are you surprised? Have you forgotten that in this kind of work it is very difficult to believe in anybody totally? Besides, remember that O'Brien is dependent upon Addison's judgment, and Addison is dependent upon someone else's. This is not the regular CIA, where normal proceedings take place. The people are autonomous, and they have the authority to proceed and to act according to the circumstances. Whatever they believe is in the best interest of the country is what they do. Remember, this is like a chain that never ends. That is why when someone gets killed, nobody knows where the order came from."

I got chills in my stomach, remembering what my cousin in Las Vegas had told me. I asked her, "Do you think they are preparing my disappearance or extermination?"

She smiled. "Nope. I don't believe so. What you have been doing has scared the shit out of them. They have no idea how you may have prearranged to use what you know if something does happen to you."

"In any case, I don't like the presence of Charlie the Cleaner with them."

"Maybe it's me. Maybe it's you. It could be anybody."

"You? Why? They don't have anything against you."

"Well, I could not hear all of their conversation because of all the people around me, but Charlie said goodbye to them one hour before the time I was supposed to meet with them. In other words, they did not want me to see him."

I grabbed her hand and tried to keep her calm. "You have not done anything crazy. Why would they do anything wrong to you? Actually, you are more like a freelancer."

Amelia smiled nervously. "You don't know. Half of the money has been exchanged in the Caribbean banks. It has been put aside to open physical therapy clinics from Los Angeles to San Diego. I am supposed to be in charge of all that."

"What is the purpose of that?"

"To process false claims to the insurance companies and to accumulate money for future secret operations."

"With all the money we have manufactured, this is not enough for now and the future and many generations to come?"

She smiled. "Have you never heard the saying here in the USA? You can never be too skinny or too rich! Well, these people think that way. I will tell you in confidence that in my trip to the Caribbean Islands and Central and South America, I made a little stop in Argentina and left a little money in my private account there. So just in case the rain comes, I will not have a bad time."

I smiled. "Have you told this to anybody else?"

"No. Only you, but you know as I do that these people have eyes and ears everywhere like Father God. It is possible—"

"Bullshit!" I interrupted. "If nobody told anybody, there is no way anyone can know. Don't let anybody brainwash you with stupid ideas. Here in this world, there is only one God. The rest are false prophets. They only proclaim themselves to be Gods."

The waitress came to our table, and we both fell silent. Then Amelia asked her for the bill, and I asked for a glass of ice water. After the waitress left, I said to Amelia, "Thank you very much for the information. I will keep my eyes open, and you should do the same."

I grabbed her by the arm. "Remember: don't tell anybody what you just told me. I am loyal to the death. Whatever happens and whatever anybody tells you I said, you check it with me before you believe it. Remember this. I will never repeat what you just told me. If anyone betrays you, always look close around you because only one who is close to you can hurt you. That is the person who knows all your moves and all your intimate goings on."

The waitress returned with the bill and my glass of water. Amelia was about to pay the bill, but I didn't allow her. We stood up and hugged each other.

"It is always a pleasure to meet with you," she said. "I always learn something from you."

"Thank you," I said. "Me, too. Especially today. I learned something very new."

While I drove to Corona del Mar, I thought of O'Brien and what he had said about my intentions to protect those who work close to me was very noble, but the intelligence community considered that a weakness and it could be dangerous for the majority in the future. He said that this weakness could bring a major problem to me one day.

I asked myself if perhaps O'Brien had been trying to warn me about what I had been doing when it came to protecting others. Maybe he was referring to the recordings, but he did not want to confront me directly. With these thoughts in my head I arrived at the house in Corona del Mar where my parents were staying. They were very happy to see me, and they had prepared a little welcome home party for me because previously I had called them and told them I would be having a late lunch with them.

To my surprise, my friends Yaneba, Elizabeth, and Hernesto were there. They all hugged me joyfully, and we sat down on the terrace to have lunch. Hernesto told me that all the work had been done and Father Salomon had already returned to Nassau. Jacobo had taken him back as I had planned and accompanied him all the way to the monastery to be sure he was okay and had no problems.

I gave each one of them plane tickets to where they had previously requested to take their vacations. I also gave them manila envelopes full of cash. I told them I hoped they would have a wonderful vacation and would see each of them back here in three months.

Hernesto opened the envelope and asked, "Is this real money?"

"Of course! Before you guys leave, however, we have to burn all the boxes in the garage closets of the house in Santa Ana because this is the way O'Brien wants it."

Hernesto was surprised. "Burn all that money? I think there is at least thirty or forty million in there, and all they have is a little tiny defect that is not even noticeable!"

"That is the way O'Brien wants it," I repeated. "He wants all those hundred dollar bills from the beginning to be burned. Go to Home Depot and buy eight or ten aluminum trash cans and bring them to the patio by the pool. Burn everything there. Nobody can see it from anywhere. If anybody asks you about the smoke, tell them you are burning some grass."

"Okay," Hernesto said, "but it is going to take quite a few days to burn all of that money."

"Fine. Try to do it quickly. The sooner you do it, the sooner you can go."

Yaneba opened a bottle of champagne and we all said cheers to a job well done and to a free Cuba. My parents got caught up in our salutes and also cheered to a free Cuba. My mother said, "I hope I am still alive when Cuba becomes free because I think that Castro is the son of the devil. God forgive me, but I hope he dies soon because that will end a lot of suffering in Cuba." Tears came to her eyes.

"Don't get too emotional," I said to her. "That can hurt you. I want you around for a long time."

She looked at me with love and tried to smile as she wiped her eyes with her hand. She caressed my face with soft hands which had become wrinkled by the years. "I love you. God bless you, my son."

The phone rang and Hernesto went inside to answer it. He came back and said, "Your friend Jacobo is calling you. He wants to speak with you."

I went inside and picked up the phone. Jacobo was a mess—crying and very disturbed. "What happened?" I asked him.

"I need your help," he gasped in between sobs. "I need your help. My wife has left me, and she took our kids with her."

"The last time I went to your house everything was okay. You guys seemed to be very happy together. What happened?"

"It's my fault. I spent all the money. Even the rent for the apartment. My wife got very mad at me. She said I am irresponsible. She said she might go back to Mexico to live with her family."

"How much do you need?"

"I don't know. Maybe five thousand dollars to pay all the bills and everything."

"No problem. I will help you. Go to Norm's Restaurant on Harbor and Victoria in Costa Mesa. Wait for me in the parking lot. Do not go inside. Do you understand?"

"Yes. Thank you very much. I really appreciate your help."

"Pull yourself together. I know you will talk to your wife and everything will be okay. If I take a little longer, wait for me. I will be there as soon as possible. I am having lunch with my mom and dad and some friends, so it might take me a little longer."

"Okay. I will wait for you," he said. "Don't rush."

"Okay. I will see you there in about an hour." When I hung up the phone and turned around, Hernesto was there. He wanted to tell me something, but he did not want the others to hear.

"Loren has called me several times," he said softly. "She is asking for you."

"What did you tell her?"

He shook his head. "Nothing. Each time she called, I just told her I would give you the message."

"Very well. Thank you. When you finish lunch here, take Elizabeth and Yaneba with you so they can help you to burn all the boxes of money that are left in the closets of the garage."

"Is it absolutely necessary to burn all that money?" he asked.

"Yes. It is money with a defect, and we have to burn it. We cannot take any chances."

"Okay. I understand."

We went back out onto the terrace to finish our lunch. About half an hour later, Elizabeth, Yaneba, and Hernesto said goodbye to my parents and left to go to Home Depot to buy trash cans.

I said goodbye and drove to my house in Newport Beach. When I arrived, I began to pack to prepare to leave town in the next couple of days. I would be going to the Caribbean Islands for a few months to relieve myself of all the tension I had been through. After I finished packing, I went into the garage and opened the trunk of the 560SL Mercedes and took out a briefcase full of bundles of $100 bills that we had printed in the beginning.

I went into the kitchen, took a grocery bag, and dumped all the money into it. There was probably between $150,000 and $200,000 there. I did not know the exact amount because I did not count it, but each bundle contained $10,000, and there were quite a few of them. I went back to the Mercedes and put the grocery bag on the front seat on the passenger side.

I got into the car and drove to Norm's in Costa Mesa. When I arrived, Jacobo was already waiting there for me. He got out of his car and came over to where I had parked. I got out of the car and said, "Let's walk. I have to talk to you."

We walked from the parking lot to the next parking lot, which was for the Salvation Army building. We entered the building from the back and went into the store.

I told him, "I brought you a lot more money than you asked me for. You must, however, act responsibly and do exactly as I tell you."

"Oh, thank you! Thank you. I will repay you every dime."

"No, you cannot repay me even if you want to. There is probably between a hundred fifty and two hundred thousand there."

His eyes bugged out. He could not believe what he was hearing. "Are you kidding me?" He smiled nervously, clearly in shock.

"No, I am not joking." Just then, I saw a little wooden barrel with six wooden glasses. The barrel had a little faucet on the front, and there was also a little wooden container under the faucet to catch any wine that dripped. It looked like an original barrel from a wine cellar. I asked the lady how much for that wine barrel.

She smiled. "Well, it is for either wine or beer. Depends on what you want to use it for. It probably cost a lot more originally, but since it is a donation, we will let it go for only fifty dollars."

"Will you please wrap it up for me? I will take it with me now."

"Of course," she replied and began to wrap it up.

I turned to Jacobo and we continued to walk around the store to get out of the lady's hearing. When we were a few steps away, I said to him, "Even though this money is of a very high quality and is made with the same ingredients as the real thing, it has a tiny defect on the neck of Franklin. His hair is touching the fur coat he is wearing. To the average person, this would never be noticed, but to anybody who knows currency, especially the Secret Service, they would know immediately that it is counterfeit.

"Precisely for this reason we are going to burn millions of dollars of this money. I took the liberty of taking some of that money that we are supposed to burn and brought it to you to help you.

"You have to give me your word of honor," I continued, "that you will only carry and use one bill at a time. If they find you with a bunch of bills, then you have no excuse. If you have only one and there is any problem and they search you, you can tell the searcher you found it on the street. It is not against the law to use or have a counterfeit bill in your possession that you found…especially since you did not know it was counterfeit.

"Please," I finished, "if you have any problem at all, under no circumstances whatsoever mention my name! Give them any excuse you want, but do not involve me!"

"No, no," he interrupted. "By no means would I ever betray you. Even if they cut off my balls, I will not mention your name."

I smiled. "Let's hope it will not ever get to that point and you can keep your balls intact!"

He rushed to reply once more, "I swear to God that I will do exactly what you tell me to do. You can sleep in peace because even if I get into trouble I will never mention your name because you have done so much for me and my family."

I looked at him straight in the eyes and saw his desperation. I knew that he would say anything at that moment in order to get the money he was expecting from me. At the same time, I felt he was sincere in what he was saying about not creating any problems for me. That is why I said to him then, "You don't have to do anything for me. You don't owe me anything. All I expect from you is your loyalty. I hope you do things the way I told you to do." I picked up my little wine barrel and paid the cashier. "Follow me," I said to Jacobo.

We went out to my car and, after I put my wine barrel on the bench behind the front seat, I told him to go around to the passenger side. I opened the doors and took the money off the seat so he could sit down. I gave him the grocery bag full of money. He took out one of the bundles and his eyes shone when he saw the enormous amount of money in the bag. He took one of the bills out of one of the bundles and held it up to the light.

"Man," he said, "if this bill has a defect I don't want to see a flawless one."

"Put that bundle back in the bag and don't call attention to yourself," I told him. "I hope this money brings happiness to you and your family."

He nearly had tears in his eyes. "God bless you, my friend." He leaned over towards me to try to give me a big hug.

Before he got out of the car, I said, "I am going to repeat this once more. Take only one bill at a time and when you have used that one then you can go back and get another one. Don't carry more than one bill with you."

We said goodbye. He got out of the car and I started the engine in preparation to leave. He came back with the bag of money in one hand and knocked on the window on the driver's side. I pushed the button to lower the window. "Yes?"

"I only wanted to tell you before you leave that if you need anything at all, you can call me and you don't have to pay me."

I smiled. "Thank you. I don't think we will be seeing each other for a while, however, because I am leaving the country for a few months."

"Well, in the future, remember—if you need anything you do not have to pay me. I will do it for you."

"Thank you," I said. "Bye, now."

I put the window up. As I drove away, he said, "Have a good trip."

# Chapter 25—Burning Money

I left the parking lot and drove to the house in Santa Ana. When I arrived, I found my friends opening bundles of money, dropping them into the trash cans, and burning them.

Yaneba looked up at me and said, "My God, it's going to take a while to burn all these boxes. The bills are not burning evenly. I don't know if it is because of the magnetic ink or because they are in bundles, but sometimes we have to move the bundles around with a stick to get them to burn completely."

We joked for a while, having fun burning the bills. Then I took the money counting machine, said goodbye to them, and left. I went to the bank in Costa Mesa and returned the machine to my friend, Mr. Laden. Then I continued to the house in Corona del Mar where my mom and dad were staying.

When I arrived at the house, my mother was very happy. She was waving an envelope at me. "I have a letter from Cuba from your son, Julito!"

I took the letter from her and said, "Why didn't you open it?"

"No, it is for you. It is disrespectful to open other people's mail."

"For God's sake, it is from your grandson."

"It doesn't matter," she insisted. "It is addressed to you."

We all went out to the terrace. We were anxious to see what the letter said. I opened it.

*Papi,*

*Even though I don't know you personally, but only through pictures, I want to tell you that I am very proud of you because of all the good things my mom, my grandma, and my grandpa have told me about you. They told me you are a brave and generous man. More importantly, they say you are not selfish. You have dedicated your life to telling the world the truth about the suffering of the Cuban people with no fear of the hardship this could bring to you and disregarding the dreadful consequences it could bring.*

*You know as well as I do that we can choose our friends but we cannot choose our families. I could not have chosen anyone better than you to be my father. You are the best example to me and the pride of my life. I feel that great pride when I tell others you are my father and my best friend.*

*I received your letters with assumed names and other letters through my grandfather and grandmother before they left Cuba. I hope they are happy by your side and I hope I, too, will be by your side one day, so I can give you a big hug and tell you how much I have missed you all these years. Give my grandpa and grandma a hug for me and tell them how much I love them. I want to ask you with all my heart to get me out of here. I don't want to leave my mother alone here, but I think she understands that there is no future for a man of my age in this country. I don't want to be in such a desperate situation as thousands of young men like me currently are. I don't want to tie a few auto tires and a few pieces of wood together with rope and get myself into the ocean and commend my soul to God and try my luck to either drown or to get free, not yet. I say goodbye to you with all my love and with all the respect in the world.*

*Your son,*

*J. Antonio del Marmol, Jr.*

*P.S.: Thank you for the motorcycle you sent to me. Thanks to that motorcycle, I don't have to get into what we call here 'the sardine cans' every day to get to my school. Hugs and kisses. Love you to death.*

As I read this letter, I became quite emotional and frequently had to wipe away the tears, which rolled frequently down my cheeks. Sometimes I had to stop because they completely blurred my vision and prevented me from reading any further. When I finished the letter, I wiped my tears away a final time. It took all my self control to keep from breaking down entirely.

My mother hugged me. She was a little scared and asked me, "Is there bad news?"

"No, no, no," I answered. "You'll understand when you read it. It breaks my heart to see the situation they are suffering with in Cuba. I remember myself when I was there and was that age. His mother is working with the government there, and he should have more privileges than anyone else. I would hate to see those who have no privileges at all. They have to deal with that horrendous way of life every day."

My mother came close to me and gave me a hug as she said, "Let's trust in God and remember that no disease can last a hundred years. No human body will take it. The monster, the dictator Castro, will have his time, too. I assure you that his death will not be peaceful or quiet.

He will probably have a violent death like his partners in crime...like Che Guevara in Bolivia."

I nodded my head in agreement and said, "But how much damage has this son of a bitch done not only to the Cuban people but to the entire world because everywhere they put their boots they plant a seed of discord and hate and death. It's like they are sons of Satan. Everywhere they go they leave destruction and death behind them."

Just then, my pager began to vibrate. I looked at the number and saw that it was Loren. I excused myself and went into the kitchen, leaving them on the terrace to read the letter from my son.

I used the kitchen phone to call Loren. When she answered, I said, "It's me. Did you call?"

"Yes, yes—I've called you many times. I need to talk to you."

"I just came back from a trip, and I am extremely busy right now."

She paused. "You told me the last time we talked and before you left my house that maybe we could still save our friendship. That's what I want to talk to you about. It will really be a pity if I don't have a chance to explain to you how some of the things happened. Now that we're both calmer, I want a chance to explain how things came to be. Please, if we can't reach an agreement and you still don't feel comfortable with me after we talk, I will never bother you again."

"Okay, but not today. I am not in a very good mood today. I will stop by your house tomorrow afternoon, and we will go someplace quiet and have a talk."

"Very well," she said. "Thank you very much. I will wait for you tomorrow. What time?"

"I don't know exactly what time right now. I have a lot to do tomorrow, but I will call you before I go to your house to pick you up."

She agreed, and we hung up. When I went back on to the terrace and rejoined my parents, they both had tears in their eyes. They had both been hit emotionally by the letter, the same as me. I sat down between them and put my arms around their shoulders. "Don't worry. I am going to do whatever is possible to get him out of Cuba. And whatever is impossible, too. He sure knows how to express his feelings. He did it so well in that letter. He touched the nerve in your hearts, too."

My father said, "You don't know how great a kid your son is. To give you an idea, he is a photocopy of yourself. He has your spirit and your personality. You need to see how he scratched the dirt to bring food to his mother in Cuba, and sometimes to us when we were still there."

"He is so sweet," my mom interrupted, "and such a good boy. He reminds me of you when you were a boy. You went to a birthday party, and they gave you a little piece of cake. You didn't eat it, and they asked you why. You replied, 'Because I want to bring a piece to my mom.' Then they gave you another piece, and you came home so happy. Your son is an exceptional boy. Of all my grandsons, he is my preference."

I smiled. "You had better not say that too loud. All your other grandsons will be jealous."

She smiled and put her finger to her lips. "Shhh."

I kissed them both and said goodbye. The sun was setting. It was a beautiful sunset. I went to my car and drove off. Then I dialed O'Brien's emergency number. He answered and his tone sounded concerned. "What's going on? Is there any problem?"

"No, no problem. It is something personal and I need to talk to you immediately. Where are you?"

"I'm in Los Angeles."

"Do you want me to come there, or do you want to come here to Orange County?"

"My plane leaves in three hours from Los Angeles. I'm going to South America. There are a few things I need to put in order before I leave here. I can meet you at the LA airport in two hours."

I looked at my watch and saw it was 6:30 in the evening. I told him I would see him in the American Airlines terminal at 8:30.

I knew I had plenty of time, so I drove to my house to change clothes and take a shower. Then I jumped into my Mercedes convertible and drove to the LA airport to meet O'Brien.

We greeted each other and went to a fast food restaurant. We sat down at one of the tables on the patio. He ordered a coffee, and I ordered a grapefruit juice. He looked at me in concern. "What's happening with you? You look disturbed."

I took the letter from my son out of the pocket of my sport coat. "It's a letter from my son. You would not understand this if I let you read it—it's in Spanish. Besides, I do not want to make you sad, too because he really depressed me. He wants me to get him out of Cuba, and he sounds so desperate that I am really worried. I have a great fear that he might get on one of those homemade rafts and drown himself or get killed by Castro's planes or torpedo boats."

"What does his mother say about this?" O'Brien asked. "Didn't you suggest to her before that you could help him get out of Cuba, and she said no?"

"I guess by now he is old enough, and she does not have too much to say in the matter. There is no future for a young kid there."

O'Brien shook his head. "I know how you feel, but remember his mother is working for the government."

I smiled sardonically. "Everybody in Cuba works for the government," I said, "because the government is the only master and owns everything in Cuba. Even if you are a carpenter or a brain surgeon, you are an employee of the government."

O'Brien raised an arm to stop me. He could see I was really angry and upset. "Listen. Calm down. With this attitude, you aren't going to get anywhere. You're only frustrating yourself more." He looked me intently in the eyes. "When I refer to Sandra, the mother of your kid, I don't refer to a normal Cuban citizen working an everyday average job. You and I both know who she's really working for and who she's living with. She's a member of the G-2 and the man she's sleeping with is one of the big honchos in that organization. That makes this very complicated and delicate. You haven't known her whereabouts for years. You don't know what she's doing. She could be making a dangerous circle like Russian roulette, either back or forth, either for or against Castro and his regime."

I stroked my chin in frustration. "For God's sake, O'Brien, you know better than anybody that nobody in Cuba works for Castro for convictions anymore because Castro only cares about his small circle. The 'first ring' are the only ones who live well in Cuba. Even they don't sleep well because they don't know what Castro in his paranoia will do to them the next day. In other words, that country is a disaster. I believe the people in Cuba all do what they have to do in order to survive because there you either pretend or you cease to exist. There is no other option."

"Very well, I get your point. I'm a very good friend of the Spanish ambassador in Cuba. Spain has had a good relationship with Cuba up to a point for the past several years. I promise you I'll do my best to get your son out of Cuba. Calm down, for God's sake, and under no circumstance try to get him out yourself. You and I both know that Castro wants you more than a boat full of gold. This could all be a trap. I'm not saying that your son is involved, but they could be putting a lot of pressure on him to get to you."

I smiled. "Doing this myself would be my last option because my life is not that important. I have already lived a good, full life. But he is still a kid. He is just beginning to live now. I will never put his life in jeopardy."

O'Brien smiled as he saw I was in a better mood. He hit me on my shoulder and said, "Come on, man. You and me, we still have a lot of things to do in this world. Don't ever say your life is full, because it's not. You can go in peace, and when you least imagine it, you might have your kid here by your side."

We stood up and I gave him a big hug. "Thank you very much."

"You're welcome. That's the least I can do for you. Remember, you don't get paid by us to do what you do, and you do it with tremendous pleasure."

I smiled, said goodbye, and left the airport a lot more calm and relaxed, thinking that O'Brien was going to do whatever was possible to get my son out of Cuba the same way he did with my parents. In a much better mood, I drove back to Orange County.

Meanwhile, unknown to me, Jacobo had arrived at the South Coast Plaza mall with his pockets full of the bundles of $100 bills. His wife and two kids were with him. They went into the Nordstrom's store. He began to do exactly the opposite of what I had pleaded with him to do. He went to the ladies' department and with the money I had given him tried to make his wife feel like the Queen of Sheba. He bought all kinds of expensive stuff and paid cash for it. They spent a total of about $15,000.

Then they went to the children's department and spent around $10,000. Then they went down to the men's department. By this time, security had called the local police, the FBI, the BATF, the Secret Service, and any other agency they could think of.

All these agents arrived and were in the security room, watching on a monitor Jacobo, his wife, and his kids through the cameras that were located all over the store. Every time they gave a bill to a store clerk, the clerk gave it to one of the security guards who were dressed like civilians, who in turn brought it to the security room. The last agency to arrive was the Secret Service.

When Agent McCain of the Secret Service saw the bill, he said, "This money, although it's of very good quality, is counterfeit—of that, I'm 100% sure." With a little pen he showed the others how the hair of Franklin was touching the fur coat.

One of the FBI agents said, "Man, you've got a really good eye. This is very difficult to catch."

McCain smiled and replied with pride, "That's what we do. That's why we're so good at it. We should wait until they leave the store; that way, we won't create a panic or risk casualties inside the store. We don't know if he's armed or not. We'll surround him in the parking lot and then arrest him."

McCain's partner, Esquivel, was a short and somewhat overweight Mexican American with very bad manners. "McCain, leave this wetback to me. I'll kick his ass so hard in the parking lot that he'll tell us immediately where he got that money from."

McCain was well-groomed and a clean type of person with good manners. He was tall and looked like a football player, and clearly felt embarrassed by the comments of his partner in front of the other agents. He frowned and looked a reprimand at Esquivel. "Take it easy. Whenever we arrest him, then we'll have plenty of time to interrogate him. Right now, the most important thing is to arrest him without causing any problems for us or anybody else."

Esquivel sighed in resignation. "Okay, we'll wait until he leaves the store."

They watched Jacobo on the cameras leave the store with his family, loaded with more packages than they could carry. It looked like Christmas. All the different agents followed him, and when he came close to his car and began to open the trunk to put all the packages in, they surrounded him with their cars, red and blue lights rotating.

They pointed their guns at him and his wife and told them to get on the ground. The children began to scream and cry, clearly scared to death. The agents then dragged the children to one of their cars. The kids were screaming and full of panic at the sight of their parents on the ground with guns to their heads. At the same time, another agent put handcuffs on Jacobo and his wife.

They frisked both of them, and when they were sure neither one had any weapons, put them in separate cars and took them to the courthouse underground floor to the Secret Service headquarters. In the offices of the Secret Service, they were separated and put in different rooms. The agents screamed obscenities at them and told them they would be in jail for twenty years. They threatened to deport them to Mexico after that. They said they would take away their children and they would never see them again. McCain asked Jacobo then, "Where did you get this money?"

Jacobo did not wait to be asked again. "Dr. del Marmol gave it to me."

# Chapter 26—Jacobo's Trap

The next day around two o'clock in the afternoon, I went to the house in Santa Ana where my friends were still burning money. When I arrived, I saw Hernesto through the atrium windows in the dinette with one box of money on his shoulder. I assumed he was taking it to the backyard where they were working. Before I closed the door to my car, I heard my phone ring. I answered, and it was Jacobo, crying like a baby, even harder than he had been the day before.

"What's the matter with you now, man?" I asked him.

He was sobbing. In between sobs he gulped, "Forgive me. Forgive me. Forgive me."

"Calm down, calm down! If you don't, you cannot even explain to me what is going on."

He tried to control himself, and after a few minutes he said, "I tried to negotiate the money you gave me with one of my friends who has connections in Vegas."

"How many times," I interrupted him testily, "have I told you not to talk about money over the phone!" I was growing irritated because he was being careless.

"I'm sorry. I'm sorry. The package you gave to me yesterday in the parking lot at Norm's restaurant in Costa Mesa. I gave the whole package to my friend so I would not jeopardize myself or cause you any problems. The son of a bitch has disappeared. When I went to look for him at his apartment this morning, one of his neighbors told me he had moved last night with all of his family. The neighbor was very suspicious because he had moved in the middle of the night, and this morning there were lots of relatively new things in the trash can and in front of the apartment. Evidently he was in such a hurry, he left behind stuff that was almost brand new."

He paused and then began sobbing again. "Now I am in an even worse situation with my wife. I had showed her all that money—the package you gave me yesterday. Now she not only thinks I am irresponsible but that I am stupid as well to entrust somebody with that. She wants to take the kids to Mexico. She says she will be leaving tonight."

I was sitting in the car, listening to his story. I shook my head and rubbed my forehead. I was infuriated. "Your wife is right. You are not only irresponsible but you are extremely stupid. Why in the world did you give it all to this guy? Why didn't you just give him half or get some kind of collateral from him?"

Jacobo sobbed again, "I have known him since we were kids. I would never have believed he would do that to me."

I shook my head from one side to the other. I could not believe what I was hearing. I said, "What do you want me to do about it? You fucked up. Piss off! I have things to do."

He said again he was sorry, and then he asked, "At least you could give me the five thousand dollars I asked for initially. That way, I can pay my rent and my bills and hold onto my wife."

"I can't believe you have the nerve to ask me for more. I have nothing else to give to you. I'm sorry. I have to hang up now."

"Please, don't hang up! I will be here in my apartment all day. If you change your mind and find room in your heart to forgive me, I will be in gratitude for the rest of my life to you. Please stop by. I beg you. I know I am irresponsible and stupid, but at the same time I am your friend. Have pity on me!"

"I'm sorry, Jacobo. I have to go." I hung up. Evidently he knew me quite well because when I hung up the phone I felt tremendous guilt and remorse. We were burning millions of dollars in the backyard and all Jacobo needed was $5,000. I walked into the house and out onto the back patio where my friends were working. I kept thinking to myself, *No, no. No more. His wife is completely right. He is an irresponsible and stupid son of a bitch.*

Everybody greeted me. Hernesto asked me, "What's wrong, brother? You look pissed off."

"Nothing. How are you guys doing?" I noticed there were more aluminum trash cans there than there had been the day before. "Did you buy more trash cans?"

"Yes," Elizabeth supplied, "we had to. There is too much. In order to burn it completely, we needed more space. We cannot put too much in one can only."

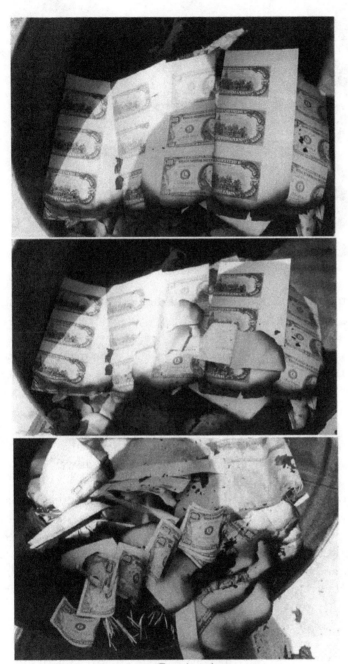

Burning the money

Millions were burned

Hernesto grabbed another box from the floor and dropped it into one of the cans. I said, "Well, at least we are getting there, little by little."

"I don't know," Yaneba said. "Did you see how many boxes are still left in the garage?"

"I think it is going to take more than just a few days to burn all of that," Hernesto added.

"Well," I said, "you guys do what you can. Unfortunately, we do not have an incinerator here, so just do the best you can as quickly as you can. We need to get rid of all this evidence. That way I can tell O'Brien that the Zipper is closed."

I said goodbye to my friends. I went into the house and got a glass and some ice from the refrigerator. I opened the fridge to pour some juice into my glass. I noticed that a few grocery bags that had been stuck in between the refrigerator and the closet had fallen to the floor. I bent over and put them back in place. They were bags from Ralph's supermarket. As I replaced them, I could not help but think of Jacobo and his family, especially his two little kids. I felt guilt and remorse again, and without thinking twice, I took one of the bags and walked through the hallway to the garage.

When I opened the door, there were two open boxes full of money on the floor. I looked up and saw a few closet doors open. They were still full of the boxes of money. I bent down and started to pick up bundles of $10,000 each and put them in the grocery bag until it was

304

about half full. I closed the bag, walked back into the kitchen, and finished my juice. I left the house and went to my Mercedes. I opened the trunk and put the bag of money in it. I closed the trunk, got into the driver's seat, and left the house, driving towards Costa Mesa. I had only gone a few blocks when the car phone rang. It was Loren.

"Hello, it's me. I've been waiting for you because yesterday you said you would pick me up today. It's almost three-thirty, and I wondered if you were going to stop by now, or later, or when?"

"Yes," I said. "Actually I am on my way to Costa Mesa. Where are you?"

"I'm here in my house, waiting for you."

"Very well. I will be there in fifteen or twenty minutes, and we will go to my restaurant. We will sit down in a quiet corner and we will talk."

"Okay," she said. "I'll be here waiting for you. When you arrive, I'll be waiting in the driveway."

"Very well." I hung up.

Twenty minutes later, I arrived at Loren's house. She was waiting in the driveway as she had said. She approached me and got into my car. After we said hello, I told her, "I have to stop at the house of a friend. Actually, it is on our way. I will just be a few minutes."

As we were leaving, the phone rang again. "Hello," I answered. I was a bit surprised to hear Yaneba's voice, since I had just seen her.

"How are you doing?" she asked.

"I'm fine. What's up?"

"Everything is fine. Our friend Alfredo from Miami just called me."

"Oh, yeah—he is the best cook in Miami. What's happening with him?"

"Everything is fine with him," she said. "He asked me when we're going to find time to go over there. That way he can cook a good *paella* for us."

I smiled. "That is not a bad idea."

"No, it is not a bad idea at all. He told me to tell you that Capitan Marrero just arrived in Miami from Cuba a few days ago. He is looking all over the place for you because apparently he has something important to tell you. Who is Capitan Marrero?"

I smiled again. "You don't remember?"

"No," she said in puzzlement. "Who is he?"

305

"Probably if you dig into your memory you will find out who he is. You were very little. Capitan Marrero is the one who prepared the raft that your family used to leave Cuba."

She paused as she tried to remember. A few seconds later, she said, "Oh, yeah—oh, yeah. He is the man who came with the Professor to my house and brought me candy when I was very little. Oh, my God! I dreamed of him and the Professor not too long ago."

"Really!" I said. "What a coincidence."

"What a coincidence indeed. Alfredo gave me his phone number if you want to get in touch with him. Do you want it right now?"

"Well, not right now. I am driving. You can give it to me later, or else you can leave it with my mom and dad. Why don't you call him? He would probably be very happy to hear from you."

"Yes, I will right now. I want to know how he is doing and it will be a great pleasure for me to talk to him."

"Well, I will be busy for a few hours, but you can tell me later about the conversation you had with him."

"I will leave his number with your mom and dad, just in case he wants to talk to you about something personal."

"Okay. Thank you," I replied. "I will call you later."

"Okay. See you later."

We hung up and Loren asked, "How are your mom and dad?"

"They are well."

"You must be very happy to have them with you, huh?"

"Yes. Very happy. I have nearly all my family out of Cuba now except my son. I am making the necessary arrangements right now to get him out of there, too."

"I hope you get him out, too."

"Thank you."

We arrived at Jacobo's apartment complex. I did not park in the regular parking area. I parked on the sidewalk in between apartments in an area very close to his entry door. I got out of the car and opened the trunk. I took out the grocery bag that contained the money. I walked to his door and rang the bell. A few minutes passed. I became impatient and almost left. Then I saw the kitchen curtain open and Jacobo's face looked out to see who was ringing the bell. He waved to me.

This caught my attention because he never had done that before. It took a few more minutes for him to finally open the door. It was as if he were doing something else first. He had a big smile on his face.

306

"Did I catch you in the middle of something?" I asked.

He smiled nervously and answered, "Yeah. I was in the bathroom when you rang the bell." He looked at the heavy grocery bag in my hand and hugged me. "I knew you would not let me down. You have a big heart. You are the best friend I have ever had. I may be stupid, but you know that I am telling you the truth and I am not trying to scam you for more money."

I tried to smile, but I only managed a half-smile as I replied, "I hope so. I hope you are telling me the truth." I had a very strange feeling in my stomach and my chest. The apartment was empty. The silence was overwhelming. "Where are your wife and kids?"

"She is still a little pissed off at me, even though I told her you would probably bring me more money."

I looked at him intently. "You were pretty sure about that, huh? I hope you will take better care of our friendship than you do of your wife and kids."

He remained silent. He put down his head and nodded. "Yes, I will." Usually, when I had been there before, I could hear his kids playing.

The silence was getting on my nerves. Whenever I had visited them before, his wife usually brought me a glass of homemade lemonade with a big smile on her face. She was nowhere to be seen.

I felt very uneasy. I was not aware of it at the time, but the Secret Service agents had installed recording devices in one of the back rooms of Jacobo's apartment and Jacobo was wearing wires on his chest that were connected to those devices. He was sweet talking me, like Judas, to trip me up in the trap the Secret Service had prepared. They were violating legal procedures and regulations, and they had entrapped me by using Jacobo as bait. They used him to get me to bring him more money. That way, they could catch me red-handed and could incriminate me with more charges, convict me, and give me more time in jail.

Of course, at the moment I had no knowledge of Jacobo's conspiracy with the Secret Service and the prearranged deal he had made with them. He had done this in order to lower his own sentence or perhaps even to have no sentence at all without any consideration whatsoever that he was betraying his best friend.

I sat down at the little table in the dining and handed the grocery bag full of $100 bills to my friend, Jacobo, with good will. "I hope that this time you will do exactly what I have been telling you to do. Don't make any more mistakes. This is your last chance. Enjoy this with your family and I hope again that you can patch up your relationship with your wife."

He grabbed the bag and opened it. When he realized it was full of money, he said, "Thank you very much, my friend. I have no words to express my gratitude to you." He put the bag on the table and reached into his pocket. "The only thing I can do for you is to give you this very small present." With that, he gave me five $100 bills and said, "Buy something for your girlfriend or for yourself, and take this as a small token of my gratitude."

I shook my head. "No, thank you. You need that money a lot more than I do. I don't need money at all."

He looked at the grocery bag, smiled, and said, "Yeah, I know. For sure you don't need money! But this is the only way I can keep my dignity. Please don't reject my gift. It is the only way I have to express my gratitude to you. You don't know how hard I had to work to get that real five hundred dollars!"

"I really appreciate it, and that is why I don't want to take it. I want you to keep it."

He stood up. "What is the big deal?" he demanded. "Just put the five hundred dollars in your pocket. That will make me feel much better."

I stood up, angered at his insistence. I snatched the money out of his hand and tossed it onto the table. "Why don't you for once think of others instead of yourself? Stop thinking of how good you will feel and of your dignity! Stop insisting. I don't want the goddamn money. I feel like you are trying to pay me for doing you a favor! Don't insist anymore!"

He realized that he had genuinely angered me and that demands were not going to get him anywhere. He changed his attitude completely. "Okay. Okay, man. You don't have to take it if you don't want it. It's okay. Don't worry about it. I'm sorry. Don't get mad at me." He opened his arms and hugged me. "Do you forgive me? I am a little nervous. I am uptight. I have not slept very much for two or three days. I don't even know what I am doing. I am sorry again."

"Okay, I have to go."

"Before you leave, wouldn't you like a glass of that homemade lemonade my wife makes that you like so much?"

"No, thanks, I have someone waiting for me in the car."

"You are not even going to accept a lemonade from me, man? You are still mad at me?" He walked a few feet and grabbed a foam cup from a long package and showed it to me. "You can take it with you. One for the road."

I was almost to the front door, but I felt bad to leave him without even taking his lemonade, so I turned around and said, "Okay, go ahead."

He went into the kitchen, and although I could not see him I heard him open the door of the refrigerator and the ice and lemonade go into the cup. A few minutes later, he came back into the living room where I was waiting and gave me the cup of lemonade, another big hug, and thanked me again profusely. His embrace was a betrayal, as he slipped the $500 in my pocket without my knowledge.

We said goodbye, and I went to my Mercedes where Loren was patiently waiting for me. I got into the car and slammed the door.

"What happened in there?" she asked. "You look pissed off."

"I don't know. Something is not right." I started the car and drove off slowly down the driveway towards Newport Boulevard. It was a very busy one-way street. Just as I was about to turn right onto the street, a white Firebird slid to a stop right in front of me. I swerved to avoid it.

Loren was scared and screamed, "Watch out!"

"What a crazy idiot!" I exclaimed. Just then, another car did the same thing. I managed to avoid him and then I drove off.

"Who the hell are these people?" Loren asked. "Where are they coming from? They are all driving crazy today!"

I said nothing. I accelerated the car to escape those stupid drivers and turned right onto Newport Boulevard. When I was on the street, I floored the accelerator to get out of there. I looked into my rear mirror and saw that both cars that had nearly hit me had red and blue lights flashing on top. I realized immediately that something was wrong.

I knew the car was clean, so I slowed down, looking for a place to pull over. "Please," I told Loren, "keep your mouth shut. Don't say a word."

She looked at me with fear in her eyes. "What's going on?"

"I don't know. We will find out."

Finally, I saw a little driveway in front of a store which went into the parking lot of Import Auto Parts. I pulled in and stopped my car. As soon as I stopped, the two cars pulled in behind me as well as another two cars. There were four men who came out of each car. They surrounded us and pointed their guns at us.

A tall guy who looked like a football player screamed, "I'm Special Agent Pat McCain of the Secret Service! Get out of the car and put your hands behind your neck."

Loren was terrified, scared to death. On the other side of the car, another guy screamed, "I am Daniel Esquivel, special agent for the Secret Service. Come on, you motherfuckers, get out of the car right now!"

I looked at these men with their guns pulled out and pointed at us like an army. There were sixteen of them! I muttered aloud, "What the hell is this?" I glanced at Loren. "Whatever you do, don't do anything to provoke these people. They are trigger happy. Don't give them any reason to shoot you."

As soon as we opened the door and tried to get out they grabbed us. We were not even able to get completely out of the car before they yanked us out. Two of them grabbed my arms, one on each side, and another one grabbed my neck and doubled me over the convertible roof of my car. They pushed me so hard that I hit my face on one of the metal bars that crossed from one side to the other to hold the convertible roof. This broke my upper lip and chipped one of my teeth. They handcuffed me.

I screamed, "You sons of bitches! What are you doing? You broke my lip! Leave me alone!"

On the other side of the convertible they were doing the same thing to Loren, placing her in handcuffs, as well. David screamed to Pat, "Very good! Very good! We got the big fish!"

Pat pointed to Jacobo, who was in one of the cars. "Bring him over here. I want him to identify this guy."

David went back and brought Jacobo with him. At the same time, Pat was searching me. I realized he was not searching my body. He went directly to the back pocket of my pants. He pulled out a little roll of bills and hollered, "Bingo! We got the whole enchilada here!"

I saw Jacobo next to me and saw the roll of bills in Pat's hand. "What the hell is going on here?"

Jacobo looked at me, ashamed. "I'm sorry. I had no other choice. It was either you or me."

I looked at him and still did not understand what was happening. "You or me? What are you talking about?"

Pat showed me the bills and smilingly said, "Jacobo is working with us. We caught him at Nordstrom's spending the money. Your boy, here, went to Nordstrom's and poured out a lot of cash. A whole hell of a lot of cash." He looked over at David. "Did you check his Mercedes?"

"Yeah," David answered. "It's clean."

Pat signaled to another car. "Clean? Go through it again. We need car evidence. This guy is as guilty and as dirty as they come."

Even though they were pushing me around, I was able to see them take the grocery bag out of one of their cars and put it into my Mercedes. I screamed at the top of my lungs, "Hey, you sons of bitches, that was not in my car! Why are you putting it in there?"

David said smugly, "It is now, pal."

They put us in separate cars and took us away to the basement headquarters of the Secret Service beneath the Santa Ana courthouse.

# Chapter 27—History's Second Biggest Seizure

They took us to different rooms and handcuffed us to our chairs. Loren was in the room next to me and they left the door open intentionally so I could see what they were doing to her.

My tooth was chipped, my lip was cut and swelling, and I had bruises on my arms and all over my body. David came close to my chair and kicked it. I nearly fell to the floor. He said, "You're going to be in jail for forty years. How old are you now? You're in your forties, no? You won't get out until you're in your eighties! You'll be in a wheelchair."

I looked at him and smiled. "I will be out of here before you know it. Everything you think you are going to get for my arrest is going to blow up like smoke out of your ass, you abusive son of a bitch!"

He kicked my chair again. "Shut up or I am going to kick your ass, motherfucker!"

"Yeah," I taunted him, "that is the kind of man you are. You like to kick a man who is defenseless. Let me out of these handcuffs and I will show you what a real man is like."

He grabbed the keys for the handcuffs and came close to me. "Okay, motherfucker. I'm going to release you. Let's see what you've got!"

Pat shouted, "David! What are you doing? Are you fucking crazy or what?" He came over to us and showed David some computer papers that he had in his hands. "I checked this guy, and everything about him is coming back 'Classified.' He escaped Cuba in 1971 and disappeared. We don't know who this guy is working for and we don't know if he's a martial arts expert or heaven knows what. And you're going to release him?"

Two more guys came into the room and took David to the room where Loren was being held. He began to scream obscenities and push her around exactly as he had done to me before. Loren was screaming at him and crying, full of panic. I heard her scream, "Don't touch me, you piece of shit!"

Pat leaned close to me. He saw I was in agony because of what was happening to Loren in the next room. He was playing the good cop. "If you want, you can stop all this. Tell me who you work for and where this money came from. Maybe then I can help you."

I looked him straight in the eyes. "Believe it or not, I have not done anything wrong."

"Well, it looks like we have different ideas of what is right and wrong, *amigo*."

David continued antagonizing Loren in the next room. She was getting hysterical. I began to realize that I had to do something to get her out of there as soon as possible. She was on the brink of a nervous breakdown and that would just complicate things more for me if she said something inappropriate. She did not know much, but she knew enough.

I decided to do something about it. I looked at Pat. "First, tell that son of a bitch to stop antagonizing Loren. Next, bring your boss here. I need to talk to the man who has the power to give immunity to her, and then I will take you to the place where I have twenty or twenty-five million sitting."

He stared at me in disbelief. "What? Twenty-five million? You've got to be shitting me."

"No, I am not. Let me tell you something. I am being very conservative. It could be thirty or forty million."

"David! Stop! Guys, come over here."

They left Loren alone, and all the agents came into my holding room. Pat pulled up a chair and sat down in front of me. He said to the others, "You want to hear something?" He gestured to me. "Come on. Tell them from your mouth what you just told me."

"Well, Loren is technically not even my girlfriend. We broke up. She has nothing to do with this at all. If you guys let her go and you bring your boss and the District Attorney here and they sign an immunity paper for Loren, I will give you between twenty and forty million dollars. I don't know how much money is there."

They all looked at me in shocked disbelief. David screamed, "Bullshit! This Cuban asshole is playing with us."

I smiled a deadly smile. "This Cuban asshole can kick your ass, you fucking moron. A mosquito has more brains than you! Remember what Pat told you just a little while ago? Everything he checked about me came back classified. Do you know who this Cuban asshole is? You don't have any idea, do you? Do you want to blow the opportunity to find all that money? It will make all you guys famous. It will probably be the biggest seizure of counterfeit money in this country. The last time I read the records, you guys made a bust in New York for about eighteen million. Imagine all the grants you guys could get for being the ones who caught me. That is not even counting the brownie points in your records for the biggest seizure in U.S. history. There is no doubt in my mind that this will exceed, even double, the New York one."

David sneered, "I don't believe it."

One agent said, "I believe it."

"I believe it, too," another agent agreed. "This guy is not bullshitting."

Pat said, "I believe it, too."

"Why do we have to negotiate with him?" David demanded. "We can get a court order and search his house. It's probably there or in his office."

I chuckled. "First of all, do you think a guy like me would have something like that in his house? And I don't have an office."

"Yeah," Pat said, "we went to the warehouse in Santa Ana. We went through that place and it was completely clean."

I thought Loren must have said something. I thanked God at that moment that Loren did not know too much about anything else. "Well, I am going to tell you, David, why you should negotiate with me." I kept my eye on the clock on the wall. I wanted to be certain my friends were all out of the house in Santa Ana before I took the agents over there. "First of all, you violated every right in the book. You have been holding me here for over six hours. You cut my lip. You entrapped me at Jacobo's house. I hope your recordings are clear enough to show that I did not want any money from Jacobo in exchange for what I brought to him. That means the dealing count is gone.

"I have a good attorney who will prove that you planted that money in my Mercedes. Remember, I saw you do it and so did Loren. Maybe one of you guys will feel remorse somewhere along the line and tell the truth. What will that leave you guys? Maybe fifty thousand in the hands of Jacobo? When you bring him to testify, maybe he will decide not to testify against me and he might say that you guys intimidated the hell out of him and forced him to plant those five hundred dollar bills when he hugged me in his apartment. What a scandal for you guys! Imagine what the press would say! It would be the biggest fiasco of your careers, especially when Jacobo gets legal advice for himself and realizes he does not have to do what you guys told him to do. You tell me what you want to do. My mouth is sealed now, and I don't intend to waste my saliva anymore. I am done talking."

Pat McCain asked me, "Can you tell us all we want to know?"

"Well, I will tell you what you need to know. I will not tell you everything you want to know because that might incriminate me."

Pat said, "Give me a minute." He took everyone out and into another room. I heard him talking on the phone to somebody. Meanwhile, I could still see Loren in the next room with both hands tied to a chair like me. I managed to bend over and signal her with my finger to my lips to be quiet. I did not want her to say anything that might screw things up. She nodded to me in agreement. Nearly an hour later, they came back.

McCain said, "What exactly do you want in exchange for taking us where you have that huge amount of money? My boss will be here in an hour. He says it shouldn't be a problem. He wants to talk to you, but he wants to know exactly what you want."

"Well, I want three things. The first thing is immunity for Loren. The second is I want my attorney and the DA here when we make this agreement. The third is I want to call my family. I have been out of the house for too long, and my mom and dad might be worried."

McCain smiled in stunned disbelief at what I had just said. "I don't see why not. I'm sure my boss will agree to those three demands. But what about you? Don't you want anything for yourself in exchange?"

"No, I don't want anything. I think I can manage."

"Okay. I have to go and talk to my boss. Do you want a sandwich or something to drink?"

"No, I don't want anything to eat, but I would appreciate it if you would bring me a cup of hot tea. That will help to settle my stomach after all these hours of being pushed around. Would you please ask Loren if she wants anything because it has been several hours."

"Sure, I'll ask her." He went into the other room and asked Loren if she wanted something to eat. I heard him say to her, "Everything is going to be okay. We're working right now on your release. You'll probably sleep at home tonight."

Loren asked him for a Coke and a sandwich because she had not had anything in her stomach all day. She asked Pat, "What about him? Will he sleep at home tonight, too?"

315

McCain smiled. "No, I doubt it. He's going to be with us for a while, unless he's a great magician. If what he's telling me is true and he has this huge amount of money, I don't think you'll be seeing him for a while."

Loren looked at me through the cracked door in sad sympathy. I had heard the whole conversation. I smiled and shook my head.

McCain left the room and told David, "Will you please go and get a sandwich and a Coke for Loren? Bring a hot tea for Dr. del Marmol."

"Actually," David replied, "we have tea right here. I can make some."

"Fine. Make the tea and then go and get her something to eat."

Pat left the room with the others to call his boss. David went to the little kitchen to make tea for me. He came back with a pot full of boiling water and a foam cup with a tea bag. The chair I was sitting in was like one used in primary school, with a wider surface like a small table on the right side so you could write. He put the cup down on the wide arm of my chair. "There you go, Dr. del Marmol. This is your tea. Do you want sugar in it, or do you want honey?" he asked with a strong tone of irony. He began to pour the water into the cup.

I looked at him but did not answer. I realized something was cooking in his mosquito brained mind and it could not be anything nice. Sure enough, a few seconds later, as he was filling the cup, he continued to pour until it was running over. He then pushed the cup with the pot, causing the hot water to spill all over my groin.

"Oh, I'm sorry!" he said as he continued to pour the hot water on me. I screamed in pain, and although handcuffed to my chair, I pushed it back and hit something behind me. "You son of a bitch!" I screamed at David. "You burned my balls, motherfucker!"

Pat and the other agents heard me scream and opened the door and burst into the room to find out what was going on. "What happened?" Pat demanded.

"It was an accident, man," David said, still holding the pot of boiling hot water in his hand.

"Bullshit!" I screamed. "He poured it in my lap intentionally! Take this sexually frustrated motherfucker out of my sight, or I will not talk to you anymore!"

David turned towards me, still holding the pot in his hand. "What the fuck did you say?"

"Your wife probably left you for another man because you have such a small weenie. That is why you wanted to burn mine! Psychopath!"

He moved towards me aggressively. He probably intended to pour the rest of the boiling water on me, but the other agents grabbed him and took him out of the room. Pat told one of the agents to release me from the handcuffs and take me to the bathroom to check for injury. The agent said, "Don't try anything crazy, please. Okay?"

"It's going to be hard for me to even walk, let alone try anything after that son of a bitch made boiled eggs out of my balls!"

He released me from the chair, cuffed my hands behind me, and took me to the bathroom. Another agent followed us closely. When we got to the bathroom, he took off my cuffs so I could check myself out. My penis and testicles were red like a lobster. It looked as if I had been sunbathing with no clothes on in the desert. I showed it to the agent. "Look! Look at this!"

"Oh, man," the agent muttered and looked away.

"I hope they don't fall off later! I need some cream or something, man!"

"Don't worry," the agent said. "Later on, when we book you, we'll tell them what happened and ask that you be examined by a doctor."

I stepped up to the sink and poured cold water on myself. It made me feel a little better. I dried myself with paper towels and put my pants back on. I washed my hands and then the agent handcuffed me again and we went back into the room.

When we returned, Pat was waiting for me. "Okay. My boss says you can make your phone call. We need the phone number of your attorney so we can call him, and the Assistant DA is on his way. The DA isn't available right now."

I said, "The card for my attorney is in my wallet over there on top of your desk." I pointed to it.

He went to the desk and looked in my wallet. "Is his name Jerry Tolan?"

"Yes, that is the man."

"Do you want to make your phone call now? I'll go to another office and call your attorney."

They changed my handcuffs from the back to the front and asked me for the number that I wanted to call. I gave them my father's number. They dialed, and a couple of rings later my father answered. "Hello?"

"Dad, it's me."

"What are you doing? Are you okay? It's nearly one o'clock in the morning!"

"Yes dad. I am sorry to wake you up by calling you this late, but I have been arrested for manufacturing counterfeit money."

"Is it true?"

"Yes, but it's not what it seems to be. I will explain to you later. Don't worry about it. I am going to be okay. Listen to me very carefully. Are you awake now?"

"Yes. Go ahead," he said.

"I want everybody around me to know what happened this afternoon," I told him. "I have been here for several hours, being interrogated by the Secret Service. I want everybody to know what happened to me. Do you understand?"

"Your friends?"

"Yes, dad. Everybody should know. Tell everyone not to worry about it. I will be okay. I will probably be released soon."

"Do you need anything?" he asked.

"Yes, tell my friends to cancel their trips because I will probably need their help eventually. I want them to stay close to you in your house and don't go anywhere else until I contact them."

Pat returned to the room and said, "I'm sorry." He signaled that I had to hang up.

I said, "I'm sorry, Dad, I have to go. Tell everyone in the family not to worry. Everything is going to be okay with me."

I could tell by his voice that my father was worried. "Are you sure?"

"Absolutely sure," I said with a smile.

"Okay. God bless you. Goodbye, son."

We hung up, and I felt much better having talked to him.

"My boss Albert is here," Pat said. "He wants to talk to you."

A tall, skinny, bug-eyed man with a long neck and greasy hair walked into the room. He dressed in an old, long-outdated polyester suit. "I understand you want to talk to me."

"If you are the man who can make the final decisions, then yes, I want to talk to you."

Pat changed my handcuffs again from the front to the back, and then they walked me to a different room where there was a long conference table.

When we were all in the room they changed the cuffs again, this time securing me to one of the chairs.

Albert sat down at the head of the table and put some papers down in front of him. "Okay, you can start talking anytime you want."

I smiled and motioned to the other men who were there. "Not in front of these people. I need to talk to you in private."

They all looked at each other and Pat said, "Oh, man. Are you going to start playing games again with us?"

"No, sir," I answered. "I am going to talk with your boss. This is between him and me only. It is off the record. If he wants to share with you guys later, that is up to him."

They all looked at Albert and he said, "Sure, why not? Would you guys please excuse us?"

They all stepped out of the room and I looked straight into his eyes. "Listen carefully to what I am going to say. I do not like to repeat myself. If you are not the one who can make the big decisions here, I want you to let me know now."

"Well, you already have what you asked for. Your attorney will be here any minute, as will the Assistant DA. We're ready to sign an immunity agreement for your girlfriend. You've already made your phone call. So far, we've gotten nothing from you except your word that you have over twenty million dollars someplace that you're going to turn over to us."

"And I will," I interrupted him. "I mean what I say, and I say what I mean. But what we are going to talk about here may be over your head. I just want to be sure that you have the authority to handle it."

"Go ahead. I've already told you I do have that authority."

"Our agreement is that Loren will be released from here tonight and will sleep in her own house, she will have immunity, and will not be bothered in the future. You know the rest.

"Now, there is another agreement that we are going to talk about. The people that are behind this counterfeit work are decent people, believe it or not, and they really love this country very much. Under no circumstances will I reveal anyone's name, but if you sweep this under the rug and stop this investigation right now as if it never happened, I promise you that in exchange I will give you information on other cases unrelated to this that will make your department the prime Secret Service office in the nation."

He leaned forward with his elbows on the table, put his head on his hands and said quietly, "Who are you?"

"Just a crazy, simple, Cuban freedom fighter."

"Freedom fighter? What is that? Who is your boss?"

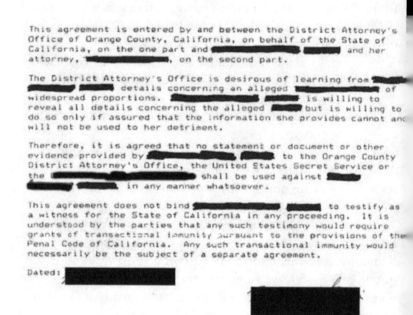

This agreement is entered by and between the District Attorney's Office of Orange County, California, on behalf of the State of California, on the one part and ▓▓▓▓▓▓▓▓▓▓ ▓▓▓▓ and her attorney, ▓▓▓▓▓▓▓, on the second part.

The District Attorney's Office is desirous of learning from ▓▓▓ ▓▓▓▓ ▓▓▓▓ details concerning an alleged ▓▓▓▓▓▓▓▓▓▓ of widespread proportions. ▓▓▓▓▓▓▓▓▓▓ ▓▓▓ is willing to reveal all details concerning the alleged ▓▓▓ but is willing to do so only if assured that the information she provides cannot and will not be used to her detriment.

Therefore, it is agreed that no statement or document or other evidence provided by ▓▓▓▓▓▓▓, ▓▓▓ to the Orange County District Attorney's Office, the United States Secret Service or the ▓▓▓▓▓▓▓▓▓ shall be used against ▓▓▓ ▓▓▓▓ in any manner whatsoever.

This agreement does not bind ▓▓▓▓▓▓▓▓▓▓ ▓▓▓ to testify as a witness for the State of California in any proceeding. It is understood by the parties that any such testimony would require grants of transactional immunity pursuant to the provisions of the Penal Code of California. Any such transactional immunity would necessarily be the subject of a separate agreement.

Dated: ▓▓▓▓▓▓▓▓▓▓▓▓▓▓▓▓

▓▓▓▓▓▓▓▓▓▓▓▓▓▓▓▓
Deputy District Attorney
Orange County, California

**Immunity document for Loren**

I sat back in my chair and looked at him. "I don't have any boss. If you don't know what a freedom fighter is, then I think we should discontinue this conversation right now."

"Alright, I know what a freedom fighter is. I know. What you ask me is impossible. As soon as we get the twenty million you say you have, we're going to call a press conference. We're going to expose it all over the world. I'm sorry, but that's too much money to sweep under the rug. That would make a mountain!"

"I don't care if you sweep it under the rug, drop it in the toilet, or throw it in the ocean. All I can tell you is all this money is trash. It is just left over from what we did. The good money is already gone, and as we are talking, it is on the way to serving its purpose. Believe it or not, I want to avoid you and your agency having the biggest embarrassment in the history of the United States. If you put this in the newspapers, then that is exactly what you will have. Please don't tell me later that I did not warn you.

"If you notice, I have not asked for anything in exchange for myself," I continued. "The reason is I know that I will get out of this untouched in a few months, if not before. Very, very soon, this will all be just smoke. There will be no trial. That would be detrimental to this nation, to your agency, as well, because of all the things you have done to me, from entrapment in the beginning to burning my balls with a pot of boiling water in your office. In other words, you should be very happy that this will never go to the court."

He looked at me in silence while he stroked his chin. Finally, he said, "Let me see if I can comprehend what you're telling me, Dr. del Marmol. You want me to release you in exchange for some future information you *say* will make us the prime Secret Service office in the nation. You want us to give your convertible Mercedes back to you. It's probably worth about eighty thousand dollars. And you expect us to sweep under the rug the twenty million you're going to give us for releasing your girlfriend? Don't you think you're asking for a little too much?"

"Not really," I answered. "Considering I am going to prevent you from making the biggest mistake of your career as a Secret Service supervisor or whatever you are and making a fool of yourself in front of the nation. This case is going to go up in smoke in a few weeks or months, and that smoke will get in your eyes and make you cry."

He smiled. "Is that a Cuban saying?"

"I only speak the truth. I am trying to help you. If the press gets hold of this and turns it around, the good principles that this work has been done for will be destroyed. This whole thing can turn out to be a political scandal and will do nothing but will destroy the future credibility of the leaders of this country."

He crossed his leg and looked at me in concern. "You mean to tell me," he asked me quite seriously, "that some of the political leaders in this country are involved in this?"

"I'm sorry," I said. "I cannot tell you anymore. It is up to you to make your decision. I have already given you my warning and I have told you all I can."

He maintained his silence for a few minutes. I looked at him, thinking that this pencil-necked bureaucrat did not understand anything I had told him. He surprised me when he answered me. "You know what? I'll call Washington and discuss this with my boss. Meanwhile, you take Pat McCain and the others to wherever you have the money and we'll talk some more later."

"No so fast, my friend," I said. "First, we sign the document that will release Loren. I want to see her free and out of here. Then I will take you guys to the money."

Just then, someone knocked at the door and Albert said, "Come in." Pat McCain showed his face around the door. "The attorney and the Assistant DA are here now. What do you want me to do?"

"We're finished already," Albert said decisively. "Send them in." My attorney came in and greeted me. They typed up the immunity letter, and the Assistant DA signed it. They brought Loren into the room.

My attorney kept a copy of the letter and gave another copy to Loren after removing her handcuffs.

Albert asked me, "Do you want one of my agents to drive your girlfriend home, or do you want your attorney to do it?"

Before I could answer, Loren said, "No, I don't want your agent to drive me."

I said to my attorney, "Mr. Tolan, could you drive her home?"

"No problem," he said.

Before they left, I said to Loren, "You go home and don't worry about me. I will take care of myself."

Albert said, "Okay, now we've done our part. It's your turn to do yours."

"Let's go," I said. "I am ready."

Loren left with my attorney, and the Assistant DA left. Before he left, Albert said to me, "We'll talk later."

Julio Antonio's mug shot

# Chapter 28–My Son's Murderers

The Secret Service agents took me to the underground garage. As we were coming out of the elevator, I saw another group of agents coming out of the next elevator. One of them, I noticed immediately, was David Esquivel. I thought they had taken him away, but here he was again. Evidently he was the "bad" cop. He walked ahead and tried to get into the car that McCain and I were going to get into.

"No," Pat yelled at him. "You go with the others in the other car."

He said nothing but got into the other car. We left, and they followed us. I told them what direction to take. We drove for a while, and when we got to the border between Santa Ana and Fountain Valley, I told them to turn onto Regent Drive.

Pat looked at me and smiled. "You son of a bitch. This is the only residence we found in your name on the computer. Don't tell me you have the money here?"

"You do the obvious," I replied, "and you throw off everybody." I shook my head. "This is probably the last place you would think a guy like me would have the money."

He smiled and shook his head. "You are fucking right."

When we got to the house, I opened the gate for them. David came out of the car screaming, "You see that son of a bitch! I told you. He's got that money in his own house!"

"Lower your voice, for God's sake," Pat said reprovingly. "It's three o'clock in the morning. You'll wake up all the neighbors."

I smiled and looked at David, who was clearly furious. We opened the garage, and to my surprise, the red DeLorean and black Mercedes sedan were still there. I smiled because I realized my friends had put them there in order to make it more difficult to get to the closets. I did not have the keys to those cars, and I told the agents I did not remember where they were. We put the cars in neutral, and David and the others had to push them halfway out of the garage. Then I opened one of the closets and showed them the boxes full of money. When they opened the first box, David's mouth dropped open.

Dr. del Marmol's residence

Residence Kitchen

"Oh, my God!" he exclaimed. "There must be millions in here."

They began to unload the boxes into their cars. There were so many boxes they had to make two trips back to the office as they could not get them all in the cars at once. When the closets were nearly empty, David dropped one of the boxes of money onto the hood of the DeLorean.

"Catch it, Pat," he said as he slid it across to McCain. "This is the last one." The box left deep scratches on the hood. It ruined the beautiful red paint, which was very hard to find. It was made especially for use on stainless steel and was used primarily on fighter airplanes to resist the weather and the high velocity. To repair the damage would cost a few thousand dollars.

I looked at David. If looks could kill, he would have been dead right there. I said, "You are not only an asshole, you are a jealous motherfucker, too."

He smiled. "Oops. The paint on your beautiful sports car is damaged. Another accident."

McCain looked at him. "Why'd you do that? The guy's cooperating with us."

"It was an accident, man," David protested. "I didn't think it would do any harm. It must be pretty delicate paint!"

I shook my head and looked at Pat McCain. I asked myself if he was actually defending me or if he was just playing the "good" cop in order to earn my trust. It did not take long for me to realize the truth.

I said, "Let's put the cars back and get out of here."

McCain said, "No. No, man. We've got to go into your house for a routine check."

"That is not in the agreement. You don't have to check my house. I did not give you consent to search my house. Besides, I don't have the keys to my house with me." I looked around and already two of the agents were pulling axes and crowbars out of the trunk of one of their cars. I glared at McCain. "You guys are a bunch of fucking liars."

"I'm sorry, man. We have to do our job." McCain put me in the car and handcuffed me once more. From the car I watched him lead the others to my house and saw them break down the door which led from the garage into the house.

My next door neighbor, Mel, apparently heard the commotion as they were breaking down the door. He stuck his head over the cement wall and asked, "Hey! What's going on out here?"

"We're Secret Service," one of the agents said. "It's none of your business. Get back to your house."

"You don't have to talk to me like that," Mel snapped back. "First of all, Dr. del Marmol is my neighbor and my friend. You made it my business when you woke me up at three o'clock in the morning with all this noise. How the hell do I know that you guys are really Secret Service? You could be robbers."

325

Pat McCain heard that and got out of the car. He flashed his badge at Mel and said, "Calm down. Dr. del Marmol is in the car. He's been arrested for possession of counterfeit currency."

One of the agents pulled me out of the car so Mel could see me. I raised my arms and showed him the handcuffs. "Thank you, Mel. Don't worry. Everything will be okay. I will see you soon."

Mel was surprised, a little angry, and kind of confused. "Okay. Okay. You guys have a good night."

McCain put me back in the car, and they drove back to the Secret Service offices. I found out later they had made a big mess in my house. They even took the only pistol I had registered from my house from under my pillow in the master bedroom.

When we got back to the offices, the agents were really happy. They were counting the money, and one of them said to McCain with a huge grin, "We've already broken the record. We've counted over twenty million dollars, and look at all those boxes that are still there to be counted. There must be three or four million more in there!"

They put me in a holding cell. I was so exhausted from all that had happened that I fell asleep for a little while. It was around 4:30 in the morning when Pat and David came to my cell. "Get up," Pat said. "Let's go. We're going to take you downtown to be booked."

"Finally," I said. "After twelve hours."

They took me to what was called "the glass house" in downtown LA. At about 5:30, the guard came over to inform me I had a visitor. I was escorted to a small interrogation room in the back. A man with black hair, graying at the temples, and wearing thick-lensed glasses sat there, still wearing his raincoat. "Sit down," he said. "I'm Sam Bailey, director of the Secret Service. I flew here from Washington just to speak with you. I expect your complete honesty. Albert told me about his conversation with you. I know this is more than strange, as your background is a complete question mark, no matter how deeply I dig. I'm here to offer you a deal. Tell me who's behind you. I know you don't have the resources to manufacture twenty-three-and-a-half million on your own. Something huge has to be behind this. If you give me a name, I promise to place you in a witness protection program."

When he mentioned the $23.5 million, I smiled and chuckled softly, since he didn't know the full extent of what we'd done. He looked at me strangely, as all he saw was a man in deep trouble smiling confidently. "Did I say something funny?" he asked in irritation.

"Yes," I replied. "You think that was a lot? That was just the trash that we were burning. The leftovers."

He looked at me strangely again. "You're either cynical or crazy."

"Maybe a little bit of both," I said.

"All I need is for you to tell me who's behind this," he repeated. "There will be no appearance; I have the power to take you from here to wherever I want."

I reclined in my chair, and said, "Mr. Bailey, as I already told your man in charge of the Los Angeles branch, there's no motive for me to make a deal, as this is bigger than either of us can realize. If I can get from you what I couldn't get from Albert, I can save your agency from looking ridiculous and save myself and my family from embarrassment by releasing this in the press, and we can prevent you from exposing something which could greatly damage the security of this nation. It's a very simple question here, and it's up to you tonight to decide. Don't put this in the newspapers, forget it ever existed, take me someplace in your car, and drop me someplace where I can take a taxi. In return, I will give you information unrelated to this that will be even bigger than you could possibly imagine. What's it going to be? You take me and the money to court, or you let me go?"

He looked at me and said, "Then you're not going to tell me who or what is behind all of this?"

"I'm making you a bigger offer than you just made to me. First of all, I don't need your witness protection program. Second, you need me a lot more than I need you. If you don't do as I suggest for you to do, you will wind up with the biggest embarrassment of your career."

He sat back in his chair and said, "I'm sorry. I can't do as you say. This is too big, and I see I've wasted my trip. You'll be arraigned tomorrow and spend the rest of your life in prison."

"No, I won't. I'll be out of this in a few months. You do what you have to do, and I will do what I have to do. Thank you for your visit."

He called the guard, who took me back to my cell.

The next morning at around 8:00, they took me to court and pressed charges against me. They put me in a room with my attorney, Jerry Tolan, to arrange our case. I was happy to see him and thought he would be compassionate and try to console me.

But the first thing he said was, "This doesn't look good at all. You're in shit up to your neck. I need twenty thousand dollars to represent you."

"Okay, no problem. This is not going to go to trial, anyway."

"Well, I need twenty thousand anyway as a retainer before I can show up in court."

"Jerry, I thought we were friends. You know they have probably frozen my accounts. Even if they have not done that, we have to be in court in thirty minutes. How in the hell can I produce twenty thousand dollars right now? Later I will give you twenty or thirty thousand, or whatever you want. But I can't do it right now!"

"What if you never get out or it takes a long time for you to get out?"

I shook my head in disbelief. "You are my friend and my criminal attorney. You have come all the way here and now you tell me I am never going to get out of here? What kind of friend are you, man? Don't you think I can beat this?"

"It's not that," Jerry said. "I'm just being realistic. I've got to look out for my interest. You're my friend, but I have to feed my family. Now, don't get touchy. I simply have to look at the odds. Truthfully, yours don't look very good."

"Okay," I said. "Okay, Jerry. How do you think I can produce twenty thousand dollars for you at this minute? We have only twenty-five minutes now before we have to be in court. I didn't sleep last night. I have been beat up, insulted, degraded, and they burned my balls, and now you, my friend and my attorney, come early in the morning to kick my ass."

Without any consideration for what I was going through, he handed me a piece of paper and a pen. "Well, you have a house. You have a bunch of cars. You have a boat. Just write down whatever you choose for me to hold as collateral for the retainer. Because you're my friend."

I threw him a withering stare. I wondered what was wrong with him—if this was supposed to be my friend, I certainly did not want to see my enemies. I took the pen and started to write. "I am going to give you a document that state you get the black Mercedes in my house on Regent Drive which is worth around thirty-five thousand dollars as collateral for the twenty thousand I owe you for representing me today and for as long as this case lasts." I signed it and put my social security number at the bottom of the page and dropped it on the table in front of him. "Is this good enough for you, Jerry? I don't want you to touch that car or take it anywhere. In the next few days, I will put the twenty thousand in your hand."

He looked at the paper. "Do you know your driver's license number by heart?"

"No, I don't remember it right now, Jerry. Why? What do you need it for?"

"Well, that would make the agreement more legal." I leaned back in my chair and shook my head. He realized I was frustrated, and so he said, "It's okay. It's fine. This is good enough. Now we're in business. Let's go. We've only got about fifteen minutes."

"Yes," I said, "but before we go I need to tell you something. I got a speeding ticket that is due in a few days. I need you to go and pay it or get an extension. I don't want any more problems from neglecting this and then it will be on my record. Please make sure you take care of this."

"Don't worry," he said. "Don't worry. Let's go. We're going to be late in court."

He took off for the courtroom and the jailer took me to the holding cell. About twenty minutes later, he came to get me and take me to the courtroom.

The judge pounded his gavel. The prosecutor said, "Your Honor, we move to deny any bail for Dr. del Marmol. We found a plane ticket to the Caribbean Islands in his possession when we arrested him."

"A one-way ticket?" the judge smiled.

"No, Your Honor, it was round trip."

"Well, then—what are you worried about?"

"He is a very well-connected man. We have reason to believe he might fly out of the country and not come back, especially since he is not a U. S. citizen. He has nothing to lose. He is only a resident of the United States. Dr. del Marmol has been caught by the Secret Service in possession of twenty-three-point-five million dollars in U.S. counterfeit currency, the highest seizure in this country's history."

"What does the defense have to say?" the judge asked.

Jerry rose and said, "Your Honor, Dr. del Marmol is an exceptional resident of the United States. He is well-established in Orange County for over fifteen years. He owns several businesses, including one beautiful restaurant. I ask Your Honor to consider all this and to grant bail to Dr. del Marmol, as he is not going to leave all this behind, including his family. His parents just arrived recently from Cuba, and he has signed immigration documents accepting the responsibility to support them and to care for them."

"Anything else, counsel?"

"No, Your Honor. That is all."

The judge raised his gavel and brought it down hard. "Bail denied."

Everything went very fast. Jerry shrugged his shoulders and the bailiff took me away to a holding cell in back of the courtroom. About twenty minutes later, they handcuffed my hands and feet, put me and some other inmates in a bus, and took us to the Terminal Island prison in San Pedro.

They put me in a holding cell with all types of inmates who had been accused of different federal violations. I leaned against a wall. A short distance away from me were eight Mexican inmates who were talking among themselves. The one who looked like he might be their leader approached me.

He held out his hand. "I am Juan. What is your name, man?"

I hesitated for a few seconds. I looked at him and saw that he was friendly and humble but also looked as if he were street savvy. At that moment, I needed a friendly face, so I shook hands with him. "I am J. Anthony. Can I help you?"

"Do you speak Spanish?"

"Yes. Can I help you with something?"

"Hey, man—you're famous in here because of all those millions you made. My buddies and I are here to help you if you need us. Remember, we all need help in here."

I smiled. "Thank you. I guess so. If you need anything, you can come to me. By the way, how did you know I made millions?"

"Man, don't you know? You are all over the TV and the newspapers and everywhere. They say in the papers you are the kingpin, the brain for the whole job."

I shook my head. "All over the newspapers?"

"Yeah, and the TV. Everywhere. You're on the Spanish channel, the Korean channel. They even interrupted the summer Olympics to broadcast your arrest."

I shook my head again and muttered to myself, "Oh, man. That guy Sam is a royal imbecile. He didn't listen to a thing I said to him."

"What?" asked Juan.

"Never mind," I answered.

Juan gestured for his buddies to come closer. The rest of the guys came all around me and introduced themselves to me, and we all shook hands.

"Hey, man," Juan said, "I need to consult you about something."

"What is going on?"

"Between us we have about ten thousand dollars hidden in our belts. Now, we know they are going to take our clothes and our belts

330

and put them someplace and give us uniforms. What do you think we should do?"

"Why don't you declare that money, and then they would have to give it back to you when you are released?"

"No, man. The last time we got arrested for smuggling illegal aliens across the border, we gave the money to the border patrol agents and they never returned it."

"This is different from what happened to you then. Here they have to record and write down everything you give to them, and they have to give you a receipt. Last time you were arrested, you were in the middle of nowhere and it was their word against yours. That is why they took advantage of you."

"Then do you think we should report it now?"

"If it were me, I would, but it is up to you. It is your decision. It is your money, not mine."

They all smiled and shook my hand again, and Juan said, "Thank you for your advice."

The guards came and ordered us to take off our clothes and brought us the uniforms to put on instead. They went through the booking procedure, and a few hours later I was in a cell with three other inmates.

That night, they took us to dinner. I saw Juan and the others and we sat down at the same table. Juan sat down next to me and said, "Be careful in here. They say out of every five inmates, one is an informant. Don't trust anyone in here, especially the one who has already been found guilty and has a long sentence. They will do anything to reduce their sentence. I know because I have been here quite a few times."

"Thank you, my friend."

We finished dinner, they put us in a line, and then took us back to the building where our cells were connected to the recreation room. A guard yelled loudly, "No food from the dining room is allowed in the cells. If anybody has any food in their pockets, drop it on your way out in the trash cans at the door. If we catch anybody smuggling food they're going to sleep in the hole tonight."

I observed a lot of guys dropping bread and muffins in the trash cans on the way out. While we were in the recreation room, they allowed us to watch TV for a couple of hours before putting us in our cells for the night.

Meanwhile, our people were spreading the money we had made all over the world. It was being used to destroy and hinder Castro's plans and intelligence everywhere, and to prevent him from taking over and controlling other countries.

For instance, in East Germany, an officer had received a briefcase full of American money at the border. In exchange, he allowed large trucks to cross the checkpoint and enter East Germany. These trucks contained blue jeans, tape recorders, and all kinds of Western goodies that were given to students all over East Germany to show them how the Western world lived. As a result of this, the students rose up in protest against the government. I was really caught by surprise to see this on TV. Massive numbers of people were tearing down the Berlin Wall with hammers and whatever they could find.

Later on, I found out from my intelligence connections that the freedom fighters in Cuba had been receiving arms, ammunition, medicine, and all kinds of aid due to the money we had made.

The police in Mexico and other countries carried out massive arrests of groups that were anti-government and had been involved in terrorist acts and had been disturbing the democratic process in those countries. In Russia, big political changes were taking place.

In Cuba, Fidel Castro was extremely angry with all these recent events. He threw a bottle of rum against the wall in his office during a meeting with his closest circle of International Counterintelligence aides. He demanded an explanation for all these setbacks.

One of his aides came close to him and put my picture on his desk. "My commander-in-chief, the Lightning is the main source behind all of this."

Castro grabbed a knife and stabbed the picture on the wooden desk. The knife stuck into the wood and vibrated back and forth. "Why can't we get this guy?" he screamed. "We can send a man anywhere to kill someone, but why can't we get this guy?"

The aide said, "This man has very strong connections with the high intelligence of the United States and other countries. He moves too fast from one country to another. We can never track him down. He never spends more than a few days in the same place." He pulled out another picture and smiled. "But he has a son here in Cuba." With that, he slid a picture of my son next to mine.

Castro smiled. "Aha! The son of a bitch! Why didn't you tell me this before now? We should have used this kid a long time ago to hurt that motherfucker!" With that, he pulled the knife out of my picture and plunged it down into the picture of my son.

A few days later, I received a letter in my cell. It was from Sandra, and it read:

*My love, it destroys me to tell you this, but today our son, our baby boy, was killed. It happened on his way home from school. He loves to ride the motorcycle you sent him and as he rode toward home, one of the army trucks came up the road behind him and ran over him. The people who saw it said he didn't suffer. Please don't blame yourself. He loved that motorcycle and was so proud of it. I will make sure he has the most beautiful funeral in all of Cuba. I know you loved him. I wish he had a chance to meet you and see what a fine man his father is.*

*All my love, Sandra.*

I began to cry like a baby. I screamed in anguish and pounded the wall with my fist until it was covered in blood. I could not have received worse news and it came at a time when I was already feeling so down and neglected. I was in agony. Juan and the other Hispanics looked over at me with pity. I was crying like a little boy.

"Why?" I sobbed. "Not my son! He was only twenty-three years old. Why him? Oh, no…."

Later on, I found out that my son was riding his motorcycle on the street in Havana when the army truck came up behind him. The faceless driver held up a picture of my son. He got close to my boy, accelerated the truck, and rear-ended the motorcycle with tremendous power. This caused my son to be thrown from the cycle, and he hit his head on an electrical pole. The motorcycle was completely destroyed. Even though my son was wearing a helmet, the impact was so tremendous he sustained a severe concussion. They rushed him to the hospital where he died moments later of a massive hemorrhage of the brain. The driver of the truck and the truck itself disappeared into thin air. No one knew who it was; they only knew it was an army truck.

At the funeral for my boy, Sandra displayed his picture. It was the same picture with my boy's smiling face that the truck driver had been holding in his hand when he ran over him. Later, my friends told me that he looked identical to me during my last days in Cuba when I escaped through Guantanamo Bay.

My son Julio Antonio Marmol Jr

I drowned in my sorrow for a few days. I was not even able to eat anything. I could only sleep. One evening while everyone else was having dinner in the dining room, I woke up sweating with a high fever. I don't know if it was my fever or what, but I saw Jesus right in front of me. He was wearing a white robe such as He wore in Biblical times, when He traveled from one village to another in Galilee. I saw His dusty feet in sandals first, and when I looked up I saw His smiling face, and there was a shining glow all around Him.

"Jesus," I asked, "what are you doing here?"

"I just came to comfort you," He said. "Your son is with Me. He will be with My Father. You should not torment yourself. It is not your fault. He is too good for this world."

I could not believe my eyes. "Is it really You, Jesus?" I asked. "Do I have a high fever? Am I delirious, or is this real?"

"No," He answered. "Your fever is not that high. I have also come to tell you that everything is going to be okay. Don't torment yourself. You will be out of this. All you have to do is what I am going to tell you now."

I listened to Him serenely. I felt extremely calm and peaceful, as if He were lifting a great weight off of my shoulders. When He finished telling me step by step what I should do, I replied to Him, humbly and gratefully, "I thank You from the bottom of my heart for Your protection and Your advice. I will do everything You told me except for one thing."

"What is that?"

"You said to tell Loren everything that has happened and to entrust her with all my heart and my soul with my deepest secrets if I want to keep her with me for the rest of my life. To be truthful with You, I don't know if I want to keep her or not. I love You and I respect You, but I cannot do that because I don't trust her. Even though You are telling me to do this and You know a lot more than I do, You were in this world in another time. People are different these days. I cannot afford to take another chance with her."

He smiled, perhaps slightly sadly. "My son, then you will lose her."

"What will be, will be," I said in acceptance.

"Sleep well. Everything will be well for you."

"I thank you, Jesus."

"You are welcome, My son. Remember, everything bad they do against you will be like salt and water. The salt will dissolve like the bad things they will try to do to you, and you will be fine."

My father was a Mason and believed in a Supreme Being whom they called the Master Architect of the Universe, or God. My mother was a Catholic, and she believed in everything. If someone told her that putting a broom with the sweeping end up was bad luck, then my mother never put the broom that way. I never embraced any religion and even though my mother was a Catholic, I was not baptized until I was eleven years old and only because my uncle insisted on it.

I believed there was a supreme being, like my father, and I believed God or somebody had created the universe, but I was never completely convinced of either theory, Creation or Evolution. But after that day when I saw Jesus, something strange happened in my life. I began to read about the life of Jesus. I did not attend church, but I came to the conclusion that any other man who had been put in the position of Jesus to save his life would have said he was not the son of God. But He didn't, and He died saying He was the Son of God. As He hung on the cross with nails in his hands and feet, betrayed by his disciple Judas and denied three times by another disciple, Peter, He still said, "Father, forgive them for they know not what they do."

I put myself in His place and imagined He must have felt a lot of disappointment. He had spent His life helping and curing others, and now they were shouting to crucify Him.

In my heart, I knew that He had to be the Son of God. I had never met a man on this earth with those extraordinary qualities. How could a man with those qualities be a liar and tell us He was the Son of God if He were not?

That is why I did exactly as He told me to do.

# Chapter 29—Mind Games

The next day I was feeling a lot better. I felt comforted and not alone anymore. I called my father, and he told me that everybody was safe. No one was in trouble. I asked my father to make sure that if Loren needed help of any kind, he would tell Hernesto or any of my other friends.

Then I tried to call O'Brien on his emergency number for the third time. Previously there had been no answer. To my surprise, this time there was a recording that said the phone had been disconnected. I shook my head and thought to myself, *This is not good.*

After I talked with my father, I heard on the loudspeaker that I had visitors. It was Pat McCain, Albert, and David. I went to a little room where they were waiting for me. They had newspapers on the table from several different states, with various headlines:

*$23,500,000 in Counterfeit Money Confiscated by Secret Service Agents in Los Angeles. Biggest Seizure in the History of the United States. 20 Million in Bogus Bills Seized, Man Arrested. Restaurant Owner Arrested in 22 Million Counterfeit Case. 20 Million in Fake Currency Seized, Man Arrested, Says He Did Nothing Wrong. Mastermind Says He Did Nothing Wrong. Richest Counterfeit Bust of All Time.*

Pat said, "You are a famous man."

David said, "Not really famous. Infamous."

I remained standing. "What do you guys want?"

Albert pointed to a chair. "Sit down."

"I don't have to sit down. What do you guys want?"

David pointed to the papers and with his fingers rapped on the table on each one. "Do you see this? You better sit down and face reality! You have six counts against you, and each count carries ten years in prison! You'd better do what my boss says, or your ass will rot in here."

I looked at him and smiled, which angered him even more. "What the fuck are you smiling for?"

## Metro

### $20 million in fake currency seized, ma

By David Greenwald
The Register

When agents searched Marmol's home at ▓▓▓▓▓▓▓▓ they

of counterfeit money and dealing in counterfeit money, is being held

counterfeit currency has been seized by the Secret Service in the

"These are, to be kind, only of fair quality," Griffa said. Banks

## Deseret News

### FAKE BILLS CONFISCATED

By Associated Press

Authorities have confiscated more than $20 million in bogus bills, possibly a record counterfeit cache, and arrested a man they describe as the mastermind of the operation.

## $20 Million in Bogus Bills Seized, Agents Say; Man Arrested

By LONN JOHNSTON and KIM MURPHY, *Times Staff Writers*

Tuesday, January 31, 1989   The Orange County Register   B3

## Santa Ana restaurateur pleads guilty in $22 million counterfeiting case

By Gregg Zoroya
The Register

One of the headlines following the arrest

I shook my hands and fingers as if I was scared to death. "All this screaming! Who the hell are you trying to intimidate here? I will be out of here in a few weeks."

"Dream on, asshole," he said.

I turned to McCain. "You should take this guy home and put soap in his mouth. Everything coming out of his mouth is like diarrhea. All this pretending to be so macho. As my father says, tell me what you are trying to impress people with, and I will tell you that is the least of what you have. You see all this macho shit and screaming and obscenities he does all the time? When he gets home he probably

338

bends over, pulls down his pants, and his wife sticks her finger in his ass, and he turns around and says, 'Oh, honey, I love it!'"

He jumped up and grabbed me by my collar and pulled me towards him. I grabbed his neck with my left hand, while with my right hand I grabbed the hand he was intending to hit me with. Everything happened very fast. Pat and Albert jumped on him and each one grabbed one of his arms and pulled him off of me. His neck was red from the pressure of my fingers.

I pointed a finger at him. "I don't have handcuffs on now. I will kick your ass, motherfucker!"

"You are a piece of shit criminal," he snarled.

"David!" Albert snapped at him. "That's enough!"

One of the guards heard the commotion and came over to our room. "Is everything okay here?"

"Yeah," Albert replied. "Yeah. Everything is fine." "Are you okay?" the guard asked me.

"Yes, I'm fine." I picked up the chair and sat down. When the guard left, I told Albert, "If you want to talk to me, get that piece of shit out of here, or I will go back to my cell."

Albert said, "No, no. It's fine. David, go and wait outside for us." His tone clearly brooked no argument.

After David left, he and McCain sat down at the table in front of me. He pulled a picture out of his pocket and put it on the table. "Do you recognize this man?"

I looked at the picture. It was Romero.

"I never saw him before in my life. Why?"

"Well, I talked to my boss, Mr. Bailey, in Washington. He may come here to talk to you again in the next few days. He told me to tell you I will be authorized to drop half the charges against you if you agree to cooperate with us and tell us who was behind all this and who is your boss. We know you don't have experience in printing and you have no criminal record, so we know there has to be someone powerful behind you and all this. We also have information that this man brought a large amount of money to Argentina similar to the ones your friend, Jacobo, was passing in Nordstrom's. Also, it's really strange how this man, Romero, died mysteriously only a few days after he arrived in Argentina. Do you have any idea how this happened?"

"I don't know if you need to go to an ear doctor, but I just told you that I had never seen that man in my life. Either way, your offer is very weak because even if you cut my sentence in half, that's still thirty years. I am forty now. That means I would not get out of here until I was seventy years old!"

He opened his eyes wide. "Does that mean you know him?"

"I never said that." I turned to Pat. "Did you hear me say that?" McCain shook his head and smiled. I guess he thought I was just too much. Albert stood up. "Well, if your memory comes back, let us know. Remember, we're the only ones who can get you out of this mess."

I grabbed one of the newspapers and waved the headline at them. "Yeah. I see how much you have been trying to help me." I stood up and called the guard. "We are finished. I am ready to go back."

When I got back to my cell, I noticed my things had been moved around. I had been trained in this, and before I left my cell I always left tiny traps so if someone disturbed or moved anything I would notice it right away. I called Juan in the next cell, and he came over. "Did you see anybody in my cell?"

"No, only your cellmates. But I did step out for a few minutes. Are you missing anything?"

"No. That is what worries me."

"Okay, let me check your stuff. I have experience in this. Move out of my way." He went through all my stuff: my toothpaste, my shaving supplies, everything. Finally, he touched the collar of my overalls. He turned it over and opened it. "There is something here, man." He pulled out two tiny white plastic bags of white powder. Juan laughed and waved the bags at me. "Look, they left a small gift for you—cocaine!"

"Why, those sons of bitches!"

Juan dropped the bags in the toilet and flushed them down. "Very simple, my friend. They want to complicate your case and make you look like a drug addict. No one would take you seriously anymore. Count the minutes. You will see the guards come in a minute to search. Whoever did this will send the guards to find it."

Not even ten minutes passed when a guard came on over the loudspeaker: "Everybody in front of their cells in the J building. We are going to search your cells."

Juan was standing very close to me, and he murmured, "Here they are. They are coming to screw you. You have to watch this kind of stuff in here, my friend."

They went through everything, and they found nothing because we had already flushed the bags down the toilet. This made me very worried. I began to think that one of my cellmates had planted the cocaine. Maybe one of them had made a deal with the Secret Service or who knew who else, and this episode could be repeated in the future. From now on, every time I left my cell or changed my overalls I would have to be sure they were clear of drugs or anything else that could implicate me because they could plant that stuff anywhere. Even when I went to take a shower I would have to keep my clothes where I could see them.

That is when I came up with the idea to ask Juan if one or the other of his men could keep his eye on my stuff whenever I left my cell. I would compensate him for that. I explained to Juan my delicate situation and where I was at that moment, and he told me not to worry. He said I did not need to compensate him. They would keep their eyes on my cell, so I should not worry about it.

The next day, the loudspeaker called me again. This time, it was McCain, Albert, and his boss, Sam, from Washington. When I got to the meeting room after the routine search, they were waiting for me. Sam said hello to me. I greeted him in reply.

McCain said, "We have something here for you to hear which you will find very interesting." He pushed the play button on the recorder, and I heard Jacobo.

"His name is Dr. Julio Antonio del Marmol. He is a Cuban national. He is in charge of printing lots of money. Evidently, this is a huge operation. I don't know if the governor of California is behind this or if it is somebody even bigger. Don't play around with him because he is armed and really dangerous. Please, will you let me see my children now? If I help you, and tell you everything I know, then you will not deport me and my and take our kids away, right?"

McCain rushed to stop the tape because he did not want me to hear Jacobo begging and the voices in the background telling him he was going to rot in jail. When he finally stopped the tape, he looked at me, a little embarrassed, and said, "Do you recognize the voice of your friend?"

"Yes, and I can see also that you did a good job of intimidating and terrifying him. I don't think he will be my friend anymore after this. Whatever he said, he has no base for it. He knows nothing of what is going on. Yes, I gave him some money but I gave it to him to help him. Nothing else."

"Do you call that help?" McCain asked. "He is in a lot of trouble because of you."

"It is not because of me. It is because of his stupidity and I will talk to him when I get out of here and we will straighten this whole thing out."

"Come on, man—you're looking at thirty or forty years. You aren't a common criminal. You're smart, but the charges you have so far don't look good. That's not counting another charge you may get for dealing drugs in here. It'll be a long time before you can speak to your friend Jacobo again."

I smiled. "You are starting to sound like Castro, in Cuba. You have already convicted me. You are my judge, my prosecutor, and let's hope you will not be my defender! You say dealing drugs in here? Is that what you said? Hmmm. I wonder why you said something like that. You have checked my record and you know that I have never had any problem with drugs and have never touched drugs in my life. I wonder if you had anything to do with the stuff we found yesterday. We flushed it down the toilet."

They all looked at each other and McCain dropped the subject. Albert said, "Remember the environment you are in right now. In here, anything is possible. That doesn't mean that we had anything to do with what happened to you here."

"Yes, you are one hundred percent right, and I agree with you up to a point. You have to agree that it was very stupid of Pat McCain to tell me I might get another charge for dealing drugs in here when yesterday evening someone planted drugs in my clothing."

"It could just be a coincidence," Sam put in.

"Yep," I said with a smile. "A very strange coincidence."

Sam and Albert looked at McCain in a reproving manner. They knew he had put his foot in his mouth. McCain smiled nervously like an idiot who had been caught with his hand in the cookie jar.

"Well," said Sam, "let's get to the point: the reason we came to see you here."

"Go ahead," I said.

"Well," said Albert, "we know for a fact that this is too huge an operation for it to be a one man job. So far, we've not been able to implicate anyone else. If you give us a list of the people who've been doing this job with you, we'll make a plea bargain with you and you'll get a very lenient sentence."

"What is your idea of a lenient sentence? Twenty years?" I asked.

"No," answered Sam. "Maybe five or ten years."

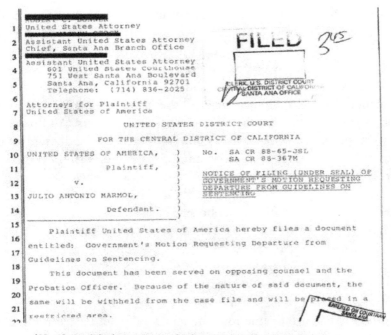

112. If the defendant were to plead guilty to all counts in both cases, the statutory maximum term of imprisonment would be 75 years and six months, rather than 30 years and six months. The felony classification would not change, nor would the term of supervised release prescribed by statute.

Respectfully submitted,

Chief U. S. Probation Officer

U. S. Probation Officer

Reviewed and Approved:

Acting Supervisor

### The indictment

"Let me be frank with you, Sam," I said. "Sam is your name, right? Or do you want me to call you Mr. Bailey?"

He raised his hand in acquiescence. "No, you can call me Sam. That's fine."

"Okay, Sam. I will tell you one thing: I will be out of here in a very short time because I know how to cover my bases. As I told Albert and you before, he should never have put this in the national and international newspapers like you guys did. This is going to blow smoke out of your asses. In a few weeks or months, when the media starts to ask you questions about this huge case and this huge case has disappeared, what are you going to say about it? Let's stop the bullshit right now and stop wasting my saliva because I will never give you a list of names. From now on, if you have any kind of plea bargain or deal you want to offer me, please get in touch with my attorney. I have nothing further to discuss with you guys. I'm sorry, Sam, but you're playing this game a little too late. All the damage was already done by you guys when you put this case into the newspapers. And not only did you put it in the local papers, but in the national and international papers, as well. They even interrupted the Olympics to broadcast my arrest. Now, you will have to live with the consequences."

Sam looked at me curiously. "Do you really work with the government as your friend Jacobo says?"

"No, Sam. I don't work for anybody. I am a freelancer. A crazy Cuban freedom fighter. That is all." I stood up and called the guard. "We are finished," I said to him. "You can take me back."

Sam stood up. "Are you sure you don't want to negotiate with me? I have the power to help you."

"Like I said, you came into the game too late. I have nothing to negotiate anymore."

"You don't care about lowering your sentence?"

"I can take care of that myself. I don't need you guys for that. Mark my words—you will never arrest anyone else in this case. I promise you."

As I walked away with the guard, I heard one of them say, "Who the hell *is* this guy?"

I returned to my cell after the routine search. Not even half an hour later, I got another call. My attorney was visiting me. I went back through the whole process again, and saw Jerry in the visiting room when I arrived there.

"I know I've not been myself lately," he apologized, "but I've got good news for you. I finally got the judge to agree to grant you bail of five hundred thousand dollar, and I'll continue to work to get it down more. That way, you'll be able to get out of here and be with your family until we get a trial date."

"Jerry, how many times do I have to tell you that there will be no trial?"

"Of course there'll be a trial. Everybody has a trial!"

I leaned close to him and said in a low voice. "I am not going to waste my time explaining details to you. Listen to me very carefully.

You arrange whatever is necessary to protect my legal rights and I will handle the rest. I have been in here for nearly a week, and all you have managed to do is get bail for me. Five hundred thousand dollars! Wow! I spoke with someone this morning over the phone, and they informed me that you had picked up my Mercedes from the house in Santa Ana. They have been keeping their eyes on you, Jerry. You have practically trashed that car. You drove it to Vegas, Arizona, San Francisco, and you have put almost four thousand miles on that goddamned car in less than a week. Of course, this devalues the car. You have abused our friendship and our agreement. My friends released the car to you because you told them I said it was okay. I never authorized you to take the car. On top of you being a shitty friend, you are also a liar! How can I trust you anymore, Jerry? You are fired. I am going to get another attorney!"

I stood up, and so did he. "I'm sorry," he said. "I'm really sorry, man. I know I screwed up. I left you high and dry. Honest to God, I'll never do that to you again."

I shook my head. "No, you won't. You are fired. I don't want you around anymore. I can't trust you. You are a fake. On top of that, you are a lousy friend and a piece of shit attorney."

He started to cry, tears streaming down his cheeks. "Don't do that to me, man. Not at this moment, when I have all these problems with my finances and my wife. This could ruin my career and destroy my family." He grabbed my hand and held it tightly. "Don't fire me now, I beg you. Please, not now."

"Why should I care about you? You don't care about me at all."

Jerry had completely broken down now. I could see he was really scared. "You don't understand. If you fire me now, it'll be all over the news. Your case is high profile, and everybody everywhere is watching this. If you fire me, nobody will ever hire me again."

I walked around the room, shaking my head. I could only repeat, "You have not done shit for me so far. You have been a crappy friend and I will never forget that you asked me for twenty thousand dollar a few minutes before we walked into court. You didn't give a damn how I felt at that moment, when I most needed your compassion and support."

"I know," he cried, "I know I've been a shitty friend and not a good person at all! But please—give me another chance."

I thought for a minute. I shook my head and glanced at him. He was looking at me, filled with anxiety and nervous anticipation. "I'll tell you what—I have already talked to another attorney. If you screw up one more time, you will be fired immediately. In other words, don't screw up anymore because that will be the last thing you will ever do. You know I can cause big trouble for you."

Jerry gasped with relief. "Thank you! Thank you! I swear I won't screw up again. You don't have to worry about it. I promise you, I'll handle your case with the respect it deserves."

"Very well." I sat down again and motioned for him to do likewise. "In my opinion, the Secret Service has a very weak case. They have been here twice already trying to work out a deal with me and threatening me with having to spend seventy or seventy-five years in jail. They told me if I would give them information regarding the case they would be willing to drop half the charges. That causes me to believe that their case is either very weak or they don't have shit at all. I think they have violated every single rule in the legal system. They intimidated and coerced Jacobo to do what he did: entrap me and bring me to his house. They probably did not even read him his rights when they arrested him. I want to make sure Jacobo has an attorney; if he does not have one, then you get one for him. Also, they broke the law by telling Jacobo to plant those hundred-dollar bills in my pocket. If you can get in contact with Jacobo's attorney or get one for him, then maybe we can get Jacobo to testify to this."

"Are you sure it happened that way?"

"Absolutely! Also, through the discovery they have to present the evidence they have against me to the court and to you. I want you to demand the tape they recorded of the conversation between Jacobo and me when I was arrested at his house. This tape will prove I declined to accept that money several times when Jacobo tried to give it to me. So how in the hell did it get into my pocket?"

Jerry smiled. "You are one smart cookie." He shook my hand vigorously.

"Calm down, calm down! I know you are happy, but calm down! One thing more—I don't want you to bring your personal problems with your wife to me when you come here. I have enough problems myself."

"Okay," he said, "okay. I'm sorry."

"Since you ruined my car already, I don't want you driving it one more day! I want you to take that car when you leave here to a used car dealer or to a Mercedes dealer and get as much as you can for it after you put four thousand miles on it! Whatever money you get that exceeds twenty thousand dollars, give it to my father. When I get out of here, I will compute how much of the depreciated the value of the car and I will deduct that from your fee."

"Okay. Okay. I understand."

"The last thing is, don't pay too much attention to reducing my bail. I will wait for one more week and if my people don't do what I expect them to do, I will take charge and do something about it. I will be out of here in a couple of weeks for sure."

We said goodbye, and he said, "Don't worry about it. I'll do what you tell me to do."

"Remember, don't sign anything on my behalf until you consult with me. Don't enter into any plea bargaining without checking with me first."

"Of course. Of course—it's illegal to do anything without asking you first."

"Well, it was illegal to go into my house and take my Mercedes and drive it all over the place without my consent, but you did that anyway. You violated our verbal agreement that you should hold that note that I gave you or put the car in storage."

"I'm sorry, man. I'm sorry."

"Don't apologize anymore. Just be half decent."

I walked out of the room and went through the usual procedure to go back to my cell. I tried unsuccessfully to make a phone call to O'Brien again. I dialed every number I had for him, and all were disconnected. I even dialed his pager, just to be thorough, even though prison phones don't allow incoming calls—it, too, was disconnected.

I decided to give O'Brien one more week to see what they would do for me. That night, after dinner, I lay in bed and tossed and turned. I could not sleep nearly all night. I looked around me to see everybody else sleeping. I got out of bed and got on my knees. I put my hands together and said, "Our Father, who art in Heaven, hallowed be thy name. Thy Kingdom come, thy will be done, on earth as it is in Heaven. Give us this day our daily bread, and forgive our trespasses as we forgive those who trespass against us." I lay back down and fell asleep.

One week later, I called my father. I told him to tell Hernesto and Elizabeth to release the first packages to the priority one address. He said, "Okay, I will. Is everything okay? Are they treating you well?"

"Yes, everything is fine. They are treating me a lot better than they would in Cuba."

347

I could hear the smile in his voice. "That is not too much consolation. Do you want to talk to your mother? I have not told her anything. I did not want to scare her, but she knows anyway because they interrupted her soap opera on the Spanish channel and showed your face. They said you were associated with the Mexican mafia. Who in the hell authorized the printing of all this rubbish and put it on TV?"

"Dad," I said, "that is democracy. They say whatever the hell they want and then retract it and apologize later. That is good enough. That is what we call freedom of speech."

"This is too much freedom when you destroy other people's character. I call that lying and misinforming, not responsible press. I hope they do something about that in this country in the future. Anyway, your mom is here."

"No, dad, I don't want to talk with Mom. She might get too emotional, and that is not good for her health. Tell her I am fine and I will probably be home next week."

With that, I said goodbye to him and went back to my cell.

# Chapter 30—The Package

The next morning, I heard on the loudspeaker that I had a visitor in the attorney's room. I went through the usual routine, and when I entered the room I saw a man in his late forties or early fifties. He was dressed in black, with a black hat, sunglasses, and a cane. I had never seen him before.

He shook my hand and said, "Mr. O'Brien said to tell you hello and to give you a hug and to tell you to hang in there. Everything will be okay. We'll get you out."

"Man, it's about time! It's been almost three weeks. My patience is nearly exhausted. I was wondering where everybody was hiding."

He smiled as he replied. "Your package was very influential. It created a big controversy at high levels. Why have you been keeping all this from us? We're your friends. Do you intend to use this against us?"

"No. By no means—but what kind of friends are you guys? Why have you left me here with no help, no communication, or anything? I couldn't even call anybody because you guys disconnected all the phones."

"This is normal procedure. You know that. You also know that phone conversations in this place are recorded."

I smiled and relaxed in my chair. "I know that. I am not going to say anything stupid or incriminating to anyone over the phone. But it would have been comforting to hear a friendly voice in the middle of this turmoil telling me that everything was going to be okay."

He took off his hat and put it on the table. He ran his fingers through his hair. "Well, you made a big mistake, and I believe you were warned about making mistakes in public. That's a big no-no for us. You know how much we hate publicity and being in the press."

"I am really sorry, but we all make mistakes. One mistake trying to help a friend is not justification to leave me here for seventy years."

He nodded. "Yes, we know, and conventional wisdom shows us that we've more to gain by helping you than by leaving you here on your own. Besides, the high powers in the government have ordered us to get you out of here immediately. When they received the package from you, they started to feel that maybe you were going to break down and release everything you sent us to the press."

"Let me tell you, and you can tell O'Brien and the others, I would never do something like that. I love this country too much, and I know how much damage that would do politically. Don't forget, I have been helping you guys out, too, for many, many years with no pay. I have never asked for anything in return except what was absolutely necessary for my survival and to help me to continue whatever I was doing. That was only economical information. You know what I mean. I am not going into detail."

He looked at me and smiled again. "Yes, I know. Obviously, some people underestimated you, but let's move ahead with this. Right now, as we are talking, someone is talking to the judge, and he'll lower your bail as low as is allowed by the law. We don't want to call attention to your case or create any problems for the judge. That's why we're asking you to do your part. Use your house as collateral for the bail, and if you need any extra cash, since your visual accounts are frozen, let us know. We'll use someone legitimate to loan you money so you can get out of jail by tomorrow."

I smiled. "I like that." I nodded and listened to the rest he had to say. We had a long conversation that went on for quite some time.

The next morning, November 21, the front door opened at Terminal Island, and I walked outside. I took a deep breath of fresh air. I had never appreciated the air and the feeling of freedom so much in my life, except when I had arrived, tired, wounded, and thirsty in Guantanamo Bay after swimming for so many miles, after escaping from the persecution of the Castro regime.

Across the sidewalk I noticed a black car and a man coming out with a huge grin on his face. He opened his arms to me. It was O'Brien. "Unless you want to walk," he joked, "I'm here to take you home."

"I was really starting to worry about you. Where in the hell have you been all this time?"

He put his arm around my shoulder. "You, better than anybody, know that this is normal procedure. We have to protect ourselves in case there are any leaks. That way, no one else can get hurt."

I looked at him. "Do you really think I will talk?"

"No," he smiled. "I know you very well. The others don't, but I know you'll not talk, even if they kill you."

"That comforts me a little because the only leak I did was when I went to the bathroom."

He laughed. "Is that another Cuban joke?"

"Well, sometimes they work and other times people look at me as if I were crazy."

"I always understand you, man, your Spanglish," O'Brien said, smiling fondly. "I want to take you to lunch. Where the hell do you want to go?"

"I know a place in Long Beach. I want a big, thick, juicy steak. By the way, if you don't understand my English by now after spending so many years around me, you better go back to school to learn English again."

He chuckled. "It's funny that you say that. Every time we're interrogating a Cuban, they call me and ask me what he said. I tell them, 'Man, why ask me? He's speaking English.' The guys respond to me that they don't understand shit that he said and ask me to translate for them."

"If you don't stop making fun of my people, I am going to kick your ass," I said.

We arrived at the restaurant in Long Beach and ordered two one-pound porterhouse steaks.

O'Brien was salivating. "Oh, man! I never saw such a steak in my life. How do you discover these good places?"

"Because I love good food. I don't like to put junk in my stomach."

"Well, we finally got your bail reduced. How was life in prison?"

"Don't ask, man. It was hell. It was hell, but I guess I was lucky because I found a group of young Mexican men, and they actually offered me protection. They were very decent."

"Well, at least you didn't have it that bad in there, and the Zipper is complete."

"Thank God I worked out a deal with the Secret Service and the federal attorney, and got immunity for Loren to get her out of the picture before she did any damage."

O'Brien looked at me slyly. "What the hell were you thinking when you brought her with you when you knew you were going to drop off money to your friend? That's not like you at all. Are you in love or something?"

I smiled and shook my head, and raised my hand in protest. "Don't even mention it. I went through hell in that Secret Service office when they were interrogating her, and she was crying hysterically and screaming. At that moment, I was afraid she would crack. That is the only reason I made a deal with them and gave them all that counterfeit junk we were burning. If Loren had not been there with me, I would never have made any deal with them because I know for a fact that no judge in the world would have given them a search warrant with such a weak case—not to mention they had violated so many of my legal rights. In spite of all that, they are still singing like a canary about making the biggest counterfeit bus in the history of the United States."

I shook my head in disgust. "What a moron that pencil-necked bureaucrat Albert is, and what an abuser and sadistic person that David Esquivel is. The best of the whole trio was Pat McCain, and I think that was just because he tried to play the good cop."

"Well, my friend, even though this may sound a little annoying to you, I think you need to play head games with these Secret Service guys and do what you're already a master of—pretend that you're just a little fish and that you'll help them to catch the big fish."

I raised both arms in objection and leaned back in my chair. "Oh no, man—why can't you tell their bosses what is really going on and take them off my back?"

O'Brien leaned in close to me and spoke quietly. "It's exactly like going to the chief of police and asking him to tell the whole police department that we're going into the grocery store to steal all the goodies, and they have to look in the other direction and let us do it. We would jeopardize ourselves not only with the police chief, but also with the entire police department. Where's the secrecy?"

I raised my hand in resignation. "Okay. I understand. What am I supposed to do?"

"It's very simple. What have you been trained for? You're going to convince the guys from the Secret Service that a few guys came from Argentina and convinced you to do this. You weren't thinking straight, and you went along with it. They used you. You were a victim. You used Romero's name. He was the leader. Now you find out from the Secret Service that he's dead. Actually, more than anything else, you were concerned for your life. You were afraid they might come back and kill you because you screwed up."

I looked at him incredulously. "Do you think those guys are going to believe this shit?"

He smiled. "You don't care whether they believe you or not. All you care about is that they put in their pre-sentence report that you're cooperating with them, and that you'll make a deal with them and be an informant for them in exchange for a lenient sentence. We're going to talk to the judge. Assuming the pre-sentence report is good, the judge will have no problem letting you go with a very lenient or even no sentence."

"Why don't you guys talk to the judge in private and explain what the whole thing is about?"

This time, he was the one who leaned back in his chair. He smiled a bit smugly, and said, "What makes you think we already haven't done that? But that's not enough. The judge is scrutinized by the public, and he has to have clean hands to let you go. In other words, he cannot jeopardize his position. You have to make things easy for him. Is that clear enough now?"

"Yes. What is my next move?"

"Tell your attorney to start doing the plea bargaining arrangements. The Secret Service is going to be delighted with this kind of deal because they think they're going to get more people involved. This would make the case bigger and better for them. They're going to play all kinds of games to implicate you more deeply in this because they assume you're a common Cuban coming from a banana boat and they can jerk you around." He paused and grinned. "They don't know who they're dealing with! A big surprise is going to come out of the sky for them! They certainly don't expect the Cuban Lightning to be burning their asses!"

We both laughed. We had almost finished our lunch, and he told me, "I'm going to give you three different addresses with three different names. These will be the names of the associates of Romero, the Argentinean who did the counterfeit currency with you. Give these names to the Secret Service, and you take them to those places. We'll arrange for people to be in those places, and they'll corroborate the existence of those people—but, they'll say that unfortunately, those people don't live there anymore, and they don't know where they are. So that's not your fault. You tried to help the Secret Service. They'll have to put that in the report—you were cooperating with them. I'll try to find a couple of hundred thousand dollars from the junk that Romero printed in the beginning. I believe I have some that wasn't burned someplace. I'll give it to you and then you call the Secret Service and tell them that you found it in a place that they didn't search in your house. They should put this in their report, and it'll be in your favor.

"Make sure they come to your house to pick it up and you tape record it when you give it to them—just in case they conveniently forget to put it in their report, you can prove they maliciously left it out in order to hurt your case. Also, be sure to get a receipt from them for the money." He smiled again.

Meanwhile, Doby the Panda Bear was circulating among the patrons of the restaurant, selling flowers. He walked all around, but stayed in the area where O'Brien and I were sitting. Unnoticed, the panda had a tiny camera in his hand and was taking pictures of us.

"Well, I guess I am going to become an informant for the Secret Service now. What will be next?" I mused.

"Man," O'Brien said, "whatever we have to do to get you out without creating problems for ourselves. Don't worry—I'll coach you in every step. I'll be your guardian angel."

"Well, I think I have a lot more powerful guardian angel behind me. I just talked with him in prison. But thank you, anyway. I appreciate all the help I can find."

"Do you want to share with me who that powerful guardian angel is?" he asked in curiosity and wonder.

"I am sorry, my friend, that is classified information."

"Okay. By the way, don't get close to Amelia because you don't want to complicate yourself. Now that you're out on bail, you have to walk on eggshells. That way, you won't create any problems or give them any excuse to send you back to jail."

"What are you talking about? Is there anything wrong with Amelia?"

"Well, evidently Amelia talked more than she should, and now she has a problem. Her ex-husband is accusing her of being involved in a major medical scam and of making false claims to the insurance companies. She's under investigation by the state, and since she did business in other states, they're trying to make this a federal case."

I looked up at him in surprise. "Excuse me. This is not my business, but doesn't Amelia work with you guys?"

"No, she's a freelancer. She does whatever she wants. Occasionally she does things for us." He shook his head. "I hope she doesn't get into big trouble for this. She's a good woman, after all, and a very hard worker."

"Uh, huh," I said. "I thought she worked for you guys. She never admitted as much to me, though. She told me exactly what you are telling me now, but nothing surprises me anymore."

We finished our lunch. He called for the bill, which he paid. "Would you mind taking me to my house? I am anxious to take a shower and put some cologne on my body and some decent clothes."

He smiled. "What house or whose house?"

"The one in Lido Island. It is not in my name. It is in someone else's name, but you know the saying: my house is your house! Their house is my house!"

As we walked out of the restaurant, he said, "Okay, Lido house. Let's go. Is this another one of your Cuban things?"

I smiled. "Yeah, probably. You know how things get lost in translation."

On the way to the house, I began to think how Amelia had explained to me before I was arrested that she was going to be doing some kind of work for them in relation to what she was in trouble for now. I wondered if she had any idea that O'Brien or his group was not going to interfere or help in any way in her problem. I figured that they considered it her problem because apparently they were not involved, after all.

After O'Brien dropped me off at the house, I showered and got ready to see my family. I wanted to see my mom, my dad, and my friends; however, I called Amelia before I left. She answered the phone and I told her I needed to talk to her immediately.

She was surprised to hear my voice, and said, "Oh, my God! You are out of jail. The newspapers and the TV said you would be incarcerated for seventy years with no bail!" She paused, and I could imagine her smile. "But I told everybody you would be out of there in a few weeks. I know you a little bit."

"Hey, don't you ever believe everything you hear or see in the news. Thank you for your confidence."

"Congratulations. Enjoy your freedom. Where do you want to meet me?"

"I will see you in two hours in the French café across the street from South Coast Plaza."

"Okay. *This* time, I will pay!"

"Okay. I will see you there in a couple of hours."

I went to the garage and took my black Jaguar sedan. As I backed out of the garage, I noticed a green Ford Taurus with two guys with baseball caps watching my house. I immediately recognized them as Secret Service.

They tried too hard to disguise themselves. Sure enough, when I drove away they followed me. I drove slowly and decided to give them a trip around the area. I drove to Balboa Island and waited for the ferry. When my turn came to get on the ferry, they tried to get behind me, but the guy on the ferry closed the gate. I got out of the car. I was wearing a white suit with a white hat. I took off my hat and saluted them with it.

When I got to the other side of the peninsula, I drove to Corona del Mar. Evidently I lost the Secret Service because there was no one behind me. I arrived at the house, and everyone was overjoyed to see me. My mom was crying, and I hugged Yaneba, Hernesto, and Elizabeth. My dad told me that they had marinated steak, chicken, and filet mignon for three days. "That way," he said, "whatever you want to eat, we have it here."

Yaneba said she had to leave town tomorrow for a few days. "I'll be in Florida, to check in with Capitan Marrero about some important information. I will talk to you in a few days." She took me slightly aside and said in a very low voice, "I have a new recording for you, of your conversation today with O'Brien. While I am out of town, Elizabeth will continue to record for you."

My father looked up. "We actually gave a few thousand dollars to Loren to take care of some personal things." That was just as I had instructed them to do.

"How is she doing?" I asked.

"She looks to be okay," my dad answered. "We don't understand each other too well because I don't speak English and she doesn't speak Spanish."

Hernesto asked me, "Do you want us to take care of Jacobo? That son of a bitch—what he did to you is unspeakable."

"Let me take him someplace and teach him what honor and friendship is all about," Elizabeth added.

"No, leave him alone," I replied. "Don't even get close to him. He is probably being watched by the Secret Service twenty-four hours a day. I don't want you guys to complicate things any more. Everything will be okay, and he will most likely back out. He will probably never testify or talk to the Secret Service again. He already has legal counsel, and they will tell him what is best for him. The Secret Service will not be able to intimidate Jacobo anymore." I smiled at them. "Thank you all for postponing your vacations."

"None of us are going to leave you alone until this situation is resolved," Elizabeth said firmly. "In fact, regarding what we discussed a while back—I've realized that all that's happened with recent events that I cannot stay away. I need to see this fight to the bitter end. I'm not going *anywhere*!"

"I really appreciate that. Thank you very much."

"Well," she said, "evidently the Zipper is working because not only has the Berlin Wall come down, but all the European communist countries are collapsing like dominos, one after the other."

"I would like to congratulate you," my father said. "I never dreamed I would see something like this happen in my lifetime. We need to celebrate."

With that, he went into the house. He brought back a bottle of champagne and opened it. We all cheered for a new and free world, thanks to the Zipper.

# Chapter 31—Fraud

A few hours later, I met with Amelia in the French café. She was not her usual smiling self—the clearest sign of her stress.

"Well, I am in a little trouble," she replied to my inquiry as to how everything was with her. "I might need your advice."

With a very serious face, I said, "Well, I think you are in even more trouble than you think. Let's sit down, and I will tell you about it."

We sat down, and I ordered a glass of wine. She ordered a glass of wine and a fruit salad.

I said, "You told me before that these guys were putting millions of dollars into whatever job you were doing with your clinics, right?"

"Yes. Why?"

"Well, I just met recently with O'Brien. I did not mention anything to him about what you had told me, but he told me they had nothing to do with what you are doing. He said to stay away from you because you are too hot right now and are under investigation."

Her mouth dropped open and her eyes grew wide. "That is what he told you?"

"Yes, that is what he said. Do you want to tell me what is going on with you? Because I have been out of circulation for a few weeks."

She took a sip of her wine and put a hand to her face as if she were in distress. "To be completely honest with you, I don't even know what the hell is going on! All I can tell you is that at three o'clock in the morning, the D.A. and the Highway Patrol authorities knocked on my door with a court order. They turned my house upside down and took all my medical files, my computer, my personal files. All they told me was that I was under investigation for insurance fraud. They told me not to leave town. The next day, they did the same thing at my clinic in Santa Ana. They scared the hell out of my patients and everybody there. They did not arrest anybody, and they told me they would be in touch. They were abusive and impolite, and they even took my personal bills so I have not been able to pay them."

"Do you have any idea what caused all of this?"

"No. I have no idea. They didn't tell me anything. They came with a search warrant and didn't give me any explanation."

"Have you talked with O'Brien, and have you told him what is going on?"

She smiled and waved one hand. "Every time I call him, they say he's out of town. I think he is hiding from me because I have not been able to talk to him at all."

I leaned towards her and said in a low voice, "Listen to me very carefully. I have knowledge that the person who initiated all these problems for you is your ex-husband. I hope you have personal insurance with O'Brien and his group to cover your ass because if you are doing something for them, and you don't have insurance, you could spend a long time in jail. This is the way things are because none of these people want to take responsibility for anything that looks even remotely illegal. Imagine something that is completely illegal! We both know that everybody does it, even the squeaky clean Secret Service. I have very personal experience in these past weeks. Remember, the point is, don't get caught doing it or you are on your own!"

She looked very disturbed. "No, I have not protected myself as you did. Now I regret it."

"Well, please don't acknowledge that I told you anything. This is our last meeting. If you need me for anything, contact Hernesto."

I wrote down on the napkin the number and slid it over to her. "Unfortunately," I continued, "I am going through a huge problem myself right now, and my battle with the legal system is just starting."

She nodded her head. "I understand. Thank you very much for your advice and your information. I did not have the slightest idea until you told me just now that my ex-husband was my troublemaker. Can you believe it? That son of a bitch called me last night. He was so friendly— it never crossed my mind that he could be the one."

I stood up. "When something goes wrong, always look at the people closest to you, and at the tight circle in which you move." I took the bill in my hand and put some cash on the table. "We will talk later. I have to go now. Good luck to you."

She tried to smile bravely. "You are a great person. Thank you for taking a chance and coming to see me."

"You are welcome." With that, I took off and headed for home. On my way back, when I reached the intersection of Harbor and Victoria Street, I made a left into the parking lot of Lucky's Market. There were several businesses there, including a pizza parlor where my friends had informed me that Jacobo had been working, making pizzas. I did not want to scare him, but I wanted to face him. I parked my car and walked into the pizza place.

I saw him immediately. He was wearing a big white chef's hat and a white apron. He was laughing and tossing the pizzas in the air. The customers were all watching him and enjoying his antics. As he turned around toward the customers our eyes met. He froze with the pizza in midair, and it dropped to the floor. He looked as if he had seen a ghost. Everybody in the place was totally silent. They perceived something was wrong but had no idea what it was. I looked him directly in the eyes quite seriously for a few seconds, and then I winked my right eye, shook my head, and touched my hat with my hand to acknowledge him. Then I turned around and walked out.

I smiled as I walked out, thinking he would probably not sleep for a week, wondering what the hell I was doing there, how I knew he was there, and I had gotten out of jail so quickly. I got into my car and drove away with a smile on my face, remembering the guilt that was reflected in his face when he first saw me. I continued driving to my house, and when I arrived a grabbed a plastic container full of real money, got back into my car, and drove to Saint Joachim Catholic Church in Costa Mesa.

For over fifteen years, I had been dropping 10% of whatever money I made into a plastic container and every three or four months I would take it to the church and leave it at the altar of the Virgen de la Caridad del Cobre, the patron saint of Cuba. I never knew how much money it contained when I took it to the church because I never counted it.

I walked into the church with the container. Because it was dark inside, I did not see the priest, but he saw me and watched me. After I had left the money at the altar, he came to me and said, "I am Father Thomas. May God bless you, my son. So you are the one who has been leaving these large contributions to the church. Why have you not made yourself known to us? My staff calls you 'the plastic container donor.'"

"Well, Father, I consider it my obligation to help those who are having a hard time in life. I have made so much money in the past years that what I do is a comfort to my conscience. Sometimes I feel guilty to have so much."

Father Thomas put his hand on my shoulder, and said with a big smile on his face, "My son, those people who have that consciousness are the real sons and daughters of God. Some men have billions and they never do anything to alleviate the suffering of others."

"Thank you, Father."

He asked me for one of my cards or my name or telephone number or something because he wanted to see me again in the future. I gave him a card and asked him not to give it to anybody, especially right now as I was in the midst of some legal trouble. I also asked him not to reveal to anyone my donations in the past. "No," he said, "I won't. Don't worry about it. What kind of trouble are you in, my son?"

"Well, it's a big legal complication. I don't want to go into details. As a matter of fact, I have just had an extraordinary experience that I would really like to discuss with someone who has deeper religious roots than I have."

"What kind of experience, my son? Can you just give me an idea?"

I shook my head. "You might think I am crazy, but I talked to Jesus just as I am talking to you right now—it happened a few weeks ago, when I was in prison. I don't know if I was delirious with fever or if it was just a dream. But it was just as real to me then as it is right now as I am talking to you."

He grew very serious and put his hand to his chin. "My son, do you have a little time? Can you come with me to my office, and I will arrange for you to talk to the Bishop of Orange?"

"Okay, I have the time." I followed him to his office, where he made a phone call to the Bishop.

When the Bishop came to the phone, Father Thomas explained to him that by the grace of God he had finally found 'the plastic container donor' and that he was right there with him in his office. "Guess what?" he asked. "He is in need of a little counsel and guidance. He just had an extraordinary religious experience that he does not fully understand and has asked for our help. He is also going through a little turmoil in his life right now, and could use our prayers. He wants to see you."

"Send him over here right now," the Bishop replied. "I have wanted to meet him for years. I want to know who he is."

"Right now? You mean right now at this moment?"

"Yes, right away, if he can come over now."

Father Thomas put the phone down and said, "The Bishop says he can see you right now. Can you go over there immediately? If you can, I will give you the address."

"Yes, sure," I said. "I can go over there now."

Father Thomas picked up the phone again and said, "Okay. He says he can come right away. His name is Dr. del Marmol." They hung up and Father Thomas gave me a little piece of paper with the address of the Bishop in the city of Orange. He hugged me and we said goodbye. "God bless you, my son. I hope all your troubles will go away, and please come back to see me. I would be delighted to spend a few hours talking with you."

"I promise, Father Thomas."

I drove to the city of Orange and parked my car behind the church. I walked into the rectory. A lady came to me with a smile and introduced herself as Sister Theresa. "I am Dr. del Marmol," I said.

"Oh, yes, Dr. del Marmol. The Bishop is expecting you."

We walked into a very organized and clean office. The Bishop gave me a big smile as he said, "At last, I get to meet the donor with the plastic container. The Lord has answered my prayers."

"Your Excellency, to be perfectly honest, I can only tell you that I think God has always given me more than I deserve. I am not a perfect human being, and I have a lot of faults. That is the only thing I could do to feel that I am giving something in return. I wish I could do more."

"My son, you think what you are doing is little, when in reality it is not."

I offered my hand to shake as I prepared to introduce myself to him, but he instead opened his arms and hugged me. "Give me a hug! God bless you. You are one of His golden sons." That really touched me and tears sprung to my eyes. He noticed my emotion and put his hand on my shoulder. "Come on. Sit down. We have a lot to talk about."

I had arrived there at 5:30 in the afternoon. When I was ready to leave it was almost 9:30. I looked at my watch and said, "Your Excellency, will you excuse me? May I use your phone? I want to call my mom and my dad. They are waiting for me to come home for dinner."

"Go ahead, use the phone. I am sorry I have kept you for so long."

"No, don't feel bad. You are an extraordinary man. You have made me feel so good, and you have relieved me of a lot of doubts and confusion that was in my mind."

"I am glad."

I called my father and told him I would be there in fifteen minutes. "We are all starving waiting for you," he said. "But don't rush yourself. Drive carefully. We will wait. Don't worry about it."

"Okay, Dad. Don't worry. I will be there in a little while."

We hung up, and I saw the Bishop was smiling. He had heard my conversation with my father and asked, "Your dad and your mom are still with us?"

"Yes," I answered. "Thank God because I love them very much, and it will be devastating to me when I lose them."

"Enjoy them. Spend time with them. That is more important than anything else you can give to them."

"I know, and I will try to spend as much time as I can with them."

"I am leaving for Rome in the next couple of days. I hope everything goes well with you and your legal battles. I will pray for you, and I will ask the Pope to pray for you, also."

"Thank you very much. I have a little present for you and one that I would like for you to give to the Pope."

"What is that?"

"It is a book that I published in 1976 called *Cuba Ruleta Rusa de America*. It has a beautiful religious song in protest to the communist regime in Cuba called 'El Ave Maria de Julio Antonio.' It is actually my composition and I made it to protest the persecution of the Christians in Cuba by the Castro government. They pretended to the entire world that they respected all religions, but in reality they persecuted anyone who believed in God and sent them to jail or to labor camps."

I opened my briefcase and took out two books and autographed them, one to him and one to Pope John Paul II.

He smiled again as he said, "Thank you very much. I will give this to the Pope and I will call you in a few weeks when I come back from my trip to the Vatican." He stood up and gave me his blessing. I left his office with a very beautiful feeling, as if a great weight had been taken off my shoulders. I had left all my remorse, all my guilt, and all my doubts behind.

I drove back to my house in Corona del Mar, where my friends and my parents were waiting anxiously for me to arrive and have dinner. It was a great dinner. My mother had made all kinds of food: green bananas, ripe bananas, black beans, white rice, chicken, filet mignon, and porterhouse steak. She asked everybody what they wanted. We talked and had a wonderful time together.

When we had finished dinner and were sitting on the terrace, Hernesto asked me, "Have you been to the Santa Ana house by any chance?"

"No, I haven't. I have been very busy all day."

"Oh, man—that house is a mess. The Secret Service has made a huge mess in there. What a pity. They even broke the walls. They must have kicked them with something."

"Yeah, these people are all morons. They are probably all high school dropouts. They have no decency or education at all."

My mother smiled. "My son—education is not acquired in school. Education comes from your mom and dad, from your roots, from your environment, from your good morals. What you acquire in school is knowledge and technical advice and they prepare you for life and your career. But morals, principles, and ethics come to you from your ancestors, your mom and dad, and the environment where you grew up."

She was getting excited so I smiled and said to her, "Mom, it is okay. I know. I know. When I say a dropout from high school is a moron, it is just a saying. He can be a dropout from high school and still be a decent person. He can also be a doctor and still be an asshole. It's just an expression. I'm sorry, Mom, I didn't mean to discriminate against people who did not finish high school."

"I don't care," she said. "I finished high school. I just wanted to make a point. That is not an excuse to be a bad human being."

"Yes," my father agreed. "Yes, she is completely right."

I smiled at him. "You had better agree with Mom, or you won't get any more fried plantation bananas."

Everybody laughed. Elizabeth said, "You know what is strange? They went through the whole house. They made holes in the wall. They dropped your underwear from the drawers onto the floor. They even went through the refrigerator and the freezer. By the way, they left them open and made a mess in the kitchen, but they never went into the patio by the swimming pool. All the trash cans full of half burned money are still there. When your father called us, we got the hell out of there immediately and a lot of the money was still only half burned. We did not have the time to get it out of there."

"What?" I exclaimed. "You mean to tell me that the trash cans full of money are still sitting there at the house in Santa Ana?"

"You didn't know that? What kind of attorney do you have?"

Hernesto said, "He told me when he came to pick up the Mercedes that he would send a private investigator that worked with him to take pictures of all the damage and the mess the Secret Service did in the house. He said he would make the Secret Service pay for all that unnecessary damage that they did to your property. They entered your property with no search warrant, and you did not give them consent to enter your house, only the garage. But he didn't do any of that."

"Evidently not," I replied with some dissatisfaction. "This is the first knowledge I have of those trash cans full of money still being there." I shook my head. "This guy has no morals, no principles, is a lousy attorney and a piece of shit on top of that. Can you believe he had the nerve to ask me for five thousand dollar extra on top of his twenty thousand dollar retainer for his private investigator to take pictures, get data, and help him to prepare the case to go to court? This guy is a leech and an opportunist. I have helped him with several cases before this and considered him to be my friend."

Hernesto burst out laughing. "I'm sorry, brother, but he looks like a homeless person with his wrinkled suit, holes in his pocket, and food dropped on his shirt. What the hell can you expect from that sloppy son of a bitch?"

"Just a couple of things," I replied, "like decency and loyalty."

I could not wait. I picked up the phone and call Tolan. He answered the phone and said, "How are you doing, my friend? Don't forget we have a court appearance tomorrow morning at eleven thirty."

"I know that, but I am not feeling too good about your performance."

"What's happening?"

"What's happening? You didn't tell me that those cans full of money are still there, sitting on my patio at the house in Santa Ana. Why did you ask me for an extra five thousand for your private investigator to assist you in the case? He hasn't done shit. He has either been picking his nose or watching the stars fall from the skies."

"No, no, no," he protested. "I didn't even know that those cans full of money were still at your house."

"When you went to pick up the Mercedes, why didn't you take your investigator with you to take pictures of the house and the mess that the Secret Service people made? You told Hernesto you would come back later, but you never did. You didn't even bother to check the back yard or anything. What kind of attorney are you, man? Are you preparing my case for my defense or for the prosecution? Who are you working for? Remember what I said at Terminal Island, Jerry—if you screw up one more time, you are out!"

"Okay. Okay. We will talk tomorrow. I will take care of that immediately. I'll see you tomorrow in court."

"Goodbye. I will talk to you tomorrow." I hung up and said to the others, "Either this guy is a moron or else he is a son of a bitch."

Yaneba stood up. "Sweetheart, I think you should keep a very close eye on this guy. I don't think he is a moron. I think he is a son of a bitch." She gave me a hug. "I have to go to bed early because my plane leaves early in the morning."

"Give my regards to Capitan Marrero. Who is going to take you to the airport?"

She pointed to Elizabeth who waved at me. "She has a limousine service." We all smiled. Yaneba said, "Goodbye, everyone. I will see you in a couple of days." Then she went to bed.

I said goodnight to everybody and took off for my house in Lido Island. On the way, my phone rang. It was Loren.

"How are you doing?" she asked. "I talked to Hernesto today and he told me you had been released."

"Well, temporarily. Things are not over yet."

"Well, at least you are out. That is the most important thing. For a while, I thought they had thrown away the key on you and we would never see you again."

"You bought into that bullshit too that the Secret Service displayed in the newspapers and the TV?"

"Well, I have a lot of confidence in you. I know you can get out of anything. But I have to confess to you that I had my doubts that you could get out of this so quickly."

"Well then, you don't have enough confidence in me."

"It's not that. This is huge. This is really huge."

"Listen," I said. "I am not supposed to be talking to anybody about the case—especially over the phone."

"Well, we never had the conversation we were supposed to have because we were interrupted by all this ordeal. I wondered if maybe we could talk now or when—"

I interrupted her. "Listen, I have had an extremely hazardous day and it's kind of late now. I need to go to sleep because I have to be in court in the morning. But I tell you what, if you are up early I will pick you up around seven thirty and we can have breakfast together. Maybe after that you can go to the bank with me. I have to make a withdrawal, if they will allow it, and take care of a few other things. We can talk while I am running these errands."

"Okay, that's fine with me. I don't have too much to do tomorrow, anyway. I really want to have this conversation with you because all the time you were in jail I have had these terrible, guilty feelings. I have felt that, God forbid, if something should happen to you I would never have had the opportunity to explain to you what really happened with Sanchez."

"Okay, then—I will not deprive you of that pleasure."

I could hear her smile over the phone. "Thank you. I really appreciate it."

We said goodbye, and I hung up. I arrived home and poured a glass of Grand Marnier. I put a little of it on a fresh fruit tart and put a couple of scoops of toasted almond ice cream on top of that. I enjoyed it while I luxuriated in the Jacuzzi. I spoiled myself to make up for all the weeks I had been in Terminal Island.

Afterwards, thoroughly relaxed, I fell asleep.

# Chapter 32—The Gun Charge

I slept a little longer than I should have. When I got up, it was nearly 8:30 in the morning. I did not want to call Loren from my house, so I went to my car, and there were a couple of messages from her. I called her back and apologized, letting her know that I had gone to bed pretty late, had overslept, and was going to jump into the shower. I was to pick her up in one hour.

After I made myself presentable for court, I got into the car and went to pick up Loren. When I arrived at her place, she was waiting for me at the door with a smile on her face. She got into my car and we drove to the bank. "I'm sorry," I said, "but since I am running so late there is no time now for breakfast. I don't want to be late for court. Give me a rain check and we will have lunch together after court in a quiet place by the beach."

"Don't worry," she smiled at me. "I am not even hungry. I got up too early because I could not sleep, and I ate a big bowl of fruit and yogurt."

"I have to stop at the bank to see if the Secret Service has already unfrozen my business account as they promised. Jerry is working on a plea bargain deal with the U.S. Attorney, and this is one of the things they promised to do in exchange for my cooperation."

We arrived at the Imperial Bank on Harbor Boulevard in Costa Mesa. It was around 10:00 in the morning. I parked the car and told Loren to wait there for me.

When I got into the bank there was a long line. I went back out to the car and told Loren to come with me into the bank and wait in the line for me while I tried to locate and talk to the manager. I asked her to hold my European wallet, which was like a backpack, that contained my identification, my calculator, my credit cards, and bank book.

I could not find the manager anywhere. They told me that he had stepped out of the bank to take care of some errands, so I asked for the assistant manager. She came to talk to me, and turned out to be an airhead who knew nothing. "I'm sorry, sir, you have to go to the window. I am busy right now. I would have to go to the computer to find out. They can help you at one of the windows."

While I was talking to her I saw that Loren was next in line, so I said, "Thank you very much. Never mind." I walked quickly to where Loren was waiting. Just as I arrived beside her, the clerk called for the next in line. I grabbed the bag from Loren and stepped up to the window with Loren beside me. I opened the zippers and took out my check book, bank account identification, and my driver's license. I left all the zippers open and presented my ID to the teller, trying to hold the bag against the counter with my body.

Loren noticed my difficulty and said, "Don't worry—I will hold it for you."

I told the teller that I wanted to withdraw $6,000. The teller checked the account and gave me a withdrawal slip. "Would you please fill this out and sign it on the bottom. How do you want this? Do you want small bills or large bills?"

I smiled because I assumed everything was okay and she was going to the vault to get the money. While I was filling out the withdrawal slip, my bag fell to the ground. Evidently, Loren was trying to fix her hair and let go of the bag. Just then, the man who was next to her at the window took advantage of her distraction and nudged the leather bag off the counter and on to the floor. Everything that was inside of the bag scattered all over the floor.

"Oh!" she exclaimed. "I'm sorry." Before she could even bend over to gather up the mess, the man who had knocked the bag off the shelf reached down to help her.

The man was young and handsome and had very proper manners. "Don't worry, miss. I'll help you. These things happen. I'll pick it up for you. Oh—can you get that small calculator over there behind you?"

Loren was flattered and smiled flirtatiously at him. "Thank you very much." She turned around to pick up the little calculator.

The man picked up everything and put it into the bag—the sunglasses case, credit cards, and the calculator that Loren handed him. "Do you have all your pens?" he asked her.

"I think so. Thank you."

He handed the bag to her. I looked at her and at him, not feeling comfortable about the whole thing, but I said to him, "Thank you."

I looked at her and shook my head. At that moment, the teller came back to the window. "I'm sorry, sir, but your account has a hold on it and you can't make any withdrawals at this time. If you want to wait for the manager, he'll be back in twenty minutes and he'll explain to you what the problem is."

"Never mind. I don't have the time right now. I will come back later." I was furious and crumpled the withdrawal slip in my hand. I was infuriated.

We got into the car, and as I drove towards the court house in Santa Ana I asked Loren, "What happened in there? You told me you were going to take care of my wallet. You know that my entire life is in that little leather bag. How did it fall on the floor? You told me you were going to hold it."

"I'm sorry. I screwed up. I just fixed my hair for one minute and it fell down."

"Never mind. I am just pissed off. I know it was an accident. Pat McCain told Jerry that my account would be cleared. These people are such liars. I cannot even get any money out of my account."

We drove into the parking lot of the courthouse. "Do me a favor and park my car for me. Wait for me in the car. I am going to talk to McCain in the office of the Secret Service. I want him to tell me to my face what is going on with my business account. I have to be in the courtroom in twenty minutes. It should not take too long. I will be back, and we will go to lunch."

I walked into the federal building, got into the elevator, and went to the Secret Service office. When I got into the hallway, I went to the door of their office and pushed the buzzer. There was a camera above the door. I waved to the camera and then I heard a buzzer and a voice saying to come in. I walked in, and David Esquivel was the first person I saw.

"How are you doing?" he asked.

I gave him a dirty look. "Fine. Is Pat McCain here?"

"Yes. Come on, man. No grudges here. No hard feelings. I was just doing my job."

I followed him to McCain's office and said, "You are doing a lot more than your job. You are abusing your job."

"Man, how can I know if you're a good guy or a bad guy? If I don't harass you, how can I find out?"

"Sure," I said, more out of politeness than conviction. "Sure."

We got to McCain's office, and Esquivel said, "Look who we have here, Pat. Your friend, Dr. del Marmol."

"How are you doing, my friend?" McCain said. "Sit down, sit down."

"No," I declined, "I don't have time. I have to be in court in twenty minutes. I just wanted to ask you what is happening with my accounts. I just went to the bank to make a withdrawal and they would not let me."

He smiled. "You know how these bureaucrats work. It'll probably take a couple of days, but we've already given the release to your attorney."

"Yeah, that is what he told me yesterday, but today I went to get some money and I can't."

He stood up. "Don't worry about it. It'll probably be released this afternoon or tomorrow. These things take time." He pointed proudly to the wall behind his desk, where there was a new award hanging: *To the Los Angeles Secret Service Team for the Biggest Counterfeit Currency Bust in the History of the United States. $23.5 Million. Congratulations on a Job Well Done.* It was signed by Sam Bailey, the Secret Service Director in Washington, D.C. McCain smiled. "Soon we'll catch the biggest fish ever that's behind all of this, with your cooperation. You *are* going to help us, aren't you?"

"For sure," I said. "I will do my best."

Esquivel patted me on the back. "You're going to be one of us, now. We have to put all these negative things that happened before behind us. We were only doing our job."

"Sure," I said cynically. "I know. It's okay. It's like the mafia says, it's nothing personal, only business. That included burning my balls, too."

"Come on," McCain said. "Come on. Let's forget all those bad things. Let's put all that behind us. Come on, we'll walk with you to court. Don't worry. We're going to put in a good word for you with the judge."

I nodded my head, still not believing them. We walked out of the office and into the hallway and took the elevator. While we were in the elevator, I commented, "That award you got for my arrest looks like it is made of gold or some kind of metal. It must be hard and heavy."

He smiled. "Yes, it's heavy. We had to use two nails to hang it on the wall." I smiled and nodded my head. "What?" he asked.

"Something is coming to my mind," I answered. "They should have made it with paper."

He looked at me in wonder. "Paper? Paper doesn't have any value. This is actually a great honor for our team."

"Maybe paper is not that valuable and to receive the award on paper is not that honorable, but paper has a great advantage." I leaned close to him and said quietly, "At least you might be able to use it as toilet paper to clean your ass in a few months."

He shook his head at me and said nothing. The elevator door opened, and Jerry was waiting for me in the hallway. Both McCain and Esquivel waved at him. He waved back and smiled at them. They walked away down the hallway towards the courtroom.

"Where have you been?" Jerry demanded. "I've been waiting for you for half an hour."

I looked at my watch, and there were still ten minutes before we were due in court. "You are such a compulsive liar. I came here twenty minutes ago and you were not even here. I have been in the Secret Service office, trying to find out what the hell is going on with my money. I went to the bank and my account is still frozen."

"That takes time. Probably a few days. You were supposed to be here before the court starts. We needed at least half hour to discuss our strategy."

"What the hell would be the use of my being here an hour before court if you are not here anyway?"

He was frustrated and waved his arm towards a door. "Come over here. I need to talk to you about something in private."

We stepped back into the lobby and left the metal detector behind us. Both of the guards were looking at us, having seen us arguing. The older one, a man in his late forties who already had gray hair at the temples said to me, "Attorney problems?"

I smiled at him. "You know how difficult attorneys can be, right? You see them every day here, huh?"

He smiled and nodded his head in approval. Jerry said, "Now you're going to make fun of me with the guard, too?"

I stopped. "What the hell is wrong with you, man? Did you wake up on the wrong side of the bed this morning? Or did your wife kick you out of the bed too early? I would appreciate it if you would change your goddamn attitude. If anybody has a reason to be pissed off, it's me because you have not been doing your job with competence!"

He looked at me. "I could do my job with more competence if you would help me. I got a call in the middle of the night from the Secret Service. They told me you approached the only witness in this case, Jacobo, at his work place and you tried to intimidate him."

I looked him straight in the eyes. "This is the second time I am questioning myself about who you are working for and what side you are on. It seems strange to me that I just left the Secret Service office, and neither McCain nor Esquivel mentioned anything about this to me. You saw with your own eyes them coming out of the elevator with me. They had plenty of time to ask me about that. Are you not aware that this is the kind of game the Secret Service plays all along? All I did last night was get a pizza on my way home. I was in a public place where anyone can go to get food. When I saw Jacobo there, I didn't even order anything. I turned around and left. Is there anything illegal in that?"

He calmed down and looked at me in disbelief. "You didn't know he was working there?"

"No. I don't have a crystal ball."

He shook his head in resignation, realizing there was nothing there to accuse me of. Even if there were, they could not prove it. "You have to stay away from Jacobo, please. That can create more problems for us."

"I have no intention of getting close to him."

We walked back through the metal detector and into the hallway that led to the courtroom. The guard with the white hair asked, "Did you guys kiss and make up?"

I took my watch and my ring out of the little bowl we had to use to get past the detector. "This guy? No, man. I don't think so."

We walked down the hallway towards the courtroom. Just as we were opening the door, we heard the metal detector siren go off. We both looked back down the hallway, and to my surprise Loren was standing by the detector, looking at us. I turned around and began walking back towards it to see what was going on. Jerry followed me.

The guard was instructing Loren to empty the bag, and they found a little .25 caliber pistol. The man with the white hair pulled his radio out of his belt and made a call. Meanwhile, the other guard was putting handcuffs on Loren. As we drew near, the white-haired guard raised his hand with the gun in it. "We found a gun!"

"Is that your bag?" Jerry asked me.

"Yes, but I don't know where the hell that gun came from!" Then I remembered the man who had flirted with Loren at the bank. When she spilled the contents of my bag, he helped her pick everything up. He must have slipped the pistol into the bag when she had her back turned.

Jerry looked at me in disbelief and shook his head. "What the hell is she doing with your bag? What's she doing here?"

I was infuriated. "I told her to wait for me in the car! Stupid and careless! I don't know what the hell she is doing in here."

"Man, nobody ever, as far as I know, has brought or even tried to smuggle a gun into the federal courthouse here in Orange County. This is going to be huge! It's going to hit the papers again! Whatever you do, don't tell the guard that bag belongs to you."

"Jerry, the bag is mine. It has all my credit cards and identification in it. How the hell can I deny that it is mine?"

"Don't worry about it. You tell them it's not yours. Let her take the fall. It'll just be a misdemeanor for her, and I can get her out in a few days. Just go back to the courtroom and wait for me there. I'll handle this."

"I'm sorry, Jerry, I cannot do that." The guards surrounded Loren and started to take her away. "Hold it! Hold it! That bag does not belong to her. It belongs to me."

"Oh, my God," Jerry said disgustedly. "You're such a fool. They're going to revoke your bail and send you back to prison. You're going to be in deep shit now!"

I moved close to the guard with the white hair. "All my ID is in there. That is my bag, but I have no idea where that pistol came from. It is not mine."

Jerry watched me as I talked to the guard. He covered his eyes. One of the guards said, "Oh, really? It just flew into your bag and nobody knows anything about it?"

I expected that my admission that the bag was mine would exonerate Loren, but instead they handcuffed me, too, and they were about to take both of us to the holding cell behind the courtroom.

Jerry said, "Would you mind unlocking those handcuffs? We have a court appearance in a couple of minutes."

One of the guards said, "Yes, I mind. They're both going to the holding cell. You can take this up with the judge."

I told the guard with the white hair. "Listen, I told you the bag is mine. Why do you have to arrest her?"

"Because she brought it in. You'd better be quiet. You have an attorney, remember? He does your talking for you. Now, let's go."

Then they took us both back to the holding cell. I said to Loren, "Is this bad luck or what? It's like déjà vu all over again. Why the hell did you come into the court, anyway? I told you to wait in the car."

She started to cry.

"It's okay, sweetie. Whatever will be, will be. *Que sera, sera!*"

She tried to smile, and then they put us in separate cells in the back of the courtroom. Meanwhile, the judge and everyone in the court house were outraged. They had already heard that someone had tried to bring a gun into the building. The news spread quickly. In a very short time, there were reporters from all the newspapers there.

Meanwhile, in the courtroom Jerry was trying to explain to the judge that I had no idea where the gun had come from. The judge ordered the guards to bring us into the courtroom. The situation was discussed by both sides, and after the closing arguments, the judge pondered the problem with the gun.

At that moment, a woman from the Pre-Sentence Court Service brought in the report and handed it to the judge. He read it and looked at me gravely. "Dr. del Marmol, this report does not put you in a very good light with the law."

"Your Honor, may we see that report?" Jerry asked.

The judge ignored him and continued, "This pre-sentence report is one of the worst I have ever seen."

"Your Honor," Jerry insisted, "can you give us the results of the findings? At least let us know what's in the report."

"Essentially," the judge said, "it says that Dr. del Marmol did not cooperate with the Secret Service in any way, and he obstructed their investigation at every opportunity he had. He lied on several occasions to them and he also has an outstanding warrant for his arrest for failure to appear for a speeding ticket."

I looked at Tolan as if I could kill him. I whispered, "You irresponsible son of a bitch. I even gave you the money because you told me you had paid the ticket for me. What happened?"

Tolan signaled for me to be quiet and said to the judge, "Your Honor, we would like to request a delay to examine our position. We will need an extension."

"If that is acceptable to all parties," the judge replied, "then it is fine with me. However, Dr. del Marmol, I will have to send you back to

Terminal Island because of the gun. You violated the terms of your bail."

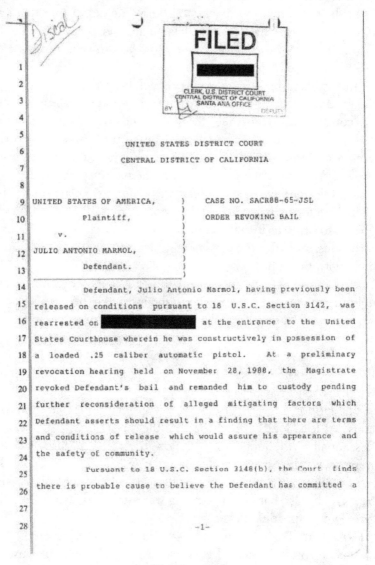

FILED

CLERK, U.S. DISTRICT COURT
CENTRAL DISTRICT OF CALIFORNIA
SANTA ANA OFFICE
BY _____ DEPUTY

UNITED STATES DISTRICT COURT

CENTRAL DISTRICT OF CALIFORNIA

UNITED STATES OF AMERICA,     )     CASE NO. SACR88-65-JSL
                              )
        Plaintiff,            )     ORDER REVOKING BAIL
                              )
    v.                        )
                              )
JULIO ANTONIO MARMOL,         )
                              )
        Defendant.            )

Defendant, Julio Antonio Marmol, having previously been released on conditions pursuant to 18 U.S.C. Section 3142, was rearrested on ▒▒▒▒▒▒▒ at the entrance to the United States Courthouse wherein he was constructively in possession of a loaded .25 caliber automatic pistol. At a preliminary revocation hearing held on November 28, 1988, the Magistrate revoked Defendant's bail and remanded him to custody pending further reconsideration of alleged mitigating factors which Defendant asserts should result in a finding that there are terms and conditions of release which would assure his appearance and the safety of community.

Pursuant to 18 U.S.C. Section 3148(b), the Court finds there is probable cause to believe the Defendant has committed a

-1-

## The Gun Charge

"But, Your Honor," I protested, "the gun is not mine!"
"Shh," Tolan warned me. "Thank you, Your Honor."
"Jerry, why don't you do something?" I asked him.

"There is nothing we can do right now. Your Honor, I move to release Loren Thompson. She is only a companion to Dr. del Marmol and had no knowledge that there was a gun in his bag."

The judge said, "If the other side has no objection, then I will order her release."

"We have no objection, Your Honor," the prosecutor said. "Very well, she can be released from custody now. Court is adjourned for one week."

Tolan then said to me, "Dr. del Marmol, I'm sorry to tell you, but this is a new case. Now we have another charge against you. I need time to put the whole thing together. This might cost you a little extra. I'll handle it."

"You will handle it like you handled my speeding ticket?" Just then the guard approached our table and he began to escort me away.

Jerry stayed at our table and said, "Oh, shit. He's going to kill me."

Loren looked at him in rage. "You're not kidding. He has more than one reason."

Tolan glared at her, clearly blaming her for the current situation. "You have to stick around for a little while until I get the papers for your release."

The guards were walking me out of the courtroom. As I passed the table where the prosecuting attorneys were sitting, I saw McCain and Esquivel were smiling with satisfaction. I looked at them and shook my head as I thought to myself, *He who laughs last, laughs with more satisfaction.*

I went through the whole booking process again. In the back of the court house, the white-haired guard said jokingly, "Man, you hit the jackpot again. You made the headlines in the newspapers again."

I turned to him. "I will gladly give you all that fame if you want it."

He smiled. "Well, I don't know. If you include your girlfriend in the deal, I might consider it!"

I smiled back. "Don't you think you are a little too old for her?"

"I'm just joking, man. I have a beautiful wife waiting for me at home."

I smiled. They took me back to Terminal Island where my Mexican bodyguard friends received me with joy. They asked me how I was doing while expressing their regrets at seeing me in prison again.

Juan said, "Don't tell me they set you up, man. I warned you before. You have to be careful with these motherfuckers. They hate to be wrong and they will do whatever is necessary to prove they are right."

"You are right, my friend," I replied. "I was not cautious enough and they set me up. They must have planted that gun in my bag at the bank. It was my last stop before I got to court. They caught me by surprise. I knew they were bad, but I did not imagine they were that bad."

"Man, you are going to be the most famous man in this country. Look at the papers already! One of them says, 'The 23.5 million dollar man brings a gun to the federal courthouse!' This other paper says, 'The million dollar man gets busted again bringing a gun to the court to try to assassinate the judge!' Man, I didn't know you were such a heavyweight. Did you really try to kill the judge?"

I shook my head. "No, Juan. This whole thing is a setup. They wanted to send me back here. They just wanted to put pressure on me in the hope that I would tell them who is behind all this."

That night in my cell, I began to re-examine the events of that day. I replayed the whole day in my mind. I began to doubt everybody completely, including Loren. Was it just a coincidence, or was it something else that both times I had been arrested she had been with me? Could it be that she was just bad luck to me, or was there more to it than that?

I tried to convince myself that it was just bad luck, but I still had a sour taste in my mouth, and I could not completely shake my doubts. I was extremely distressed. I could not sleep for hours. I tossed and turned in my bed. No matter what, I was grateful because one of Juan's friends had been released. Since my original cell was occupied, they put me in the cell with Juan and his men. I knew my situation was getting extremely complicated now because breaking my bail stipulations and the gun charge could add years to my sentence—as if I did not already have enough to worry about.

I fell asleep with all this torment in my brain, and I had horrible nightmares. I dreamed that Charlie the Cleaner had snuck into the prison and was dressed like a guard. He put a pillow over my head and shot me several times using a pistol with a silencer. He walked out, and nobody noticed him. I was lying in bed, bleeding but unable to talk, so I could not ask for help.

I saw Pat McCain, David Esquivel, and O'Brien, all laughing at me. They all three grabbed me out of the bed while I was still living and took me close to the ocean where I saw the dolphins coming. They swung me and dropped me into the water. The dolphins turned into sharks, and grabbed and ripped me into pieces. I could feel the pain and I shuddered and jumped up. I sat on the side of the bed with sweat pouring off of me.

When I opened my eyes, Juan and the others were sitting around me. They had been pulling my arms to wake me up. Juan said, "Are you okay, man? Are you okay? You have been screaming. You woke us up."

"I had a terrible nightmare, man," I replied. "I dreamt somebody dropped me in the ocean and the sharks were eating me alive. They were ripping off my arms and legs and they were swimming off with my body parts! I have a horrible migraine!"

"It's been too much for you lately, man. Stress can kill you. You have to try to calm down and relax. Do you want a couple of aspirins?"

"No. Not two. I want four!"

One of the guys went for a glass of water and Juan gave me four aspirins. I put them in my mouth and chewed them.

"Oh, man!" Juan exclaimed in revulsion. "You give me goose bumps. How can you chew that? Doesn't it taste horrible?"

"Yes, but only for a few seconds. This way it goes directly into your bloodstream and you don't have to wait until your stomach digests it."

It was around 4:30 in the morning. I lay back down on the bed, and evidently I fell asleep. When everybody else went to breakfast, I remained in bed. The guard came and asked me why I was not in formation to go to breakfast.

"I feel sick," I told him. "I don't feel good."

"Do you want to go to the infirmary?"

"No. I will probably feel better in a little while. I just did not sleep well and I have a headache now."

At about 10:00 the others came back. They brought some fruit to me that they had managed to sneak out of the kitchen. I was feeling a little better, but the headache was lingering. I ate the fruit, and that seemed to help.

They called my name on the loudspeakers, stating that I had a visitor in the attorney room. I washed my face quickly and went to the visitor room. I was angry because I thought I was going to meet Tolan, and my headache increased. To my surprise, when I walked into the room there was a young man with a nerdy face and greasy, 1960s-style hair sitting at the table.

# Chapter 33—My Attorney's Paris Vacation

"Excuse me," I said as I started to back out the door. "I think I am in the wrong room."

"Dr. del Marmol?" he inquired. "Yes. Who are you?"

"I'm Ricky Johnson, your new attorney. Jerry Tolan had to go on a trip to Paris. I'll handle your case until he comes back. And when he returns, I'll continue to assist him because this is my first federal case and I need the experience. That's good for you because you'll have two attorneys for the price of one!"

I looked him up and down in utter disbelief. "You are going to be my attorney? Are you joking, or what?"

"No, I'm not, and yes, I'm really your attorney."

"Why did Jerry have to go to Paris? Especially now, when my case is even more complicated and I am in extreme jeopardy?"

"Sit down, Dr. del Marmol," he said very politely, "and I'll explain to you what happened. It might seem strange to you, but I know what I'm doing. Even though this is my first federal case, I've had many state cases and I've never lost a single one of them."

"I am very happy to hear that, but why is Jerry not here? He is the one who is familiar with my case."

He smiled enigmatically. "Well, unfortunately, his wife said if he did not take her to Paris, she was going to divorce him because he had not taken her on vacation for five years."

I threw up my arms in total disgust. "You mean to tell me that the big emergency that caused him to leave me here? I paid him twenty thousand dollars, and we are in the middle of an extremely delicate situation, but his wife wanted to go on vacation!? On top of him being an irresponsible attorney, a lousy friend, and a negligent individual, we have to add that he is pussy-whipped, too!"

Ricky shook his head. "I know. But that's the way Jerry is. But he's a good guy. He's got a good heart."

I looked at him and took a deep breath. "If Jerry has a good heart I don't want to be anywhere near a person who has a bad heart."

Ricky smiled again. "Come on, Dr. del Marmol. We have a lot of work to do in order to get you out of here. We have to prepare your case for when we go to court. You have to spill your guts and tell the whole truth to the Secret Service. That way, we'll make things easier and we'll get them on our side. These are the recommendations Jerry left for me to tell you." He then opened a file and showed me a note from Tolan.

I leaned over the table. "Listen to me very carefully. I don't even know you. I don't know where you came from. Now that you have shown me that note, I have no doubt in my mind that either Jerry sold his soul to the Secret Service or he is a complete moron. I am not opening my guts to anybody! You got that? If I open my guts it will stink so badly that everybody all over the country will have to hold their noses. Now, all I want you to do is get the papers from the court house and I will arrange bail. You have to fill out those papers for me. You know the legal mumbo jumbo. Do you think you can do that with no mistakes?"

"Of course," he said. "Of course I can do that."

I gave him a phone number and said, "This is the phone number for Miss Loren Thompson. Contact her, and she will put up the money for the bail, and I will get out. I will arrange that with her. Please don't do anything else for my case because there is not going to be a trial. It would just be a waste of paper and money. If you know where Mr. Jerry Tolan is staying in Paris, please send him a telegram and in capital letters tell him *he is fired*! I never want to see him again. I will pay for the telegram!"

Ricky looked at me in surprise. "Are you sure you want to do that? You're getting two attorneys for the price of one!"

"I don't go to the swap meet to shop for an attorney. You, Ricky, stick around. If I need any legal paperwork done, I will call you. Please tell that son of a bitch to not even dare to come near me ever again! Send me a check for whatever money has not been used and itemize my bill."

"I'll fill out the paperwork for you and get in touch with Miss Thompson."

I said goodbye to him and went back to the recreation area to call my father. I told him the situation as best I could. I said that I had been taken back to jail and whatever amount of money Loren asked of Hernesto, he should give it to her, as she was going to arrange my bail.

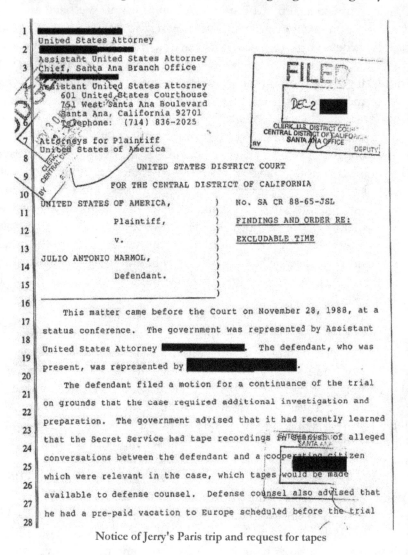

```
 1
     United States Attorney
 2
     Assistant United States Attorney
 3   Chief, Santa Ana Branch Office

 4   Assistant United States Attorney
        601 United States Courthouse
 5      751 West Santa Ana Boulevard
        Santa Ana, California 92701
 6      Telephone:  (714) 836-2025

 7   Attorneys for Plaintiff
     United States of America
 8
                          UNITED STATES DISTRICT COURT
 9
                    FOR THE CENTRAL DISTRICT OF CALIFORNIA
10
     UNITED STATES OF AMERICA,      )   No. SA CR 88-65-JSL
11
                  Plaintiff,        )   FINDINGS AND ORDER RE:
12
            v.                      )   EXCLUDABLE TIME
13
     JULIO ANTONIO MARMOL,          )
14
                  Defendant.        )
15                                  )
16
            This matter came before the Court on November 28, 1988, at a
17
     status conference.  The government was represented by Assistant
18
     United States Attorney ▮▮▮▮▮▮▮▮.  The defendant, who was
19
     present, was represented by ▮▮▮▮▮▮▮▮▮▮.
20
            The defendant filed a motion for a continuance of the trial
21
     on grounds that the case required additional investigation and
22
     preparation.  The government advised that it had recently learned
23
     that the Secret Service had tape recordings ▮▮▮▮▮▮▮ of alleged
24
     conversations between the defendant and a cooperating citizen
25
     which were relevant in the case, which tapes would be made
26
     available to defense counsel.  Defense counsel also advised that
27
     he had a pre-paid vacation to Europe scheduled before the trial
28
```

FILED
DEC 2 ▮▮▮
CLERK U.S. DISTRICT COURT
CENTRAL DISTRICT OF CALIFORNIA
SANTA ANA OFFICE
BY_____ DEPUTY

Notice of Jerry's Paris trip and request for tapes

"Don't you want us to handle that for you?" he asked.

"No, Dad. I don't want you or any of my friends to get anywhere near this problem. I do not want them to be implicated or exposed in any way. I need them on standby, just in case something goes wrong and I need their help. I will be out of here in a few weeks at the most."

"God bless you, my son. I hope to see you soon."

"Don't tell Mom I am in prison again. Tell her I am on a trip and I did not have a chance to say goodbye."

"I'm sorry, son. They interrupted her soap opera on TV with your picture and said you had been arrested again for bringing a gun into the federal courthouse."

"I'm sorry, Dad. I was trying to avoid her despair because I know her heart is not in the best condition. You take care of yourself."

We said goodbye and I told him again not to worry because I would be out in a few weeks at the maximum.

A week later, I was called back into the visitors' room. The man with the black suit and the black sunglasses had come again. When I walked into the room, he shook my hand and said, "How are you doing?"

"Not too good. I have been in here for a week already and my attorney is in Paris on vacation on my money. The substitute attorney has to be twenty times worse than my attorney. Birds of a feather flock together. I believe this is the third time he has filled out the papers for my bail, and they reject it each time because he did something wrong."

The man shook his head. "Where do you get these people? Even the judge told me to tell you to get a new attorney. You're making this process very difficult for us."

"I am sorry. I understand. This will never happen ever again. They caught me by surprise."

"You have to understand how many favors we're calling in to get you out of here. We can't do this again. If you give money to the wrong person or if your girlfriend screws up and brings another gun into court or any other type of thing like that, you'll make it very difficult for us. We cannot continue to intervene because we don't want to call attention to ourselves. Do you understand this?"

"I understand completely. I am sorry."

"You have to be extremely careful because the Secret Service is out to get you, and they're going to break every rule in the book to do it. They don't want to look like imbeciles in front of the whole nation and get to the point where they have to wipe this out like it never happened." He stood up and put his hand on my shoulder. "You know you have to do things right this time. I know you can because you have the capability and training for it. Do me a favor—start to walk alone as you did in the past. Stay by yourself when you're doing something important. At least, until you get out of this mess. I'll take care of your release from here. All your attorney has to do is fill out those forms properly."

"Don't worry about it. I will take care of that right now as soon as you leave."

We said goodbye and he hailed one of the guards. "We're done," he said and then left.

I went back to the recreation room and called my father. I told him to tell Hernesto to pick up Loren and go to any attorney in town that he thought was good and could fill out that form properly. "Don't let that moron Ricky touch any of my papers anymore," I finished.

"I don't think you need to worry about that. Loren has already filled out the bail papers and they are ready to take them to court tomorrow."

"Okay, Dad. Listen to me very carefully. Tell Hernesto to go with Loren to any attorney and pay whatever is necessary to review those papers to make sure nothing is missing. I don't want to spend any unnecessary time in here as a result of another stupid error. Tell Loren to please come over to see me after they file the papers. I will put her name on the visitor list for tomorrow at six p.m."

"Very well, my son. I will tell Hernesto, and it will be done the way you want it. Unfortunately, Hernesto wants me to tell you that Yaneba and Capitan Marrero had a bad accident. Evidently they went off the road on the highway to the Keys, close to Isla Morada. Their car turned over several times and went into the ocean. They nearly drowned and barely managed to survive. They're in both critical condition at a hospital in Miami."

"Oh, no, Dad. This is terrible. She is a wonderful woman. Please pray for them, and ask Mima to pray too."

"I will," my father said, then added, "Yaneba is very strong. She will probably survive."

"Yes, she might, but Capitan Marrero is an old man. He is, however, very strong, too. He spent all his life on the sea. The poor man went through hell in Cuba, and after he finally managed to get out of there, look what happened to him. Let's hope they both get better. Tell Hernesto to keep me posted about them."

The next day, Loren came to visit me. We sat down in the visitors' room, and she got a couple of cookies from the vending machine.

"Did you come by yourself?" I asked.

"Yes, I did."

"How did the filing of the papers go? Is everything okay now?"

"Yes," she responded, "it's already done. You should be out of here by tomorrow or the next day. We took them to an attorney as your father asked, and he said everything was well done and ready to go. He didn't have to do anything. It was a waste of a hundred dollars."

"I think it's better to spend a hundred dollars than to spend another week in here."

"Hernesto told me about your friend Yaneba and the accident she had. He's very concerned because he doesn't think they're going to make it."

"I know. Let's hope for the best. Do you need any money?"

"No, unless you want me to pay for something. I have my personal accounts and I'll be okay for a long time with the money you gave me in Vegas. I also have a few thousand dollars that your father gave to me the first time you were arrested. I didn't want him to feel bad, so I took it and put it into your bail money."

"Thank you. The reason I called you is to thank you for everything you have done for me and all the errands you have run for me since I have been in here. I've been asked to lie low until this whole situation is clarified, and I don't want anything bad to happen to you under any circumstances. I'm asking you to get a job and try to detach yourself from this whole situation. That way, if anything happens, you will not be hurt. You almost got in trouble the other day again, and I still don't know who put that gun in my bag."

"I understand." She touched her belly. "I will do that, not only for myself but for this treasure I am carrying. Do you believe that jerk, Ricky, asked me out?" she continued. "Who does he think he is? He told me I should start dating some other man because you'll be in jail for a long time. I told him I would tell you that. He didn't like that too much, but I don't care. Instead of concentrating on doing his job correctly and getting you out of here, he was spending more time trying to get under my skirt!"

I shook my head. "Why does that not surprise me? Well, don't worry. He is no longer my attorney. I don't need that kind of legal defense."

We said goodbye. Just then, a storm broke over the island.

Loren left the prison parking lot and drove her car down the coast road. The storm hit hard. Lightning flashed, high winds blew, and the rain poured down. Loren was caught in this horribly stormy weather as she tried to drive home, with winds frequently reaching hurricane force.

I tried to call a couple of hours later to find out if she had arrived home safely. However, the lightning strikes had caused a blackout, and the phones went dead. I was unable to reach her to ascertain that she had arrived home safely.

My head began to pound as another horrible migraine came on. I had a gut feeling that something was not right, especially after what had happened to Yaneba and Captain Marrero in Miami. I was not really convinced that it was just an accident.

Meanwhile, on the road, Loren's car entered a turn on a steep part of the road. She put her foot on the brake, but the car didn't slow down. She pumped the brakes madly, but on the next turn they failed completely. The car began to slide on the wet road, completely out of control. On the next turn the car slid off the road through a guard railing. Just as the car went off the road, Loren opened the door and jumped out. She managed to catch hold of the guard rail as the car went over the cliff. It rolled over several times, and was completely smashed by the time it hit the bottom.

Loren clung to the railing for dear life and managed to painfully pull herself back up the side of the cliff to the highway. She was bruised and cut, and her blouse was ripped, one of her sleeves hanging by a thread. It was raining hard, but she managed to spot an approaching highway patrol car.

She waved hysterically at the car, but it did not stop. She wondered whether they had even seen her, or if some other factor was at work.

Shortly after the highway patrol car had passed her by, a station wagon driven by a man and his family stopped. The man got out and asked her what had happened.

"I had an accident," Loren said. "My car went over the cliff." She then collapsed. His wife told the kids to stay in the car, and helped her husband carry Loren to their car to get her out of the rain. The man called an ambulance, and they stayed with her until it arrived. She was unconscious, and there was blood all over her skirt and legs.

When the paramedics arrived, they carried her out of the car and put her in the ambulance. Then they put an oxygen mask over her face. The man's wife asked, "Will she be okay?"

"I don't know," one of the paramedics answered. "It looks like she's lost a lot of blood. We have to get her to the hospital right away." With that, they drove off and took Loren to the emergency room.

I continued trying to call her house with no luck. I was unable to sleep because I was so worried. First thing in the morning, I called Loren again. There was no answer. Then I called my father and told him I had not heard from Loren and was concerned. I told him she had left the prison the night before, the weather was really bad, and I had been unable to contact her.

"I am sorry, my son," he said, "but the hospital called Hernesto early this morning. They found his number in Loren's purse. She had a bad accident and they said she is not in too good a shape."

"Oh no, Loren…?" My head hung for a moment. "Thank you, Dad. Tell Hernesto and the others that I might be having dinner with you guys tonight. They told me this morning that the papers for my bail just arrived here and are finally in order, and that I should be released this afternoon."

He made a happy sound and said, "Good! Good! We will see you tonight at dinner!"

A few hours later, they told me I needed to arrange for someone to pick me up as I would be released in an hour. I called my father again and told him to tell Hernesto to pick me up in one hour, and that they had told me I would be released by then. I said goodbye to Juan and his friends and walked out of Terminal Island for the second time. Hernesto and Elizabeth were waiting for me in the parking lot, and we hugged each other.

"God," said Hernesto, "this is the second time you have been in this place."

"Let's hope there will never be a third time!" I said. "Tell me, how are Yaneba and Capitan Marrero?"

Elizabeth replied, "I called the hospital in Miami this morning. They said both of them are still in a coma."

"That does not sound good," I said in concern.

Hernesto asked, "Don't you think it is too much of a coincidence that Loren had an accident last night, too?"

"Yes. Too much of a coincidence. That is the reason I want you and Elizabeth to find out where Loren's car has been taken. I want you to go there immediately before anybody else gets to that car and find out if there is anything suspicious or abnormal that could have caused that accident. Right now, though, I want to stop for a few minutes at the hospital and see how Loren is doing."

A little while later, we arrived at the hospital. Elizabeth parked the limo at the rear entrance of the hospital by the emergency entrance.

We all went in and to the desk where a nurse was sitting in the middle of the hallway.

I approached her and asked, "Could you please tell me where Ms. Loren Thompson is?"

"Yes," she answered. "Can you tell me who you are? Are you a member of the family?"

"I am Dr. del Marmol."

"You are a doctor?"

"Yes."

"Let me call her doctor. He can give you a better update on her condition." She picked up a speaker. "Dr. Reynold. Dr. Reynold, please. Dr. del Marmol wants to see you here in the E.R."

A few minutes passed, and a half bald man wearing a light green lab coat appeared in the hallway. He approached me and asked, "Are you Dr. del Marmol?"

"Yes. These are my friends, Hernesto and Elizabeth."

"Are you Ms. Thompson's family? Are you related?"

"I am her boyfriend, and we are all good friends."

He wiped his forehead with his fingers. "Well, actually she's conscious right now, but she's lost a lot of blood and is very weak. She has a small fracture in her elbow and right shoulder. Are you aware she was carrying a child?"

I looked at him sharply. "Yes, I know that, but what do you mean—*was* carrying a child?"

He put his hand on my shoulder. "Well, I'm sorry to tell you that she lost the baby."

I shook my head and we all looked at each other, momentarily struck silent. "Can we see her, please?"

"Of course. But she's very weak. She needs rest."

"I understand. We are only going to be with her for a few minutes." When we got into the room, we saw Loren had tubes in her nose, blood going into one arm, and an IV in the other. She was bruised, had a few cuts on her face and forehead, and the right side of her face was swollen. When she saw us, she looked at us, groggy from the sedatives. She said very softly, "Hi, guys."

Elizabeth walked close to her and asked, "What happened? Can you talk?"

Loren spoke with difficulty, but she managed to say, "My brakes didn't work. They were gone completely. The strange thing is that when I left Terminal Island my brakes were fine. I don't understand. It just seemed to happen in the middle of the road."

The three of us looked at each other. I came close to her, held her hand, and said, "Don't worry, sweetie. We will find out what happened. Whoever did this to you will pay for it."

"I'm sorry," she said. "I can't deal with this craziness anymore. As soon as I feel a little bit better, I'm going to leave town. I want to get as far away from here as possible." Two tears ran down her cheeks. "You know I loved our baby. You know I lost our baby. This is too much for me."

I nodded my head. "I understand. Please keep in touch. If you need anything, just call me. You know where you can find me, always." I bent over and gave her a little kiss on her forehead. "Try to rest. The doctor told me you will be okay."

Hernesto said, "Get well, and God bless you." He and I stepped out of the room. Elizabeth stayed with her a little longer. He looked at me seriously. "This was not an accident. Somebody tried to take her out of the way. I have an idea how they did it. I will let you know by tonight."

We waited for Elizabeth in the hallway for a little while. When she came out of the room, she was wiping tears from her eyes. She never told me what Loren told her, but whatever they had talked about had made her very emotional. We walked out of the hospital, got into the limo, and drove towards Newport Beach.

I picked up the phone in the limo and called O'Brien. "How are you doing?" he asked when he answered. "Is everything okay?"

"Yes. I am out already."

"Thank God. I don't know what university those attorneys of yours went to, but all they did was screw everything up. I want you to keep very low because you're actually walking on glass right now."

"Yes, I will, but I need you to do me a favor right now. I need a copy of that pre-sentence report today. I want to know in detail what the Secret Service told these people to make the judge say that was the worst report he had ever had in his hands."

"Okay. I'll put it in your hands in a couple of hours."

Elizabeth and Hernesto dropped me off at my house on Lido. Not even an hour later, O'Brien called me and said he wanted to meet me at the Balboa Bay Club in half an hour.

389

# Chapter 34–Pre-Sentence Report

Half an hour later, I met O'Brien on the yacht. We sat down and each got a glass of wine. He handed me some documents. "You aren't going to believe what the Secret Service said about you in this report."

I took it in my hand and read it thoroughly. When I finished, I was livid. "What lying sons of bitches!"

He handed me a piece of paper with a telephone number on it. "This is Ms. Foster's direct line."

"Thank you very much. This time I will take care of this once and for all."

We parted after giving each other a hug, and I walked out and got into my car. I picked up the phone and called the number.

"Pre-sentence Report Office. Ms. Foster speaking. Can I help you?"

"Yes, Ms. Foster. This is Dr. del Marmol. I know you are an extremely busy person, and I assure you I am not going to waste your precious time. I just need to clarify that malicious information you got from the Secret Service about me. The information is completely false. Yes, they do lie, and I can prove it. I believe you are a decent person, and you want that report to be accurate, don't you?"

"Of course I do," she answered. "That's my job."

"Give me the opportunity to meet with you for a few minutes and I will prove to you the truth."

"How long will it take for you to get over here? We are in Los Angeles."

"I know where you are. Give me a couple of hours because I have to gather some information to complete my report to you."

"Okay. I'll wait a couple of hours for you."

As soon as I hung up, I called the Secret Service office and asked to speak to Pat McCain. When he came on the line, I said, "I understand you have my leather bag that Loren brought to the court that contained the pistol. Can you please return that to me because it has my driver's license, check books, and everything? It has all my identification and documentation."

"You're out already?" he asked in surprise. "Either you have a great influence over the legal system or you've got a great attorney."

I smiled. "No. Neither one. Justice always prevails. May I pick up my leather bag, please?"

"Sure. Come on over. We'll wait for you. Actually, I want to ask you a few questions about Jacobo and your friend Amelia."

"Sure. I will be there shortly."

About twenty minutes later, I was in the office of the Secret Service. I rang the buzzer and Esquivel came and opened the door for me.

"How are you, my friend?" he asked. "It's good to see you. You look good."

"Thank you," I replied. "Where's McCain?"

"He's waiting for you. Follow me."

When we got to McCain's office, he asked, "How are you? How are you doing? I love that suit you're wearing. It must be very expensive. My God, that watch you're wearing! Is that a Rolex? It probably cost twenty or thirty thousand dollars, right?"

I smiled but did not answer him. Instead, I said, "Hey. How are you guys doing? It's good to see you. Have you made any new arrests from all that information I gave to you?"

"No," McCain said. "Everything turns into smoke."

"How come?" I asked in astonishment. "I took you to my associate's house and the houses of all those guys who financed the whole thing. I even took you to one of their businesses—that used car dealer. Why have you not been able to arrest anybody?"

He scratched his head. "I don't know. Maybe we made too much noise with the newspapers and the TV. Every time we move to arrest somebody, they've either moved or are nowhere to be found."

I shook my head. "I told your boss not to put it in the paper. He didn't listen to me. That's what you get. Scared the birds. I did my best. I cooperated with you guys. I did my best."

"You did more than your best," McCain assured me. "You even risked your life putting wires on yourself when we went to find those people. You went overboard to help us, which most people won't do."

"I have a question for you," I said. "If you feel that way, how the hell did that woman from the Pre-sentence Office get all that bad information about me that made me look and sound like Al Capone?"

"I don't know," he answered. "She's a young bimbo. She doesn't even know how to wipe her ass yet. I don't know how they give people like that positions of such responsibility. I never told her anything bad about you. Isn't that true, Esquivel? Did you ever say anything bad about Dr. del Marmol to her?"

Esquivel reclined in his chair. "I had nothing to do with it. She's a lying bitch who screwed up that report on purpose, just to make you look bad."

"I believe you guys," I said. "I totally believe you because you, Esquivel, burned my balls with hot tea and you kicked me and gave me a fat lip and pushed me around and held me for twelve hours in that basement. You humiliated me and screamed all kinds of obscenities at me and Loren, and even touched Loren sexually to make her freak out. I never raised a finger to complain about you guys."

"You guys were lucky that was all you got," Esquivel said.

"Listen, Esquivel," I said, "whatever happened is water under the bridge. I am only trying to find out why that woman made such a lousy report about me."

"I can't believe they let idiots like that work for their office," he said. "But don't worry; Pat and I are going to straighten things out in the courtroom."

"You are?" I asked in surprise.

"That Pre-sentence Office bitch totally screwed this whole thing up. When we straighten this crap out in court, I'll be she loses her job. It'll be a great laugh. She'll look ridiculous because we're going to put her in the hot seat when we deny everything."

I noticed McCain was listening to Esquivel with interest.

I said, "I really appreciate this, guys. I feel a lot better. You asked me to trust you when I gave you all that help. I played informant for you, and I have never been an informant before in all my life. McCain, you told me that I probably would not spend even one more day in jail because of all these great things I have done for you guys."

"Oh, yeah," McCain said, "you were great. You did more than most people. You really helped us out on lots of investigations. I've no problem with you at all."

"Since you feel that way, McCain and Esquivel, would you mind giving me a little note saying how you feel? You know, stating how great I've been at helping you guys and what a wonderful person I am. That even though I have been involved in this counterfeit situation, I am not a criminal and these guys actually used me and took advantage of my good nature."

"Actually," said McCain, "we can't do that because of the regulations in our department. They prohibit us from getting involved in court proceedings. But man, this is going to be better for you. This is going to be a surprise to Ms. Foster. Imagine her coming to court with that stupid false report, and Esquivel and I'll say we never told her that. It's all lies. She'll want to crawl in a hole like an ostrich."

I smiled. "Okay, McCain. I am going to trust you guys. Please don't screw this up. My life is on the line here, okay?"

McCain stood up. "Man, don't worry about it. You're great. You've really helped us a lot in our investigations, and we won't let you down. Oh, I have a couple more questions to ask you before you leave. Do you have any involvement with Amelia? She's under investigation for major insurance fraud. Jacobo told us that you're very close to her."

"Really close to her? I cannot say I am really close to her. I just went to her clinic a few times and she gave me some therapy for a couple of accidents that happened in the past. I don't know anything about any fraud or anything she has done that is illegal. To me, she is an extraordinary woman and a very hard worker. She is a single mother struggling to raise a child by herself."

"Okay," McCain said. "That's all I want to know. Thank you."

I left the Secret Service office with a big smile on my face and walked out of the federal building to the parking lot and my red DeLorean. I grabbed the phone as soon as I got into the car, took two tape recorders off of my chest that had been taped to my skin, and called Ms. Foster.

"This is the Pre-sentence Report Office, Ms. Foster speaking. May I help you?"

"Hello, Ms. Foster. This is Dr. del Marmol."

"Yes, Dr. del Marmol?"

"I am leaving Orange County right now. I will be there a little early if that is all right with you."

"That's fine," she said. "As a matter of fact, that's even better for me because then I can leave earlier, too. By the way, my supervisor, Mr. Wilson, wants to be here and will be a part of our meeting, if that's okay with you."

"Absolutely. I will be delighted to include your supervisor in our conversation. Tell Mr. Wilson I am on my way right now."

When I arrived at the Pre-sentence Service Office in downtown Los Angeles, Ms. Foster met me with a tall, half-bald man with a not-too-friendly face.

"We've been waiting for you, Dr. del Marmol. Come on in."

I followed her into a conference room in silence. When we were inside the room, she introduced us. We shook hands and sat down at the long table.

Mr. Wilson said, "Well, Ms. Foster has informed me that you have very conclusive evidence that the Secret Service has been lying to us and playing us for fools."

"Not only you, sir," I responded, "but they have also been playing me for a fool. I have been breaking my back trying to help them, and look at the kind of information they have given you about me." I pulled the report they had presented in court and laid it on the table.

Mr. Wilson's manner became hostile. "How did you get that report?" he asked sharply.

I looked him directly in the eyes and answered quite seriously, "I have my sources. I am sorry, but I cannot reveal them to you. The important thing is that this whole report is based on complete lies, distortion, and misinformation. They told me they would give me a good report because of all the cooperation I gave to them. That is nowhere in this report."

Ms. Foster said, "They didn't say you cooperated. They said you stalled them at every opportunity you could. I never had any reason to question them, or any other government agency."

"Yes, I know," Mr. Wilson replied. "That's policy. But our report must be beyond question for us to survive, and it has to be completely truthful. We cannot afford to not be or we open the window for anyone who wants to destroy a person to do just that. That's why we're here now. You'd better have good evidence for us to even consider submitting a changed report to the judge. If we change our report, we're admitting to the judge that we were wrong and didn't do our job properly in the first place."

"With all respect, Mr. Wilson," I replied, "I understand exactly what you have just told me." I took the cassette player out of my briefcase and said, "I am going to play this for you. This is a conversation between me, Agents Pat McCain, and David Esquivel, less than one hour ago. After you hear this, you can do what your heart and your principles tell you to do. They were trying to put me in jail for a long time for their own personal gain and for the publicity this case involved, using your office as a weapon."

I pressed the play button on the cassette and turned up the volume. At first they both listened closely, and their mouths started to drop as the conversation progressed. Then the part of the tape began to play where the two agents started to talk about what a great job I had done for them, even risking my life by allowing them to put recording wires on my body when we went on the goose chase of trying to get the ghost people who ostensibly worked with me on the counterfeit job.

Ms. Foster was so angry she had tears in her eyes. Mr. Wilson was shaking his head. "I can't believe this!" he says. "We were completely taken in by these two. We believed they were telling us the truth."

"I never liked those two," Ms. Foster fumed. "There was something about them I didn't quite trust, but I never dreamed someone from the Secret Service would do that to us."

Mr. Wilson asked, "Dr. del Marmol, can you please leave me one copy of this tape?"

"With pleasure. I made two just in case one failed. Do you want the mini or the regular tape?"

"Either one is fine with me. I'll call the judge first thing in the morning and request permission to make a new report, even if I have to drive myself personally to Orange County. I'm going to play this tomorrow for the judge. I'll request the judge to give us an extra week for your appearance to prepare an addendum to the pre-sentence report that will override the initial one that we presented."

"Does this mean that you will make a good report this time that will be in my favor?" I asked.

"I'm sorry, Dr. del Marmol, but I can't reveal what we'll put in that report. It's only for the judge's eyes. But off the record, I'll tell you that you can go back home and sleep very well."

"Thank you very much, sir." I looked at Ms. Foster sympathetically. "You are a wonderful and decent woman. You are nothing like those indecent men described on that tape."

She smiled. "Thank you, Dr. del Marmol. You're a very decent man, too, and I'm sorry for our mistake."

"We'll call you tomorrow," Mr. Wilson added, "and let you know when your next court sentence date will be. We'll also notify you by mail."

I left them and was so happy that I nearly exploded as I stepped into the elevator.

I drove back to Orange County and to my parent's house in Corona del Mar. They were overjoyed to see me.

My mother hugged me with tears in her eyes. "No more jail, all right? You be a good boy."

My father smiled, looked at me, and shook his head. "Mima, leave him alone. He has enough problems without you reprimanding him."

"I am not reprimanding him," she protested. "I am tired of seeing him on the TV, interrupting my soap opera!"

Dad and I both laughed, and I said, "Oh—it's your soap opera you are concerned about, then, and not me!"

She smiled and my father shook his head again. The day was nearing an end and the sun began to set. It was a beautiful sunset in Corona del Mar that night.

UNITED STATES DISTRICT COURT
CENTRAL DISTRICT OF CALIFORNIA
PROBATION OFFICE

*FILE COPY*

████████████████
██████████████████████
IF PROBATION OFFICER

O U.S. COURT HOUSE
2 N. SPRING STREET
IS ANGELES, 90012

SUPPLEMENTAL

Honorable J. ██████████████████
United States District Judge
United States Court House
751 West Santa Ana Boulevard
Santa Ana, California 92701-4599

        Re:  MARMOL, Julio Antonio
             Docket Nos. SA 88-0367M &
                         SA 88-00065

Dear Judge ████:

According to the criminal minutes, dated July 17, 1989, the Court ordered the Probation Officer to submit a supplemental report. Sentencing was continued to September 8, 1989.

Defense counsel wished the defendant's continued cooperation with authorities, additional character reference letters, revised financial status, recent Department of Motor Vehicles (DMV) records, and an alleged U.S. Court translation of the defendant's conversation transcripts, be reviewed and considered.

The defendant provided a DMV order of reinstatement, dated April 17, 1989. This statement reflects action taken against his driving privileges has been canceled. Defense counsel contends the reason the defendant's license was suspended was due to a ticket, which went to warrant while he was detained on the present charges. Accordingly, such matter has been resolved.

Additional character reference letters were provided to the Probation Office which are attached for review. They collectively reflect the authors' opinion that the defendant is an honest, trustworthy and intelligent individual. Furthermore, he is viewed as one with high values who has a cause, and will defend his beliefs. The defendant reportedly assisted his family in their endeavors to leave Communist Cuba and arrive in the United States, a country he loves. He is seen as having a big heart, never greedy, and always available to help others.

Supplemental Pre-Sentence Report

My mother announced, "Dinner will be ready in about an hour. Are you hungry?"

"Yes," I replied, "I am starving!"

"Okay. I am going to bring some fried finger meatballs and banana chips. What do you want to drink?"

"A glass of wine would be great, Mom," I said.

"Me, too," my father said.

My mother smiled and said, "I'm making *duck à l'orange*. I don't want you guys to get all filled up and leave my main course untouched."

I laughed. "Mom, I could eat a cow! Especially with all that lousy food I have been eating in prison."

Dad and I sat down on the terrace and enjoyed a glass of wine and a beautiful sunset. He asked me if I had any news lately from Cuba about his grandson. I looked him directly in the eyes and knew I could not lie to him. I had tried to keep this bad news from them, but decided this was the moment to tell him what had happened.

"Dad, I am sorry to tell you that Castro and his people killed my son. Probably in retaliation for what I have been doing to them. Since they could not get to me, I think they decided this was the best way to hurt me. I did not tell you because this happened in the middle of all this trouble I have been having, and I did not want to bring any more frustration and sorrow to you than what you already were dealing with."

His eyes filled and tears rolled down his cheeks. He put his glass of wine down on the table and put his right hand to his forehead as he tried to wipe away his tears. "Why? Why my grandson? He was such a good boy. Do you know how this happened?"

"According to the information I have, a military truck hit him and ran over him while he was on his motorcycle. He hit his head against a light pole. If it is any consolation, they told me he went into a coma and died shortly after they took him to the hospital, so I don't think he suffered too much."

"I don't know how Mima is going to take this," he said. "She loved him so much, the same as she loves you. I think it is best that we keep this from her for a while. Her heart condition."

"I have no intention of telling her, Dad. I told you because you asked me and I thought it only fair for you to know."

Just then, Mima came out on the terrace with a plate of snacks. We stopped talking, and she asked, "Why are you guys so silent?"

My father grabbed his glass of wine, stood up, and pulled himself together. He turned around so Mima could not see the tears in his eyes, and walked to the railing. He pointed to the ocean and the sunset and said, "Why should we be talking when God has displayed this beautiful sunset for us to see?"

Mima came close to him and rubbed his back. "You are getting romantic in your old age! I like it." She took the glass from his hand, sipped a bit of it, and handed it back to him. She kissed him on the cheek and said, "Enjoy your beautiful sunset." She turned and went back into the kitchen.

After she left, my father came back and sat down by me. "She is so happy to see you back here. We should not ruin her happiness." I nodded and he continued, "Let's try to keep this to ourselves for as long as we can. I don't think it will be too long because you know how smart your mom is. She will probably find out soon."

We stayed on the terrace until Mima called us to dinner. We went inside, sat down at the dining room table, and began to eat.

# Chapter 35—The Rude Awakening for the Secret Service

Meanwhile, Hernesto and Elizabeth, dressed in black, made their way to the fence of the wrecking yard where Loren's car had been taken. Two big Doberman pincers ran to the fence and began barking at them. Hernesto took two big chunks of ham out of a plastic bag. He tossed them over the fence, one to each dog. The dogs stopped barking immediately and started to eat the ham. My friends walked to some nearby bushes and sat down on a rock to wait.

Elizabeth asked, "Will they die?"

"No, they will probably sleep for a day or two, though."

"A day or two! How much sedative did you put in that ham?"

"I'm only kidding. They will have sweet dreams for several hours. They will be in dog heaven maybe overnight."

About twenty minutes later, he checked on the dogs. They were out cold. They climbed over the fence and walked around the yard, looking for Loren's white Ford Bronco. It took them nearly half an hour to find it because there were so many cars in there. Finally, they found her car and examined it with a small flashlight.

Elizabeth said, "Oh, look at this. I found Loren's little fox jacket that she wears all the time. It was crammed under the back seat. It had a rip in one of the sleeves."

"Will you please point the flashlight under the car on this side?" Hernesto asked. "I see something funny hanging there. Forget about the coat, woman. We have to get out of here quickly. Loren probably has several of those jackets, anyway."

She came over to point the flashlight where he wanted it. She was also carrying the jacket. "You men! This could be her favorite jacket. Anyway, it's hers. I am going to take it back to her!"

"Son of a bitch!" Hernesto exclaimed. "Look at this!" He pulled down a rubber tube that looked like a hospital IV drip tube with a valve attached to regulate the amount of fluid to be eliminated. This tube was connected to the brake line master cylinder with a thick needle. He carefully removed the line and showed it to Elizabeth. "It's unbelievable, but with this little thing you can kill somebody. All you need to do is calculate the distance the person is going to drive and where you think the worst place will be for the master cylinder to get completely empty. Then they have no brakes at all!"

"Son of a bitch!" said Elizabeth. "Who do you think would do this?"

"It could be the Secret Service because they did not want her around helping our friend, or it could be the MQ1 because they know by now what probably happened with Sanchez, or it could be anybody with a motive unknown to us." He wrapped up the IV line and put it into the same bag that had contained the ham for the dogs. They jumped the fence again and drove away with the headlights off.

Hernesto called my father, who gave the phone to me, saying, "Hernesto wants to talk to you."

I took the phone from my father. "What's up, you guys? Is everything okay?"

"Yeah," Hernesto replied. "We have a good surprise for you."

"Hurry up. My mom made a great *duck à l'orange*, and you don't want to miss it."

A little while later, they arrived at the house and Hernesto waved his hands. "Mmm. It smells good in here. I have to wash my hands, but I will be back in a minute."

Elizabeth looked at him. "You didn't use gloves?"

"A cat with gloves cannot catch a mouse," he replied. "I had to remove them in order to disconnect the IV line." He took a paper towel from the wall and placed it on the kitchen counter. He took the plastic bag and waved it at me. "You're not going to believe what we found in Loren's car." Then he began to wash his hands.

"You guys excuse me," Elizabeth said. "I am going to wash my hands in the bathroom. I am not going to change my clothes, though. I am too hungry."

"Don't worry about it," I said. "You are at home. You don't have to change clothes."

"I will start to serve your plates," my mother said.

In a few minutes, they both came back to the table and began to eat. We were nearly finished, but we waited for them to have dessert.

Hernesto told me, "They put an IV line to drain Loren's master cylinder. That was not an accident."

Elizabeth said, "That is one of the oldest tricks in the world when you want to kill somebody and leave no trace. What I don't understand is why they didn't send someone to remove that IV line before we got to it."

"They might already have sent someone," Hernesto said, "and they could not find the car or else they could have been intimidated by those dogs."

"That doesn't make sense to me," Elizabeth disagreed. "People who would do that to Loren would not stop just because of a couple of Dobermans."

"It took us nearly half an hour to find the car," Hernesto pointed out. "Maybe they came and could not find it. They might go back or they might assume the car is in another yard and they could be checking out another place."

Elizabeth nodded her head. "Well, maybe you have a point. Maybe we were just a step ahead of them."

"Who would want to kill that poor girl?" my father asked. "She is harmless. She looks like an angel."

Elizabeth looked at Hernesto, and they both looked at me. I said, "Let's hope it was not because of me that they tried to kill her. But Dad, everything in life is not always the way it appears to be."

We had a great dinner. I examined the IV line and wrapped it in a second plastic bag before putting it in my briefcase. I left the house and called O'Brien on his emergency line. We agreed to meet at the Santa Ana train terminal, about half an hour later. When I arrived, he was already waiting for me on one of the benches in the terminal. After we greeted each other, I sat down beside him and opened my briefcase. I handed him the plastic bag. I also handed him a pair of rubber gloves.

He put them on, opened the bag, and examined the IV line. He shook his head. "This is very strange. This is not from someone we know. Either the Secret Service just tried to scare her and not kill her, or else someone is trying to send you a warning."

"What do you mean?"

"I don't know for sure, but it could be someone in our own intelligence group with no clue as to what we're doing. Anyway, I'm not sure. Give me a little time, and I'll try to find out. By the way, congratulations. You did a great job convincing the people in the Pre-sentence Office of your innocence. I saw the new report. It's like night and day compared to the other one. The judge is very happy with this. I'm glad everything's working out for you. You'll probably just spend a few months in a federal camp, so enjoy your vacation. You know how those federal camps are. There's an Olympic swimming pool, no iron gates—just a line on the ground that limits the areas where you can go, a chapel, a library, and great food. This'll give you the time to write that book you've wanted to for a long time. When you write that book and you talk about me, be gentle. Don't describe me as a grumpy old man."

I smiled. "You are not a grumpy old man. You are just a little complicated sometimes."

"I wasn't planning to tell you this until I was sure, but since you're in such a good mood now, I want to make you feel even better. The love of your life is extremely pissed off at what happened to your son in Cuba. I'm really sorry about that, by the way. We've been arranging in the past weeks to bring her to the United States through Mexico. She can be a great asset for our intelligence community because of the position she had in Cuba."

I shook my head in stunned disbelief. "You must be kidding! Right? She is not going to leave her family there."

"My friend, she has no family left there. Her father died a few months ago, and her mother died only a few weeks ago."

"Shit! Do you think it was natural causes, an accident, or were they killed?"

He shook his head. "In this business, we never know. It can look like natural causes or an accident, but there could be a third hand hiding behind the real cause."

"So, you are not kidding?"

"No. We're still making arrangements, but I think in a couple of weeks you and I will be taking a trip to Cancun, and maybe we'll be bringing your honey back with us."

"Well, I don't know. It has been a long time, but I will be very happy to see her. Probably my mom and dad will be happy to see her, too. Make sure our trip does not conflict with my final appearance in court."

He smiled. "Don't worry. You know how we arrange things. Besides, you'll have to travel under an assumed name because of the restrictions on you right now. We don't want to get you into any more trouble."

I patted him on the shoulder. "Thank you, my friend. Isn't it strange how God makes things happen sometimes in our lives? No matter how many times we go around in the world, sometimes we end up in the same place we started!"

We parted company and I went back to my house on Lido Island.

Ten days later, Elizabeth, Hernesto, and I took Loren to the Los Angeles airport. Loren, Elizabeth noticed, was wearing a black fox jacket. She smiled and said, "You did a great job sewing that jacket. It doesn't even show where it was ripped before."

Loren smiled back at her. "Believe it or not, I don't sew. J. Anthony sewed it for me."

"You sewed that, man?" Hernesto exclaimed.

"That is one of the many things my mom taught me," I replied. "It really has come in handy. More than a couple of times, I went to bend over and my pants ripped open like a machine gun, and my whole butt all the way to my balls was exposed. You could see my underwear. I had to go to the gift shop in the hotel where I was staying and buy a little sewing kit and then go back to my room with my back against the wall of the elevator. When I got back to my room, I sewed up my pants, and I was back in business!"

Elizabeth and Hernesto laughed. Hernesto said, "Are you kidding? Is that really true, man?"

"Yes, it's true. You are no less macho just because you can sew and cover your ass!"

Hernesto, who was sitting in the passenger seat in the front of the car, asked Loren, "Would you mind taking off your jacket so I can see what he did?"

"Why do you want to see it?" she asked.

"I want to see it close up. I saw it ripped. I am the one who took it out of the car."

"Liar," accused Elizabeth. "I am the one who took it out of the car."

"Okay," he conceded, "we both took it out of the car. You found it."

Loren took off the jacket and handed it to him. He looked at it closely and marveled, "Man! You cannot even see the thread here. How did you do this? This is great. I have a couple of things in my wardrobe that need repair. Would you mind helping me with them?"

"Dream on," I said. "I am not your tailor. I will teach you, though, and you can do it yourself. I guarantee you will not be less macho for that."

He smiled. "Okay. I will take you up on that offer whenever we have the time."

We got into the airport, and I told Elizabeth, "Don't park in the garage. Just drive around a couple of times. Pick us up right here at the same gate in a little while. We won't be long."

Elizabeth stopped in front of the terminal gate at the loading zone. One of the luggage attendants approached us immediately when he saw the limo. He put Loren's luggage in one of the tenders and gave her the tickets. Another man took the plane tickets, processed them, and told her where she had to go. Elizabeth hugged Loren and said goodbye. Hernesto and I walked with her into the terminal and accompanied her all the way to the waiting area. She hugged Hernesto and said, "Don't let anything happen to him." Then, with tears in her eyes, she hugged me. "Well, this is it. You take care of yourself, okay?" She gave me a tender kiss on my lips.

"You take care of yourself, too."

"I'm sorry it didn't work out for us," she whispered. "I hope you find what you are looking for one day."

We said goodbye, and she turned around and walked away.

Hernesto and I went back out to the front of the terminal where Elizabeth had dropped us off. We waited a few minutes until she arrived. We got into the limo and took off.

A few days later, I called O'Brien. "Is everything still as planned? Are the cigars coming from Cuba or not?"

"Well, the cigars have some wrinkles and we've got to iron them out. We'll probably be able to smoke them after your court appearance. Don't worry. Nothing's changed. It's just taking a little more time. You know how customs work—there's always a lot of red tape and paperwork."

"Okay. No problem."

I hired a new attorney who would only represent me in court when I was sentenced. His name was James Barnett. He was very professional and told me not to worry. He said I would have no problem at all; he also had no idea of what was going on. I smiled at his assurances and said "Yes, I know. I will see you at nine a.m. on the appointed day."

When that day arrived, we went to the courtroom, which was now completely empty. The case had been ordered sealed, and only interested parties were allowed—no newspapers or TV people. Only the prosecutors, the Secret Service, the Pre-sentence Service people, Mr. Wilson and Ms. Foster, and my parents were there. The judge was waiting for Mr. Wilson to present a new report.

"Your Honor," Mr. Wilson said, "this second report is being presented as a revised report because the first one was based on false information."

The judge slid his glasses down on his nose, looked over them, and said, "Really?" He appeared to be surprised. "I don't remember your organization ever doing this before!"

"That's right, Your Honor. But accuracy is what we base our reports on, and in this particular case there were some very strange distortions of the facts. We were very lucky to discover the truth just in time."

The judge was holding the report in his hand. "Is this one accurate now?"

With a smile on his face, Mr. Wilson answered, "Completely, Your Honor. It's very rare that I say this, but Ms. Foster and I have personally and meticulously investigated this, and we've come to these conclusions together."

After the judge read the report, he looked at me. "Dr. del Marmol, will you please stand up? Before I pass sentence on you, I am pleased to inform you that this court has received over fifty letters on your behalf, telling us what a great individual you are. The names of some of your supporters are startling. They reflect very highly on your moral character. I have to tell you also, as long as I've been sitting on this bench, that I've never received so many letters on behalf of anyone!"

"Thank you very much, Your Honor."

"Considering the details of this case, you should never have even been charged, let alone gone to jail. I am dropping the charges in reference to your bringing in a gun to the courtroom. My findings prove that you had no connection with that weapon. Actually, you should not even be here right now. However, I am obligated to impose a minimum sentence of at least of one year. You are going to receive six months credit for time served. That leaves you with six months. You will serve that time at the Boron Federal Camp. With good behavior, you will probably be released sooner. Let this court know how much time you need to put your business affairs in order, and

405

then when that time has expired, you will present yourself to the authorities at the Boron Federal Camp Facility. Don't prove me wrong, Dr. del Marmol."

"I won't," I said. "Thank you very much, Your Honor. You have been very fair."

He brought his gavel down hard on the top of his desk. "Court adjourned."

Mr. Barnett, the new attorney, stood up and said, "Congratulations, Dr. del Marmol. I don't know how you did it, but I've never been in a courtroom where the judge liked the person he was about to sentence so much."

Mr. Wilson also came over and shook my hand. "Good luck to you, and thank you very much for your honesty and for being so straightforward with us."

"Thank you, sir," I replied, "for being such an ethical and moral individual."

"I'm only what's right," he said, glaring at Pat McCain and David Esquivel, who were looking at me in absolute incomprehension, their jaws dropped. "It's my job."

Ms. Foster hugged me. "Good luck to you, Dr. del Marmol."

"Thank you very much," I replied to her, "and good luck to you also, Ms. Foster. I hope you last many years in the Pre-sentence Office because you are an extraordinary human being."

My mother came up to me. "You have to go to jail for six months, my son?"

My father smiled. "Mima, it's okay. We will explain everything to you at home. Thank God that is all he got!"

Elizabeth and Hernesto were waiting outside in the limo. When I broke the news to them, Elizabeth started to cry and Hernesto gave me a big hug. Mr. Barnett approached me and said, "Before you leave, go into the office of the Secret Service. They just informed me that they have in their possession six thousand dollars in real money that they confiscated from you when you were arrested the first time. They want to return it to you. Do you want me to go with you?"

"No," I said, "it is not necessary. Go ahead and finish your paperwork and please send me the bill."

"Your retainer is more than enough," he said with a rueful smile. "I will issue a refund check to you. This case was a lot easier than I expected."

MR. JULIO ANTONIO MARMOL

Santa Ana, CA  92704

DATE ▇▇▇▇▇▇▇▇▇▇▇

Docket No. 88-00367
Exp. Date: ▇▇▇▇▇
DOB: ▇▇▇▇▇▇

YOU ARE AUTHORIZED TO TRAVEL TO _____ MEXICO _____

LEAVING ▇▇▇▇▇▇▇▇▇▇▇▇ AND RETURNING ___Indefinite___

WITHIN 24 HOURS AFTER YOUR RETURN YOU WILL CONTACT THIS OFFICE.

PURPOSE OF THIS TRIP:  TEMPORARY RELOCATION TO HOME ON MISSION SAN FERNANDO.

SPECIAL INSTRUCTIONS:

▇▇▇▇▇▇▇▇▇▇▇▇▇▇▇▇
UNITED STATES PROBATION OFFICER

Post Sentencing Release Papers

I told Hernesto and Elizabeth to take my parents to the limo and to drive around the block. I figured I would be back and waiting for them on the sidewalk in about ten minutes. I went into the federal building and to the office of the Secret Service. When I got there, I rang the buzzer on the door and looked into the camera. A few seconds later, McCain opened the door. A blonde lady in her forties was standing by him.

"Oh, hello, Dr. del Marmol," McCain said. "Speak of the devil! By the way, this is Deborah—she represents the highway patrol office."

"I've heard a lot about you!" she said.

"Oh, yeah. It must be all good, no?"

She shook her head. "Not exactly."

"Oh, well, you cannot please everybody." I turned to McCain. "I am here because my attorney informed me that you guys want to return some money that you took from me when you first arrested me."

"Yeah, yeah," McCain said. "Follow me to my office. You'll need to sign some papers." I followed him, observing that Deborah followed as well. When we got to McCain's office, he pulled out a manila envelope. He pulled out the money that was inside and gave it to me. "Sign this paper. It's a receipt verifying you received six thousand dollars from us." I took the bundles and spread them out. There were three bundles. I checked to be sure they were the same height and put them back in the envelope. "Don't you want to count it?" he asked.

"No," I said, "it's not necessary. It's fine."

He smiled. "What if there are a couple of hundred dollar bills missing in each of those bundles?"

"Then you keep it, like a tip," I said with a smile.

Just then, David Esquivel came into the office. "Hell! You got away with murder! You lied to us from the beginning."

I turned around, still smiling. "My father told me to never call someone else what you really are. You are the liar! That's why you think everybody else is like you."

"David," McCain said, "calm down. Everything's over. The court of law's made its determination. Actually, I'm surprised, too. I can't figure out how you did it."

"Remember what I told you a while ago about your award that was hanging behind your desk?" I asked a trifle smugly. "I only see two holes there now. What happened?"

He shook his head and smiled cynically. "Let's not talk about that, okay? By the way, Deborah wants to ask you a few questions about Amelia and her insurance fraud."

"I am through talking with anybody about anything," I declared. "It seems to me that every time I say something you manage to maliciously turn it around and try to crucify someone. I have learned my lesson and I have put a zipper on my mouth."

Deborah said, "Dr. del Marmol, I would really appreciate having a few words with you. I can make your life difficult because Amelia said you had knowledge of what she's been doing. Remember, you still have a warrant for your arrest for failure to appear for a speeding ticket."

I looked her up and down. "I think you should update your information. My ticket has already been taken care of. Check my record, and you will see that it is clean. In reference to Amelia, yes, she is my friend, but the last I heard about her, she was out of the country. She is in South America, and I don't believe a word of what you are saying. I believe Amelia is a smart woman, and telling you something like that implicates her even more than she already is."

She grew very upset and began to threaten me. "I will get her wherever she goes. If you don't cooperate with us, I am going to make your life a fucking living hell."

I backed up towards the door and shook both my hands as if I were terrified. "Are you sure you and David are not married? If not, then you should be because you guys are identical. And, for a lady, you have a very foul mouth! You are lucky my mother is not here. I am positive she would wash it out with soap!" I walked to the door. "McCain, would you let me out of here, please?"

As I left, Deborah said, "Dr. del Marmol, you had better pray to God that we don't catch you breaking your probation because we're going to send you straight back to prison where you belong!"

I turned back to her. "What makes you think I will be on probation? How do you know that? You know what, lady, using your own foul language, why don't you *go fuck yourself*?"

I left the office, slamming the door behind me.

# Chapter 36–Sandra's Return

On the drive back home, I told my friends and parents what had just happened. Elizabeth said, "These guys just don't give up, do they?"

Hernesto said, "You have to be careful because they are going to be watching you like a hawk. These people are really mean sons of bitches."

"Uh-oh," Mima said. "We have a bad boy here."

Hernesto blushed. "I'm sorry, Mima. Sometimes these people get me so upset I forget my manners."

My father tried to make Hernesto feel better. "It's okay, my son. You just said what I have been thinking."

My mother hit my father on the shoulder. "Don't encourage him."

I said to Hernesto, "You see? You got my dad in trouble. He will not have fried plantation bananas tonight." We all laughed.

The phone rang and Hernesto answered it. "Yes, he is here. Everything went very well." He looked at me. "Pick up the phone. O'Brien wants to talk to you."

I took the phone and O'Brien said, "Congratulations. Hernesto said everything went well."

"Very, very well. Thank you."

"Don't mention it. It's all right. I owe you a lot more. Meet me at the location we just used. Don't drive yourself. Have somebody bring you over there. You know what I mean, right?"

"Yes, I do. What time?"

"At two in the morning. That way, you'll be able to tell if you're being tailed. Take all the precautions necessary because we're going to bring the tobacco home."

"Thank you. I will be there." I hung up the phone. "Which one of you wants to stay up late tonight or get up very early in the morning? I need someone to drop me off someplace. I am going to take a little trip."

"What time is your meeting?" Elizabeth asked.

"Two o'clock in the morning."

"That's fine with me," she said. "I'll take you."

"That's okay," Hernesto told her. "You have been working hard. You need some rest. I will take him."

She smiled. "You are a good brother."

My mother looked at me. "You are leaving again?"

"Well, Mom, this time I am going to bring a very, very beautiful surprise for you."

Naturally, she did not know what I was referring to, and she said, "I don't want any surprises. I just want you to rest and to stay home for a while. You never sit your butt down for more than fifteen minutes in the same chair."

"Mom, this is part of my work. This is what I do."

"What kind of work is that when you have to leave at two o'clock in the morning to go someplace?"

My father hugged her. "Mima, leave him alone. He is not a baby anymore."

She smiled. "He will always be my baby."

I hugged her, as well. "Mima, you are so sweet." I gave her a kiss on the cheek.

We went home and I spent the rest of the day with them. My mother cooked a great lunch as well as a terrific dinner, during which I said, "You see, Mom? I have spent the whole day with you."

We celebrated my release with a bottle of champagne, and when it got late, everybody went to sleep except Hernesto and me. We sat down on the terrace and talked. At about 1:30, he took me in the Range Rover down to Balboa Island. We had plenty of time to go around in circles for half an hour to make sure nobody was following us. When we got to the French café, O'Brien was waiting for me in the parking lot. I said goodbye to Hernesto, and he took off.

I got into the black Ford sedan that O'Brien was driving, and we headed for the Mexican border. We crossed into Mexicali in Baja, and we waited in the parking lot of my bank until it opened. When the bank opened, I told O'Brien, "I will be back in a few minutes."

I went inside the bank and the branch manager greeted me. "You are our first customer today. I have not seen you for a while."

"I have been out of town for a bit."

"What can I do for you?"

"Well, I want to get to my safety deposit box."

"Oh, sure. Come in. I will take you myself." We walked into the room where the boxes were, and I filled out a little slip and signed it. He walked me through the room over to my box. He left me alone in the little room, saying as he left, "Call me when you're finished."

I closed the door after he left and went through the box, searching the different passports there with my picture but different names. I found the one I was looking for—"Ricardo Valentin." I also took out a small pistol and a handful of cash. I closed the box and called the manager.

I said goodbye and went out to the parking lot and met O'Brien.

I apologized for taking longer than I had anticipated, and O'Brien said, "No problem. You didn't take long at all."

We drove to the airport and an hour later, we flew out of Mexicali. On the plane, they showed a John Wayne movie.

"Wow," O'Brien said. "Look at this. John Wayne is my favorite actor."

I smiled. "No kidding. If I had known that, I would have gotten an autographed picture for you from him."

He looked at me in astonishment. "You're kidding me. You knew him?"

"I not only knew him, but he used to live only a few miles from me."

"You're kidding me! How'd you meet him? You never told me about this."

"You never asked! I didn't know you liked cowboy movies."

"What kid doesn't like cowboy movies?" O'Brien said. "We grew up with cowboy movies."

"I must be very weird, then. I don't like cowboy movies, with a few exceptions. The cowboys always end up killing all the Indians. If you see one movie, you have seen them all."

He looked at me in surprise. "How can you say that, man?"

"I'm sorry, my friend. Do you want me to be honest with you or not? I don't like the way they portray the Indians in the movies. They always make them the bad guys. I must be a rebel because I don't get any joy out of watching those movies."

"Okay, okay," O'Brien said. "I got it. You don't like cowboy movies. How did you meet John Wayne, then, you lucky bastard?"

I smiled. "Under very unusual circumstances. I was in a Hughes market on 17th Street at the border of Costa Mesa and Newport Beach, where I always go to buy my live Maine lobster. By a fluke, I was picking up a large order for a bunch of guests I was having, when he came in for some lobster. He jokingly asked me if I was going to leave any for him, and I explained what I was doing with such a large order. The attendant realized that I didn't recognize who I was speaking with, which also amused Mr. Wayne a great deal. We spoke about Cuba and my book, and he was very interested in hearing more details about my escape. We exchanged cards, and it was then that I noticed that we were virtually neighbors. We discussed the dish I was going to make, and he asked me over to his house the next evening so I could teach him how to make it—Lobster thermidor."

O'Brien asked me, "What happened with the book? What happened with all that stuff?"

"Well, he sent me to his writers, but they could not do anything for me. They were very nice people, but they mostly did Western films. I did not really put too much emphasis on it then because of the projects I was working on with you guys which didn't leave me much time. I can tell you, though, that he was an extremely nice man. I met with him on several occasions and he even invited me on his yacht.

"He loved to tell the story of when he came to California with holes in his shoes, and his feet got wet even though he had heard that it never rained in California. For the first week after he arrived, all it did was rain! He had to put cardboard in his shoes and carry his socks in his pocket to avoid getting them wet. That way, when he arrived where ever he was going, he had dry feet!"

"What a great story," O'Brien said. "You never told me that."

"It never came up."

"He passed away, right?"

"I saw him in his last days," I said. "I had gone to visit him and a very tall, beautiful brunette brought him home from the hospital. He was having chemotherapy treatments. She needed help to get him out of the car and into the house. Fortunately, I was there to help, but it broke my heart to see him in such a poor condition. He was all bent over and very weak and was hardly able to walk."

"Sometimes," O'Brien said, "life is shit. Such a big, strong man. That must have really affected you."

"Yes, it really did," I replied. "It bothered me for a long time."

The next day, late in the evening and on an isolated beach in Cancun, O'Brien and I were sitting in a jeep watching the ocean. Out at sea, a small boat made its way towards the shore. Gradually, it became more visible as it got closer. Finally, it got close enough for us to see four figures on the deck. The boat came to within a hundred feet of the beach and stopped. A small skiff was lowered into the water, and one man got in to row and another sat in the back. The man rowed the skiff to the beach, and the other man hopped out.

A young man hailed from the boat, "We have the tobacco here."

O'Brien replied, "I have the lightning and the box with me. Bring the tobacco in."

I just laughed as I heard all this mumbo jumbo. The small skiff came closer to us, and I saw Sandra sitting in the back of it. "Sandra!" I called.

"Julio Antonio!" she yelled back. I ran into the water, picked her up, and carried her to the dry sand on the beach. I put her down and kissed her. Sandra threw her arms around my neck, and we locked in a deep kiss. She had tears in her eyes as she looked into my own eyes. "I never thought this would ever happen," she said.

"I can't believe it," I said. "We are finally together. If you want, we can stay like this forever."

She was sobbing with joy. "So many bad things have happened, and there has been so much pain in my life. Let's hope nothing spoils it this time. Something always seems to happen to prevent us from being together. I want with all my heart to be with you for the rest of my life."

"Then let's pray to God that nothing bad ever happens to us again."

We said goodbye to the men in the skiff. They turned around and disappeared as they rowed to the main boat. We all got into the jeep and drove back to Cancun. A few days later, we were in California. My parents could not believe it when I brought Sandra to the house in Corona del Mar. They cried and hugged, and then my mother asked the question I had been dreading.

"Where is my grandson?"

Sandra turned and looked first at me and then my father. She was caught by surprise. "Mima," she said, "didn't you know? Julito died a while ago."

"NO!" my mother screamed. She put her hands to her mouth and collapsed in my arms. My father and I carried her to the bedroom and laid her on the bed.

"Oh, my God," Sandra said. "What have I done?"

"No," I reassured her, "it's not your fault. It's mine. I should have told her a long time ago."

I told my father to bring some cold water and some alcohol. I took my mother's pulse and it was fine. I put some cold water on a towel and put it on her forehead. I soaked some cotton in the alcohol and let her smell it. She started to come around a few minutes later. All three of us were sitting by her on the bed. She looked at all three of us, and then asked my father, "Did you know this?"

"Yes," he answered.

She began to cry very hard. "Why him? Why not me? Such a good kid. He was so young!"

"Mima," I said, "I know the pain you are going through. We are all in pain. You have to control yourself. Remember what the doctor said. I don't want to lose you, too." I began to cry.

She held my face. "Oh, my son—why do these things happen?"

"Mima, this is life," I said. "We are only here temporarily. Jesus talked to me in my revelation or dream, and He said Julito was too good for this world. That is why He took him with Him. He is sitting by the Father in heaven. He does not want to see you crying like this."

She made a sad face and tried to stop crying. She grabbed Sandra's hand and pulled it towards her. "I know how you must feel, my child."

For the next three weeks, I spent all my time with my parents and Sandra. I tried to soften the pain my mother was feeling because I knew how drastically it was affecting her. She was depressed and did not even want to eat. Finally, in the fourth week, I saw her smiling with Sandra in the kitchen. Sandra had burned the bananas and the boiling oil she poured in the sink nearly burned the whole kitchen.

"I have to teach you to cook, my child," she said to Sandra. "In order to get to a man's heart you have to get to his stomach first."

I decided on that day I could now go to check in at the Boron Minimal Security Camp and serve my sentence. I called my attorney to make the arrangements to go on the Monday of the coming week. Hernesto and Elizabeth drove me in the limo to the camp. I did not want my parents or Sandra to come with me, so I had said my goodbyes to them at home in Corona del Mar.

I met some very interesting men in that camp from all over the country, including some very high-level business people. I connected with and became friends with many of them. Six months later, I walked along the pathway to the front gate. Many of my new friends congregated around the main entrance to say goodbye to me. Two of the guards shook my hand, and one of them said, "Good luck to you, man. Let's hope we never see you here again."

Sandra and Elizabeth were waiting for me in the limo. Sandra got out of the back door, and Elizabeth, naturally, got out from the driver's side. They both waved to me. The guard saw them and said, "Man, it looks like the president of the United States is leaving this camp!"

The other guard said, "Wow! Not only are there two beautiful women waiting for him, but they're in a fantastic limo!"

I smiled and continued walking, saying nothing. I crossed the white line that was painted on the ground, which indicated that I was now a free man. I approached the limo and hugged Sandra. "You look beautiful," I told her. "I have missed you more than I can tell you."

She smiled. "I missed you, too. More than ever."

Elizabeth said, "What about me?"

I let go of Sandra and gave Elizabeth a big hug. "I really missed you, too!"

She smiled. "Welcome back to freedom."

We got into the limo and drove off. A few weeks later, Sandra, Hernesto, Elizabeth, and I said goodbye to my parents for a few months. We took a taxi to the Los Angeles airport. As we were boarding the plane to Miami, I noticed two men were watching us. One of them was wearing a white suit and dark glasses—it was Charlie the Cleaner. The face of the other man was extremely familiar to me, and it was connected in my mind with something bad. I saw them write down something on a tablet.

About an hour later, I was resting in my seat. It came to me like a flash, and it gave me goose bumps and chills all over my body. That face I had seen in the airport with Charlie was the one I had seen many years earlier, in Alfredo's restaurant, the El Pelicano in Miami. It was the man who had come in and sat down at the table next to us with something in his hand. Alfredo had called me into the kitchen to answer the phone, and while I was gone this man placed the package under his table. It subsequently blew up and killed all of my friends.

I did not want to tell Sandra because I did not want to scare or worry her. I signaled to Hernesto to meet me in the restroom. I walked down the aisle and we pretended we were waiting in line for the restroom. I said to him, "I don't want to scare Sandra, so don't tell her what I am about to tell you. You can tell Elizabeth. If my memory is correct, I think I saw the man who was responsible for killing my friends in the restaurant in Miami. I saw him in the airport as we were boarding our plane. My worst concern is if that was really him, what was he doing with Charlie the Cleaner? Charlie works directly with Addison and O'Brien for our intelligence community."

Hernesto's eyes opened wide and his mouth dropped open. "Shit! This is really fucked up!"

"Just keep your eyes open when we land in Miami and tell Elizabeth to be on her guard, too. Do me a favor, brother—as soon as we get to Miami, please put two loaded pistols and spare magazines under the mattress of my bed on the yacht where we are going."

A few hours later, we landed in Miami. There was a limo waiting for us that Elizabeth had arranged for through her contacts there. When we got to the limo, Elizabeth and Hernesto both hugged the young Cuban driver and Elizabeth said, "This is Dr. del Marmol and his love, Sandra." She turned to me and said, "He is one of us."

We greeted each other and he said, "I am Rodolfo, at your service, Dr. del Marmol. It's really a great honor to meet a man like you."

"It's an honor for me to meet you, too. You are the new generation who will probably bring freedom to Cuba."

He smiled and we got into the limo and drove off. He put the glass down. "There is chilled champagne in the refrigerator there," he explained. "I put in six bottles because I know you have something special to celebrate. The most wonderful gift a human being has—freedom."

We opened a bottle and we all began to drink and toast. Rodolfo asked, "Where do you want to go?"

Hernesto said, "Just cruise around the marina for a little while, and I will tell you where to go."

He drove around the area, which was beautiful. We drank more champagne and we ate some appetizers that he had placed on the table in the limo. After we had cruised for a while, finished the first bottle of champagne, and opened a second, Hernesto told Rodolfo, "Just turn right at the next corner, and go all the way down to the end of the dock."

Rodolfo parked the limo, and we all got out except Sandra. She said, "What are we going to do here? Are you going to drown me?"

"Drown you?" I said. "Anybody could kill you any other way, but not drown you. I remember that you can swim like a fish." She giggled and was a bit tipsy. "Come on," I said. "Don't be lazy. Get out of the limo. I want to show you something."

She got out and we began to walk towards a big yacht at the end of the dock. Hernesto was talking to Rodolfo. The two of them went to the trunk of the limo. Rodolfo opened it to reveal a big leather case within. He opened the case, which was full of many different caliber guns. He said to Hernesto, "Take your pick."

Hernesto bent over and looked at the guns carefully. He chose two nine millimeter pistols and a few extra magazines. He put them inside a plastic bag, and Rodolfo gave him a towel. Hernesto wrapped the plastic bag in the towel and put them under his arm. Then he walked behind us.

We arrived at the beautiful forty-six-foot yacht, and I pointed to the stern. In big letters, it read *My Sandra*. Sandra said, "Ohhh! You named your yacht after me?"

"Yes, but it is not my yacht. It is our yacht."

She hugged and kissed me. "Is this my surprise?"

"Yes," I said. "We are going to navigate it all over the Caribbean Islands, and we can wave to Cuba as we cross close by."

She looked at me. "You are crazy! You should not even be within a thousand miles of the Cuban coast!"

"I was just kidding. Don't worry."

The big Macaw parrot, Lucky Angel, was sitting on the stern railing. He was walking back and forth, happy to see me. He said, "Oh, God bless me. God bless you. Brraaak! Hello, sweetie. Welcome aboard. Welcome aboard."

Sandra laughed. "Oh, how cute! Where did you get him from?"

I smiled. "It's a long story, honey. That is Lucky Angel. He was my only company for many days on an island where I almost died from lack of food and water. He is the one who flew to the boat and let them know I was there. That is why I call him Lucky Angel. He saved my life. I will tell you about it later on the cruise."

We all got on board. Hernesto brought our luggage into the cabin and put the guns under the mattress in the master bedroom. We sat down on the yacht for a little while, talked, and drank more champagne. Hernesto went to the limo and brought Rodolfo back with him. He joined us and drank only one glass of champagne because he had to drive.

After a while, Elizabeth said, "This is a beautiful yacht. It is very modern and has very contemporary décor. That is why I like it. Normally, boats are not like this."

"Oh, you have never been here before?" I asked.

"No."

"I thought Hernesto had brought you here before. Let me show you and Sandra around."

We walked around the yacht, and they were both fascinated. They both liked it very much, and Rodolfo said, "Boy, I would love to have my honeymoon in a place like this."

"When are you getting married?" I asked him.

"September, next year."

"We will be back long before then. Arrange it with Hernesto. That will be my gift to you for your wedding."

"Thank you," he stammered. "Thank you. I didn't mean—"

"No problem," I interrupted. "I am happy to do that for you. Hey guys, why don't we have an early dinner before Sandra and I leave Miami? Let's go to the Pelicano restaurant and at the same time I can say hello to my good friend, Alfredo."

Everyone loved the idea, and Elizabeth said, "Alfredo will be delighted to see you."

We left the yacht, and Rodolfo drove us to the El Pelicano. Alfredo greeted us when we arrived. "Oh, my old friend!" he exclaimed. "I have not seen you for years! How are you? You're a famous man. And, like I told you before, celebrities don't have to pay."

"Come on," I said, "you don't have to do that."

"Oh, I know. It's just my way of saying thank you for coming to my restaurant and bringing such a lovely lady."

"This is the love of my life. This is Sandra." Sandra smiled shyly and pretended to hide behind me like a little girl.

Alfredo looked at her as if he was appraising a gold ring. "Can she cook?"

"Like my mama, and even better!"

Alfredo smiled in approval. He nudged me and pretended to whisper, "I think she will be very good for you and you two will have many, many children."

We all laughed, and I said, "Alfredo, you are a good friend and you have the best food in Miami. You have the best service, the best atmosphere, and you are the most gracious host. Why would I want to go anywhere else?"

"Ah, Dr. del Marmol," Alfredo said, "you do my heart good. Come with me. I have a special table, just for you." He took all of us to a table in the back, where we could watch the front door and were secure. We all sat down. I ordered a big *paella* for five people. When our dinner arrived, we ate it and had a wonderful time.

Sandra said, "I can't believe this. After all we have been through, and now we are right here in Miami. Finally, we are going to be happy. I have wanted this all my life. Remember when we used to play baseball?"

"Remember?" I said. "Of course. You always wanted to pitch, and you cheated."

"What? I never cheated! How did I cheat?"

"Because you knew I couldn't hit that inside pitch. I always thought it was a good pitch, but you made it hit my knuckles."

Sandra threw her head back in laughter, and then she kissed me. "Hmmm, okay, maybe I did cheat, but it was just good pitching."

Alfredo came to our table. "Excuse me, my friends. Would you mind if I stole Dr. del Marmol from you for a few minutes?"

Everyone was fine with it, and Hernesto joked, "As long as you bring him back in one piece."

Alfredo smiled. "Don't worry—he will be in good hands."

Hernesto raised an arm. "Are you sure you don't want me to go with you?"

"No," I said, "it's all right. Everything is fine now. So far, everything is quiet."

I followed Alfredo through the kitchen to his office. He closed the door behind us. He went to his desk and pulled out a bottle of Grand Marnier. "Take this with you. Drink it with your lady in my name. By the way, I wanted to tell you that Yaneba and Capitan Marrero are doing a lot better. We have them in an undisclosed location under high security. We think that what happened to them was not an accident. Somebody tried to kill them deliberately."

"Are they okay now?"

"Not completely, but they are recuperating."

"It was six or seven months ago!" I exclaimed.

"They almost died. They were in very critical condition for months."

"I am going to investigate what really happened to them when I return from my trip," I said.

"Thank you. I hope you will get to the bottom of that, and we will find out who was really behind such a cowardly act. Miserable sons of bitches, trying to kill a woman and an old man!"

"Don't worry. I will get to the bottom of it, and whoever it was will pay for it."

We went back to the table, and Hernesto said, "Oh, good! He came back in one piece!"

We all laughed, said goodbye, and walked out of the restaurant. Alfredo came outside with us and waved to us as we drove away.

# Chapter 37—The Last Days of the Dolphin

Rodolfo took us back to the yacht. We said goodbye to Hernesto, Elizabeth, and Rodolfo, and I told Elizabeth and Hernesto that I would see them in three months but would keep in touch with them periodically. I asked them to please make sure that if Yaneba or Captain Marrero needed anything to provide it for them. Everyone came on board for a farewell glass of champagne. While Sandra chatted with our friends, I went to the cabin, changed my clothes, and put on my captain's jacket and hat. After I came back on deck, Sandra retired to change clothes. She put on a red bikini with a white see-through robe on top. When we finished our champagne and said our goodbyes, they left the yacht. Hernesto untied the ropes on the dock and tossed them onto the boat.

We waved to them from the upper deck as we sailed out of the harbor. Sandra brought me a glass of lemonade. Lucky Angel started to talk, pleading for water. I smiled and extended my glass to him. He jumped to my shoulder and took a couple of sips from my glass. "Water. Water. Braakk." He looked at Sandra. "Hello, sweetie."

Sandra looked at me and we both laughed. I continued piloting the yacht out of the harbor. She walked in front of me and I looked at her body, tanned by the tropical sun. She looked like a Greek goddess with her long, black hair mixed with strings of copper from the sun shining through her hair. We continued crossing the marina.

She gave me a kiss and hugged me. "I will be back in a minute." She went down to the cabin.

I navigated the yacht to the open sea. After a little while, I saw three dolphins playing and swimming around our yacht. They crossed back and forth, from one side of the boat to the other. I said into the intercom, "Come up on deck. You have to see this. There are three dolphins putting on an unbelievable show for us. Hurry up. I don't want you to miss this."

I slowed down the boat so that we wouldn't hurt them. They were jumping out of the water and over the rear deck, from one side to the other. They seemed to have practiced doing this before. I heard Sandra laugh, but she did not seem to be too surprised or excited. I repeated, "Please hurry up, or you are going to miss it."

"Okay. Okay. I will be there in a minute."

The dolphins continued doing their show. They did not seem like regular wild dolphins. They acted more like trained animals. When Sandra came up to the upper deck where I was, I was surprised. She had changed into a rubber scuba diving wetsuit. She had fins in her hand as if she were ready to jump into the ocean.

"Did you change to make a show for me like the dolphins, or do you intend to catch some lobster for me for dinner?" I asked.

She came over to me and kissed me with a big smile on her face. "Why don't you stop the engines, drop the anchor, go down to the cabin and change into your scuba suit? We can play with these beautiful animals for a little while, and maybe we will get lucky and get some lobster for dinner?"

I smiled. "Right now? Right here? Well, maybe after all, that is not a bad idea!" I stopped the engine and released the anchor. "I will be back in a few minutes, after I change into my suit."

When I came back on deck a few minutes later, Sandra was already in the water, playing with the dolphins. I was completely in shock. I went to the rail and watched her. She was on top of one of the dolphins as if she were riding a horse. The other two dolphins were swimming next to her in formation. I could not believe what I was seeing.

She directed them and they swam together in different formations, obeying her clicks and commands. I was completely in awe. I could not believe what I was seeing. She beckoned to me. "Come on. Come on. They are very friendly. You will enjoy this. It's a lot of fun."

I put on my tanks and lowered myself slowly into the water. I swam to where she and the dolphins were playing. They received me like a dog that had not seen its master for a long time.

She removed her mouthpiece. "Come over. Come over. Climb on top of one." She petted all three of them, and they got together in a line like a platform. I swam underneath them and surfaced in between them. Then I climbed on the back of the one in the center.

I took off my mouthpiece and exclaimed, "This is unbelievable! These dolphins are acting like horses waiting for a rider to climb on their backs."

She jumped on the back of the dolphin on the right and patted him on his head. He began to swim around the yacht. "This is unbelievable," I said again. "How come these dolphins respond to you like this? It is as if you were their trainer. It's like they know you."

"Don't worry about it," she yelled back to me. "Have fun. I will explain to you when we get back aboard the yacht."

The riderless dolphin was swimming, playing, and jumping all around us. We had a lot of fun. After a while, Sandra made a guttural noise that sounded like dolphins communicating with each other. All three stopped in the water, as if they were dead. She patted the one she was riding and it began to swim towards the rear of the yacht. The other two followed him. They stopped at the back of the yacht as if they knew that was where we wanted to go.

"Put on your mouthpiece," she said, "and let's go down and see if we can find your lobsters."

We did so, letting ourselves slide off the backs of the dolphins and into the water. While we were still on the surface of the water, all three dolphins came around Sandra, and she petted them all. She signaled to me to come close to her, so I swam over. The dolphins nudged us lovingly like dogs.

We dove down deep into the water, and the dolphins came with us. They continued to swim around us. I saw lobsters between the corals on the bottom on both sides of us. I pointed to her and signaled with my thumb. She understood and went down on the right while I went down on the left.

We each caught two with our knives and then I signaled her to surface. That was all we needed.

We surfaced and climbed back aboard, leaving the dolphins to frolic by themselves in the water. We took off our suits, washed them, and hung them on special hangers to dry. It was a beautiful sunset. We kissed each other, completely naked. We took the lobsters down to the kitchen and left them in the sink before jumping in the shower together.

"I have something to confess to you," she said as she kissed me. I kissed her back and began to fool around with her. I touched her breast and started to become aroused. We gave each other a passionate kiss, and then she put her hand on my chest. "Listen, I want to tell you something. We had better turn off the water here in the shower, or else we will not have any water later." She got out of the shower, dried herself, and went to the bed. I stayed in the shower and rinsed myself. Then I got out and dried myself.

She patted the bed. "Come here. I have a confession to make to you. I want to tell you before we make love today."

I smiled and asked jokingly, "Is it an indecent confession?"

She smiled back. "No. On the contrary. It is very decent. I want to tell you the truth about a few things that you have no knowledge of."

That stimulated my curiosity. I went to the bed and lay down beside her. "Um-hm. Have you been a naughty girl? What have you been doing that causes your conscience to bother you and makes you feel that you have to confess to me?"

I petted her wet hair and continued in a loving voice, "Sweetie, whatever you have done in the past is in the past. I have had several relationships and I never found anyone who could take your place. That is probably true for you, too. If you didn't love me, you wouldn't be here right now. Let's not talk about past relationships."

"Shh," she said and she put her finger to my lips.

"Okay. I am all ears. Make your confession."

The expression on her face changed completely. She looked very serious and was deep in her thoughts. "Those dolphins that you and I have been playing with all afternoon are not common dolphins. They are professionally trained. I have spent nearly all of my life with them. I have been with them ever since I was a child, when my father put me in that counterintelligence training school." She paused, and I looked at her in stunned disbelief. "Just hear me out because what I am going to tell you puts my life in your hands. I, like you, grew up as part of Castro's revolution. Do you remember my father?"

"Yes, he was one of the biggest leaders in the Revolution."

"Well, he enrolled me in this program when I was only seven years old. We have been going through all those years spending practically nine months out of each year with the baby dolphins they bred genetically in the labs. They grew up with us. They taught us to control and train them as you would train a dog to respond to us and to do whatever we want them to do. The intention of this is to convert the dolphins into international spies. We are the trainers and the masters. We can send them to blow up a ship, a bridge, a submarine, or whatever the hell we want, and most of the time they never get hurt.

425

Each of us has three or four dolphins. We are like a team. We have been doing absolutely everything. You cannot even imagine!"

I stopped her with my hand. "Wait a minute. You don't have to convince me! I saw with my own eyes what you are capable of doing with those animals. What you are telling me now does not explain why you were arrested in Cuba when we all tried to escape from there to Guantanamo Bay. Why didn't you turn us in if you were a spy at that time?"

"At that particular moment, I really wanted to leave Cuba with you. First of all because I have always been in love with you, even when you were the Little Commander for the young military forces for Castro. However, when you shared with me your disappointment with the government and felt betrayed because of the many broken promises Castro made to all of us Cubans, I saw the truth through your eyes. I realized I had wasted all my infant and adolescent years. It was only for the selfish ambition of one man to control the world.

"Then, when we made love and I became pregnant, I knew I did not want my child to feel the same way I felt. I did not want him to go through the same disappointments I went through. That is why I decided to leave Cuba with you.

"To answer your question, my arrest by the Cuban soldiers in that train station that day happened by a fluke. A woman in the ladies' restroom identified me and called the soldiers. I knew if I offered resistance, I could break their necks and kick their asses, but because I loved you so much, I did not want to call attention to you guys and you would all have been arrested, especially after what you did in the airport. You would probably all have ended up dead in front of a firing squad. If people wound up dead or sentenced to thirty years in jail for very minor things, what they would have done to you guys after you blew up the most expensive planes Castro had in the airport? You guys would all have been dead."

She made a sour face. "I knew that with a good story, and since I was an important spy for them, I would be released. That is why I decided to keep my mouth shut in order to let you guys go."

I reclined on the bed. "Do you mean to tell me that you are the famous Cuban spy, the Dolphin?"

She turned and looked me straight in the eye. "I am one of them."

I shook my head. "O'Brien talked to me so much about you, and he warned me so many times, that I even had nightmares about the Dolphin. One of those horrible nightmares that I had was about dolphins that became sharks and ripped my body to pieces. Each one swam away with one of my body parts."

She smiled. "They give us more credit that we deserve. The Dolphin is an organization, like MQ1. We all work individually and we all have separate missions. According to our established protocol, the reports always indicate that there is only one Dolphin, when in reality there are many agents under that same name. The Cuban counterintelligence wants everyone to believe there is only one! We have all been trained to leave behind the same pattern. That way, everyone thinks it is the same person."

I looked her in her eyes. "I just want you to answer this with complete honesty. Did you have anything to do with the death of my friend, Arturo?"

"No. Absolutely not."

I asked again, "Did you have anything to do with the incident when someone pushed Yaneba out of the building and cause her to lose the baby she was carrying, which was my son?"

"No, *absolutely* not." She grabbed my hands and held them in hers. "I swear on the memory of our son, may he rest in peace, I never did anything against you or your friends. My work has been restricted to Europe and sometimes South America for many years. After the death of our son, when they knew that I knew who gave the order from the high level, probably from Castro himself, they didn't trust me anymore. I know they did this to our son because you have done so much damage to their international politics and have destroyed their secret plans. They had to do something to hurt you. That is why they killed our Julito."

Tears were rolling down her cheeks. She pulled me close to her and held my hand. She put one of her hands on my face. "They didn't take into consideration that Julito was my son, too, in spite of what I had done for the Revolution. That is one of the reasons I left Cuba and I wanted to talk to you in private and tell you my secrets and my confessions. That way, you can tell O'Brien yourself that I gave you all the details that will destroy the most dangerous counterintelligence and terrorist groups that exist in the world today. The Dolphins were created in Cuba in the sixties by special intelligence forces from Russia, Germany, and Romania. I know all the codes and names, and I have all that information in my head, and I will give it to you."

I shook my head in astonishment. "Why didn't you tell O'Brien and me all this information when we picked you up in Cancun?"

She still held my hands in hers. "We had not seen each other for many years. I had to get close to you again for a while, to feel you had not changed, to trust you, and to feel comfortable with you. We are never going to fix this world. We should stop living this crazy life. Look at yourself. You recently almost ended up in jail for seventy years. Why don't we live our lives in peace and happiness, far away from all this and maybe with a little help from God we might even have our own family?"

I looked into her eyes and I saw sincerity and a lot of love. She was talking to me with her heart in her hand. She was exposing herself to losing her life with that confession if I didn't handle it properly.

So I said, "Don't worry, honey. I will talk to O'Brien and I will make sure that nothing you say will be used against you. This has been done in the past. It can be arranged. Don't worry about it. I will handle everything for you."

She smiled and said, "Thank you, my love." She gave me a tender kiss on the cheek.

I looked at her as she lay naked on the bed and said, "In the past, I have had so many nightmares about the Dolphin eating me. Now I am going to eat the Dolphin!"

She laughed, and I started kissing her breasts. We made love for a long time. When we finished, I told her I would call O'Brien from the first port and everything would be okay.

She hugged me. "I feel at peace and safe with you." We embraced again. "Well," she said, "let me wash myself and then I will cook dinner for you. I want to make it a very romantic dinner on deck, looking at the stars and the moon."

"Well, I want to help you."

"Very well, I accept your help, but when I tell you to get out of the kitchen and go upstairs, you have to do that for me. I want to make the final touch to the meal and bring it to you. That is going to be my gift to you tonight."

I bowed as if to royalty. "Okay, my queen. Whatever you say."

"Very well, my king." She jumped out of bed and went into the shower.

Later on, after I took a shower as well, I joined her in the kitchen. I opened a bottle of champagne and we boiled the lobsters we had just caught and began to prepare Lobster thermidor. We drank some champagne while we were cooking. We actually got a little tipsy, tasting the food and drinking the champagne in the kitchen.

When the food was almost ready, Sandra said, "Okay, that's good enough. You go upstairs and sit down on the deck and wait for me." She refilled my glass and gave me a little plastic bowl of nuts. She walked me towards the stairs that connected the cabins with the deck. She brought a bucket full of ice and a bottle of champagne. I went up to the deck with my glass and the nuts, and then went back down to pick up the bucket of ice.

I sat down and enjoyed the evening. There were millions of stars and a beautiful full moon. The temperature was perfect, neither too hot nor too cold. I was wondering what I had done to deserve so much happiness. I had with me the only real love of my life. I was so happy to be there precisely at that moment.

Sandra began to bring the dinner, and every time I tried to help her she said, "No. I told you to wait here."

She prepared all the plates so beautifully. She put fresh asparagus and sliced avocado around the lobster to decorate it. Then she brought another plate of ham and cold meats, surrounded with fresh pineapple and chicken wings in white sauce. Every time she came up with another plate, I tapped my glass with my fork like a bell to announce her coming and said, "Bravo! Bravo for the chef!" She smiled, full of satisfaction.

When finally she had brought everything up, I said, "You must be tired."

She smiled. "Yes, a little. I think I am out of shape. Your mom and dad and your friends have spoiled me rotten these past six months."

"Well, I am glad. They treated you just as you deserved."

"Don't worry about whether I am tired or not. The important thing is—do you like the way I decorated everything?"

I made a gesture with my hand. "Of course! Look at this! This is beautiful. It looks as if it had been prepared by a professional chef! Look at the way you cut those relishes. They look like roses. Look at those little tomatoes. They look like little carnations. This is more than just a meal. It is a piece of art."

"Well, you have to thank your mom. She taught me all of this." She came over to me and gave me a kiss. "You have a wonderful mom."

"Okay, sit down." I pulled a little box out of the pocket of my white shirt and opened it, revealing a diamond ring. I got down on my knees and asked, "Will you marry me? I want to be with you for the rest of my life."

She started to cry and grabbed the ring in her hands. "Silly, you don't even have to ask me. You know the answer. Of course I want to marry you. I have wanted to all my life. This is beautiful. You should not have spent so much money." She put the ring back on the table. "I love you," she said, and we kissed.

"There is not enough money in this world to pay for my happiness tonight," I said. I kissed her hand, took the ring off the table, and put it on her finger. "Together for the rest of our lives!"

"Together for the rest of our lives," she repeated. We kissed passionately and laughed happily. I took the bottle of champagne from the bucket and was ready to pour more into her glass when it was empty. "No, no," she said. "I want to bring up a bottle of fresh orange juice to make mimosa."

She started to stand up and I stopped her. "No. You have been back and forth too many times. Wait here for me. I will go and get it." I walked away towards the stairs, smiling. "You went up and down ten times."

She laughed. "Did you really count how many times I went up and down?"

"Yes, I did."

"That is one of the things I like about you. You are very considerate of others."

I went down to the kitchen and opened the refrigerator. I took the bottle of orange juice out and turned off all the lights. As I turned around to go back up the stairs, something shiny like a reflection caught my attention.

I saw it through the port-hole in the kitchen, so I stopped for a minute. Then I saw it move. I walked slowly to the port-hole to try to see what was going on. I looked through it and saw a small submarine attached to our yacht and four men get out.

Each one of them was dressed in a scuba diving suit. I looked up and saw a rope ladder attached to the top of our deck. One of the men began to climb up the ladder. I saw the same reflection that I had seen a few moments before. I realized there was probably a fifth man who was already on deck, and Sandra was up there, alone and unaware.

The reflection was from the moon shining on the glass mask. As they moved their heads while climbing up the ladder, it caused a reflection to move across the port-hole and shine inside the whole cabin like a flashlight.

430

I looked down and saw the other three men trying to attach something to the side of the yacht—it looked like C4 explosive. I put the orange juice down on the counter, ran to the bed, and tried to find the pistols. I took both pistols and got them ready to fire and ran to the stairs with one in each hand.

I screamed at the top of my lungs, "Sandra! Sandra! Assassins aboard!" I ran as fast as I could up the stairs. I heard three shots and a large bump on the deck as if something heavy had fallen down. When my head came out of the stairs, I saw a man lying on the floor close to the ladder I had seen earlier. He was bleeding and had a harpoon through his neck. I saw another man's head coming up the ladder with a pistol in his hand. He pointed it at Sandra. The dolphins were flying over the boat from one side to the other, the same as they had done this afternoon. The man fired his gun anyway, but he could not aim very well because of the dolphins.

Sandra tried to take cover under the table. The man shot again and this time he hit one of the dolphins. It fell on the deck, wounded and making a very loud sound. I aimed at the man with both pistols and shot three times. He fell back into the water. "Sandra!" I yelled. "Grab this pistol!" I slid one of them across the deck to her. As she grabbed it, I asked, "Are you okay?"

"I think so," she said. With the pistol in her hand, she ran screaming towards the dolphin on the deck that was nearly dead. I went close to her and saw tears in her eyes. She petted the dolphin and kissed it.

"We have to leave," I said. "They are putting explosives on the boat. It is going to blow up any minute." I moved aft and began to unload the dinghy. I started to crank it as fast as I could. I looked at Sandra. She was still down on her knees by the dolphin. I saw the man on the floor with the harpoon in his neck, and recognized him. It was the same man who planted the bomb in the restaurant that killed my friends; his violence finally caught up to him. I screamed to Sandra, "Let's go, please! There is nothing we can do for it now. Let's go! The boat is going to explode!"

Just then, another man appeared from the hanging ladder. Before he could get up completely and shoot at us, Sandra walked towards him, shooting her pistol. She continued shooting at him until he fell down. Even then, she continued walking towards the railing and shooting in berserk fury. She wanted to make sure he was dead.

I bellowed at her, "For God's sake! Don't get close to the rail! There's another man down there!"

The man who was still on the small submarine shot her several times. She lost her equilibrium and fell over the railing and into the ocean.

I was on the opposite side, loading the boat. I screamed, "No! No! Shit!" I ran across the deck and to the front of the boat. He thought I would come straight across to the ladder, so he did not see me. I shot him and he fell onto the deck of the submarine, dead.

I dropped the gun on the deck and jumped into the water to try to find Sandra. I got close to her body. It was floating and the dolphins were supporting her so it would not go down into the water. They were making strange sounds, almost as if they were crying.

Sandra coughed twice and opened her eyes. "We almost did it," she said in a faltering voice, "but I guess it was just not meant to be."

"No," I said, my voice breaking. "No! Don't die on me, please! After I have waited for you for so long, don't leave me now!"

She looked at me and touched my face with her hand. "I love you. I always have and I always will. I see our son is coming for me. Can you see him? He is right there." She took a deep breath and died in my arms.

I hugged her very, very hard for a few minutes. I cried out as I have never before in my life, giving vent to all my anger and pain. I finally let go of her body, and the two dolphins escorted her, one on each side, off into the deep ocean. It was as if they had been waiting for me to finish mourning her death before they took her with them.

I started swimming towards the dinghy, which was floating a short distance away. I grabbed it and jumped in. I started the little engine and was ready to take off. I saw something flying towards me, and I stood up, trying to determine what was approaching me. I heard a familiar voice squawking, "Braakk. Braakk. God bless you. God bless me. Welcome aboard."

Lucky Angel landed on my shoulder, and I felt a little comfort in the midst of my sadness because I knew my bird would be okay. I petted him on his head, and he said, "Welcome aboard, Lucky Angel. Braak. Braakk. Welcome aboard. Hello. Hello."

I took off, and a few minutes later the yacht blew up in millions of pieces. I felt my heart blow up with it from the pain of losing the only and most beautiful love I had ever had in my life.

As I was navigating the boat towards the coast, the image of when Sandra and I were children playing baseball in our home town, Pinar del Rio, came back to me. I flashed back to January 12, 1958, in my

beautiful Cuba. Sandra was the catcher on the opposite team and as I
was running around the bases for my team and was approaching home
plate, she winked at me and with a smile she gave me a big thumbs up.

*To My Only Love*
If you ever left my side one day
I would now know what to do with my life
Because I love you so very much
Just thinking about that happening
Makes me want to end my life
I know you are very unique
Because your love has always been pure
Naked with nothing to hide
Pure and clean like spring water and refreshing
Wonderful to drink and beautiful to see on a spring night
I only know I love you very much
And it will always be that way
Until the last day of my life
Whatever you do no matter what and under any condition
I will always be there for you willing to give you my love and my
life
Many years could be passing by and tears might come into your eyes
It could be difficult times and almost impossible for you to survive
But I want you to remember my love and keep in your mind
The way I have loved you through all my life
This kind of love will never die

For more information on the adventures of Dr. J. Antonio del
Marmol, see the website at **www.spymasterspy.com**

# About Dr. Julio Antonio del Marmol

Born in 1947 in Pinar del Rio, Cuba, he followed in the footsteps of his father, Leonardo del Marmol, in his love of freedom and justice. His father, one of the financiers behind Fidel Castro's Revolution, had been motivated by an outrage over the excesses of the previous dictatorship of General Batista. He communicated to his son, Julio Antonio, this sense of frustration and love of homeland. Julio Antonio became a military leader when he was only twelve years old. Castro, impressed with the youth's maturity and eloquence, appointed him Commander-in-Chief of the Young Commanders of the Rebel Anny, and the Little Commander was born.

One year after the Revolution, Julio Antonio, while inside the first ring of the government, personally saw the plans the Castro brothers had for the future of the country.

He watched closely the suffering of the Cuban people, standing in long lines in the tropical sun for simple things like a loaf of bread, while the leaders of the Revolution enjoyed the most luxurious lifestyle, eating the most exquisite dishes while living in great mansions, completely disaffected from those living under the Socialist system.

He decided to abandon his own privileged lifestyle as part of Castro's elite because his integrity and moral values passed on by his father and his ancestors did not allow him to watch in silence the suffering of his people. He then formed a group of brave men who were also dedicated to stopping the Socialist regime as his uncle offered to him the opportunity to work in this resistance movement. At the tender age of thirteen, he was trained and prepared for the fight, and the most persecuted and feared spy was born, earning from his enemies his codename, "the Lightning."

**Don't believe everything you read in the papers...**
Set up, arrested, and not knowing who to trust, spy and freedom
fighter Dr. Julio Antonio del Marmol must find a way to escape!

LOS ANGELES TIMES -- Tuesday September 27, 1988

# $20 Million in Bogus Bills Seized, Agents Say; Man Arrested

By LONN JOHNSTON and KIM MURPHY, Times Staff Writers

In what may be the largest seizure of counterfeit money in U.S. history, federal agents announced Monday that they had confiscated more than $20 million in bogus $100 bills and arrested a Santa Ana man after two accomplices tried to pass some of the phony cash at a department store. Secret Service agents arrested Julio Antonio Marmol, 41, at his accomplices' home Friday in Costa Mesa and searched his Santa Ana home the next day, authorities said.

"This represents one of the largest counterfeit seizures in the history of the United States Secret Service," said Richard Griffin, special agent in charge of the agency's Los Angeles office. Earlier this year in New York City, agents confiscated $22,048,000 in bills, Griffin said at a press conference Monday in Los Angeles.

In the Orange County case, most of the phony money--along with printing plates, photographic negatives and other counterfeiting paraphernalia-- was taken from the garage at Marmol's home in the 4200 block of West Regent Drive, Griffin said.

An undetermined amount of the counterfeit money also was found Saturday in Marmol's safety deposit box at California Federal in Costa Mesa, a bank spokesman said.

"The Secret Service carted out 20 bundles of bills," said John C. Kaufman. "But we don't know how much that represented. We have a policy on what goes into safety deposit boxes: We don't want to know."

Marmol, a Cuban native, apparently is part of a larger counterfeiting ring, authorities said. Griffin added: "I think the biggest fish got caught.

There are further leads we will try and follow to make sure no smaller fish got away."

The bogus $100 notes first appeared in the Los Angeles area about two weeks ago, Griffin said. "They have not appeared anywhere else in the country," and only a "handful" have been passed, he added.

Agents were first tipped to the operation when a Costa Mesa couple tried to pass a counterfeit $100 bill at a Nordstrom department store in Santa Ana, according to court records. The couple told Secret Service agents that Marmol had befriended them two months earlier. A few days earlier he gave them $10,000 in phony $100 bills, in return for which they promised to give him $5,000 in real money later.

**Money Handed Over**

After being contacted by Secret Service agents, the couple agreed to cooperate in the investigation. On Friday, agents staking out Marmol's Santa Ana home followed him to the couple's Costa Mesa residence, where they arrested him after the couple handed him $500 in genuine currency supplied by the agents, court records show.

U.S. Atty. Robert C. Bonner filed a federal criminal complaint Monday charging Marmol with two counts of possession of counterfeit currency and one count of dealing in counterfeit currency. Each of the two possession counts carries a maximum penalty of 15 years and a $250,000 fine; the other count carries a maximum sentence of 10 years in prison and a $250,000 fine. Marmol is being held without bail at the federal prison on Terminal Island.

1988 article reprinted with permission of the *Los Angeles Times*

# Dedication

To my son, Julio Antonio del Marmol, Jr. who was killed by Castro's assassins in retaliation for the work I've been doing for freedom and democracy around the world. God has him in Heaven until we reunite one day. I hope that his blood was not shed in vain, and that one day, before I die, I will be able to see Cuba once more in bright, happy days free from tyranny and evil forever.

evidence of his high standard of integrity, he has a moral commitment to those he has worked with to tell his life story responsibly. In furtherance of that commitment, everything he writes or says publicly has been reviewed by his colleagues to be doubly certain that no lives are endangered by what he says or writes.

Dr. del Marmol is fiercely loyal to his adopted country, the United States, and would never do anything to harm her or her allies. This is one of the reasons that certain details of his accounts are altered. He is neither Democrat nor Republican, but instead is a lover of freedom. Many of the true details of life in Cuba under the Castro regime are recounted in this account and others he has yet to give. Dr. del Marmol was not only personally acquainted with Fidel Castro, but also Che Guevara, Raul Castro, and others of that regime which started in 1959. Many of his family and friends were killed by this regime, some because of the actions he took against it.

Many of the things you will read in this book may seem amazing, incredible, and some others even completely unbelievable. Yet this is truly what would be expected from the life of a spy and freedom fighter who has survived dozens of attempts on his life, traveled to all seven continents, and was trained by his master spy uncle, U.S. intelligence, and other services as well as one who saw firsthand communist intelligence practices and protocols. As you read these pages and the accompanying documentation, you will be learning about one of the most amazing operations of a master spy who actually lived to tell the tale.

# Introduction

The pages of this book represent a small fraction of a life lived in the world of espionage. The history of the operation called "The Zipper" was chosen to relate the story of the Cuban Lightning for various reasons. Among the dozens, if not hundreds of stories that could be recounted from our archives, this one is certainly one of the most amazing, compelling, and emotional. There are many amazing stories that occur before and after this event, yet even among those this account is singularly remarkable. Let there be no doubt for the reader, this story is real. As the disclaimer reads, some dates, times, and names have been changed to protect individuals. However, this story is truer to life than most of the books or movies that one might encounter which claim to be "based on a true story." Many of those stories have added characters, twists, love interests, and other elements to make the story more appealing to certain audiences. When you read *The Cuban Lightning: The Zipper*, you are reading as close an account as possibly can be given while still protecting certain people and information.

The author, Dr. Julio Antonio del Marmol, has meticulously stored photographs, documents, and other items of interest over the decades of his career which testify to this and many other stories. In fact, there were so many documents and photos detailing events in this book that not all of them could be printed. The ones selected were the most relevant to the story and a surplus of these would distract from the book.

One might ask how the author was able to receive permission to relate these accounts. The answer is simple: Dr. del Marmol was an independent "ghost" agent. He worked with many intelligence organizations but was not employed by any of them. He carefully documented many of the operations he performed, not with any desire to expose them publicly, but instead to provide a legacy of his integrity in case it was ever called into question. As you will read in this book, his habit of documenting operations saved him from a great deal of suffering. After many years, the author now feels that some of these stories can be told. As further

The most amazing stories are not works of fiction; they are the stories of real men and women who have lived extraordinary lives. One of these men is Dr. Julio Antonio del Marmol. As a young boy, he never dreamed he would end up as a spy and freedom fighter, but that is where his fate took him. He became involved in the revolutionary government before his 12th birthday as the Commander-in-Chief to the Young Commandos, a youth army he formed. Shortly after turning 12, he learned the true character of Fidel Castro and discovered the communist direction the revolution was being taken and was recruited and trained by his uncle to be the youngest spy in world history. Because he was impossible to catch, Castro himself gave him what would become his codename: the Lightning, or in international circles, the Cuban Lightning. After getting his doctorate in genetics, Dr. del Marmol worked directly for Castro in the Prime Minister's office. He was forced to flee his home country, where he was further trained in espionage by the best agents in the intelligence service. He has travelled all around the world in his fight to stop the spread of terror and tyranny, risking it all many times in the process. He has survived 56 documented attempts on his life. This story, covering the operation codenamed "The Zipper", deals with a classified intelligence plan to create currency for use in secret operations. It is one of the many incredible stories of Dr. del Marmol's life.

Dr. del Marmol is an international bestselling author of the 1976 book *Cuba: Russian Roulette of America* published in Spanish by Orbe Publication in Hollywood, CA. The European prestigious academic publisher, Lambert Academic Publishing selected this work for English translation in 2010 to be used in university political science courses. That book has also won Dr. del Marmol an international journalism award from the National Latin American Institute of Journalism.